GENERAL AND COMPARATIVE ENDOCRINOLOGY

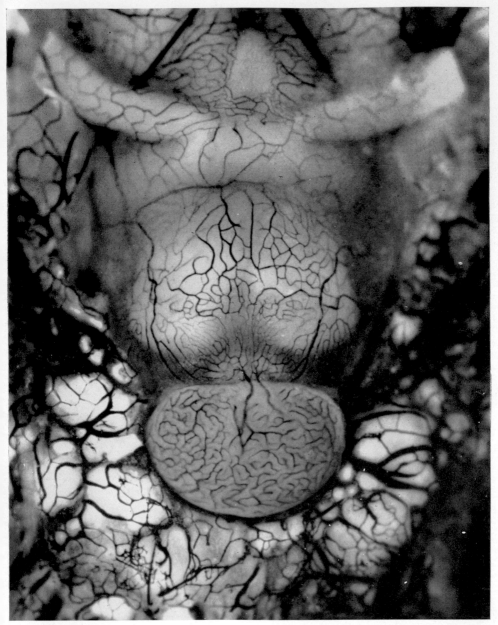

Hypothalamus and pituitary gland of the toad (*Bufo bufo*) in ventral view; the blood vessels have been injected with an Indian ink-gelatine suspension. The optic chiasma is above (anterior) and the pars distalis of the pituitary gland below (posterior), with the hypothalamus lying between them. The median eminence is at the posterior end of the hypothalamus, and two hypophyseal portal vessels run downwards (posteriorly) from it to the pars distalis. (× 24.)

(From Jørgensen *et al.*, 1960. *Comp. Biochem. Physiol.* **1**, 38–43.)

Compare with the sixteenth-century interpretation of the pituitary gland seen in Fig. 17, p. 67.

AN INTRODUCTION TO
GENERAL AND COMPARATIVE
ENDOCRINOLOGY

BY

E. J. W. BARRINGTON

Professor of Zoology
University of Nottingham

CLARENDON PRESS · OXFORD

1963

Oxford University Press, Amen House, London E.C.4

GLASGOW NEW YORK TORONTO MELBOURNE WELLINGTON
BOMBAY CALCUTTA MADRAS KARACHI LAHORE DACCA
CAPE TOWN SALISBURY NAIROBI IBADAN ACCRA
KUALA LUMPUR HONG KONG

Printed in Great Britain by
The Camelot Press Ltd., London and Southampton

F U

PREFACE

'All that Mr. Wright, the rubber estate manager, ever knew of the business was that an army patrol had ambushed a band of terrorists within a mile of his bungalow, that five months later his Indian clerk, Girija Krishnan, had reported the theft of three tarpaulins from the curing sheds, and that three years after that someone had removed the wheels from an old scooter belonging to one of his children. As it never occurred to him to look for a possible connection between the three incidents, he remained unaware even of that knowledge.'

Eric Ambler (1959) Passage of Arms (Heinemann: London)

THE science of Endocrinology has its roots set deep in clinical observations, supplemented by experiments on convenient laboratory mammals, but it has never neglected other groups of animals. This has not been merely a matter of Bayliss and Starling's Christmas goose or the goitrous trout which, in the hands of Marine, made a significant contribution to our understanding of the consequences of iodine deficiency. One is thinking rather of investigations into the reproductive endocrinology of birds, or into thyro-pituitary relationships in amphibians, or into the regulation of colour change in the lower vertebrates, investigations that are classical in their own rights and which have made fundamental contributions to the establishment of the science.

Endocrinology, in fact, has always been a branch of Biology, and not merely a specialized section of mammalian physiology, and recent years have seen a remarkable growth of interest in the extension of its principles throughout the greater part of the animal kingdom. It is the more regrettable, then, that the student who wishes to discover how the subject is developing at the present time is confronted with a formidable literature into which there is very little access except through specialized review articles in symposia reports, excellent in themselves but discouraging reading for the newcomer.

Banting is said to have remarked that he would never have undertaken the isolation of insulin had he known how much had previously been published in this field, but this anecdote sounds apocryphal, for it is difficult to believe that anything at all could have damped down that particular surge of energy. In any case, the volume of publication relating to a particular problem may well be a tribute to its interest and importance rather than an indication of exhausted possibilities, and there is no need for the young researcher to be depressed by it. In 1922, at the very beginning of modern studies on the endocrinology of colour change, 150 papers dealing with the problem in amphibians had already been published, yet entirely novel contributions are still appearing. In 1949 a review of the literature relating to the pituitary gland of a single species of toad (admittedly a famous one, for it was Houssay's *Bufo arenarum*) listed no less than 197 titles in the bibliography, yet who could claim today that we are near to a complete understanding of the functional organization of that gland in any vertebrate group?

It is clear that those who really demand sympathy in this situation are the teachers who would like to see this absorbing subject fully incorporated into contemporary biology and the students who need a path of entry so that they can explore for themselves, and it is for these groups that this book has been written. Rigorous selection and elimination have gone into its composition, for it aims to set out some of the main themes of endocrinology rather than to describe the endless variations that nature has worked upon them. These themes are explored primarily from the standpoint of the comparative physiologist, but I do not believe that such a treatment can be effective, at least in the present state of development of the subject, unless it is founded upon a clear exposition of the principles that have been derived from the study of man and other mammals. By virtue of the inclusion of this foundation the book becomes General as well as Comparative, and I hope that in consequence it may be of value to students of medicine and physiology as well as to the zoologists whose needs were my initial stimulus.

The result is probably a highly personal one, for it must be supposed that half a dozen different writers setting out with the same aim would have produced half a dozen very different books. I have myself borne in mind that I am dealing with a rapidly growing subject, and I have therefore devoted some attention to the way in which hypotheses have been developed, and have even at times followed the rather unusual course of mentioning some of the mistakes that have been made, for I believe that it is helpful to judge the present position against the background of past experience. I have also ventured into speculations and I must ask for these to be accepted in the spirit in which they are offered; there is nothing, I believe, for which some support could not be found somewhere, but they do not necessarily represent a majority viewpoint and they are intended primarily to extend horizons and to form bases for discussion.

One particular difficulty that faces all writers in this field is the problem of nomenclature, and here I have had to make one or two decisions. For example, I have rejected a good deal of the alphabetical jargon that is essential shorthand for the specialist but merely irritating to the general reader, and I have preferred the suffix 'tropin' to 'trophin' because it seems to me to be a better expression of the implied relationship. In dealing with various alternative names I have drawn comfort from the knowledge that a gathering of experts, confronted in 1959 by a motion that 'the term ICSH should henceforth be used instead of LH with respect to one of the pituitary gonadotropins' were unable to do better than produce ten votes against it and nine in support. I have felt obliged to be more selective in the disposal of my own favours, and in making my choices I have tried to take counsel from that useful legal fiction, the 'reasonable man'. If at times his influence seems less obvious than could have been wished, I can only plead that 'where reason cannot instruct, custom may be permitted to guide'.

In a book that has partly grown out of lecture material it is difficult to make proper acknowledgement of all of its sources, nor have I wished to crowd the text with references. I have therefore provided suggestions for further reading, as selective as the book itself, but containing publications which have been particularly useful to me and which should be equally useful to readers if, as I hope, they accept this book as truly an introduction and not a complete statement. I am glad to express my own indebtedness to the writers concerned, and to the personal discussions which are such a pleasant feature of contemporary science. I am grateful also to my friends Mr. T. E. Hughes and Dr. A. E. Needham, who were so kind as to read the whole of the manuscript; they are not responsible for what I have written, but they have improved it a great deal, and it has been helpful to draw on their wide experience in the teaching of comparative physiology to undergraduates.

Finally, I must express my appreciation of the care and skill which my publishers have brought to the preparation of the book for press. This stage, however, would never have been reached without the tolerant acceptance by my wife and family of the insatiable claims that the writing of it has made upon my time.

E.J.W.B.

Nottingham
1962

ACKNOWLEDGEMENTS

I AM indebted to Mr. Eric Ambler for permission to quote from *Passage of Arms*. Thanks are also due to the authors, editors and publishers of the following works and journals.

Adams and Eddy, *Comparative Anatomy* (John Wiley & Sons, Inc., New York); *Advancement of Science*, vol. 9 (British Association for the Advancement of Science); *Amer. J. Physiol.*, vol. 154 (The American Physiological Society); *Ann. Sci. Nat. Zool.*, vol. 19 (Masson et Cie, Paris); *Arch. Zool. exp. gén.*, vol. 94 (Centre National de la Recherche Scientifique, Paris); Baldwin, *Dynamic Aspects of Biochemistry*, 2nd ed. (Cambridge University Press); *Behaviour*, vol. 12 (E. J. Brill (publishers) Leiden); Bell *et al.*, *Textbook of Physiology and Biochemistry* (E. & S. Livingstone, Ltd., Edinburgh); Best and Taylor, *Physiological Basis of Medical Practice* (The Williams & Wilkins Company, Baltimore, Maryland); *Biochem. Journal*, vol. 29 (Cambridge University Press); *Biol. Bull.*, vols. 101, 102 and 109 (Marine Biological Laboratory, Woods Hole); *Biol. Rev.*, vols. 17, 22, and 27 (Cambridge University Press); *Brit. Med. Bull.*, vol. 16 (British Council, medical department); Bullough, *Vertebrate Sexual Cycles* (Methuen & Co., Ltd., London); *Can. J. Zool.* vols. 33 and 37 (National Research Council, Ottawa); Carlisle and Knowles, *Endocrine Control in Crustaceans* (Cambridge University Press); Chester Jones, *The Adrenal Cortex* (Cambridge University Press); *C. R. Soc. Biol. Paris*, vol. 154 (Masson et Cie, Paris); *Endocrin.*, vols. 49, 51, 53 and 66 (Charles C. Thomas, Publisher, Springfield, Illinois); Gorbman, *Comparative Endocrinology* (John Wiley & Sons, Inc., New York); Harris, *Neural Control of the Pituitary Gland* (Edward Arnold (Publishers) Ltd., London); Hartman and Brownell, *The Adrenal Gland* (Lea & Febiger, Philadelphia, Pa.—Publisher); Heller (ed.), *The Neurohypophysis* (for Colston Research Society, Bristol, by Butterworths & Co. (Publishers) Ltd., London); *Internat. Rev. Cytology*, vol. 8 (Academic Press. Inc., New York); *J. Emb. exp. Morph.*, vol. 8 (Company of Biologists, Ltd.); *J. Endocrin.* vols. 5, 8 and 18 (Cambridge University Press); *J. exp. Biol.*, vols. 5, 17, 31, 32, 33, 36, 37, 116, 123, 127 and 138 (Company of Biologists Ltd.); *J. Fish. Res. Bd. Canada*, vol. 17 (Fisheries Research Board of Canada); *J. mar. biol. Ass. U.K.*, vols. 31, 33 and 34 (Council of the Marine Biological Association); *J. Physiol.*, vols. 18, 28, 29, 100, 107 and 126 (Cambridge University Press); *Uitgeversmaatschappij Neerlandia* (Utrecht); *Mem. Soc. Endocrin.*, nos. 4 and 7 (Society for Endocrinology); *Nature*, vol. 188 (Macmillan & Co., Ltd., London); Nicol, *The Biology of Marine Animals* (Sir Isaac Pitman & Sons, Ltd., London); Patten, *Embryology of the Pig* (McGraw-Hill Book Company, Inc., New York); Patten, *Fundamentals of Embryology* (McGraw-Hill Book Company, Inc., New York); *Phil. Trans. Roy. Soc.* B, vol. 232 (Royal Society, London); Pitt-Rivers and Tata, *The Thyroid Hormones* (Pergamon Press, Oxford); *Proc. Roy. Soc.* B, vols. 120, 128 and 141 (Royal Society, London); *Quart. Journ. micr. Sci.*, vols. 62, 65, 77, 85, 91, 97 and 100 (Company of Biologists Ltd.); *Quart. Rev. Biol.*, vol. 24 (The Williams & Wilkins Company, Baltimore, Maryland); Singer, *Vesalius on the Human Brain* (Oxford University Press); *Symp. Zool. Soc. London*, 2 (Zoological Society of London); Traité de Zoologie, vol. 11 (Masson et Cie, Paris); Turner, *General Endocrinology* (W. B. Saunders Company, Philadelphia, Pennsylvania); *Univ. Bergen Årbok*, vol. 14 (A. S. John

Gregs, Boktrykkeri, Bergen); *Vidensk. Medd. fra Dansk Naturh. Foren.*, vol. 18 (Zoological Museum, Copenhagen); Watterson, *Endocrines in Development* (The University of Chicago Press, Illinois); Wigglesworth, *Physiology of Insect Metamorphosis* (Cambridge University Press); Willier *et al.*, *Analysis of Development* (W. B. Saunders Company, Philadelphia, Pennsylvania); Wingstrand, *The Structure and Development of the Avian Pituitary* (CWK Gleerup, Lund); Winton and Bayliss, *Human Physiology*, 2nd ed. (McGraw-Hill Book Co., Inc., New York); Witschi, *Development of Vertebrates* (W. B. Saunders Company, Philadelphia, Pennsylvania); Young, *The Life of Mammals* (Oxford University Press); Young, *The Life of Vertebrates* (Oxford University Press); *Zeitschr. Zellforsch.*, vol. 51 (Springer-Verlag, Heidelberg); *Zool. Jahrb. Abt. Anat.*, vols. 66 and 68 (VEB Gustav Fischer Verlag, Jena).

CONTENTS

NOTE ON POSITION OF PLATES

I. INTRODUCTION

1. Chemical regulation

WHATEVER the circumstances under which life first evolved, we may feel sure that living organisms must at a very early stage have developed the capacity for responding adaptively to stimulation both from within and from without, for reacting, that is to say, in a manner most likely to ensure their survival. We may assume, too, that such reactions of chemical systems would have been mediated by chemical means, and that for this purpose use would have been made of suitable substances which were present in the environment or which were arising as by-products of the organisms' own activities.

Certainly we see evidence of this at the present day. It has been observed that water from crowded cultures of *Hydra* has the capacity for inducing sexual differentiation in this animal, an effect that is apparently a consequence of the high carbon dioxide tension in the medium. Whatever the significance of this may be for the normal life-cycle of *Hydra*, we have here an illustration of members of a species being able to influence each other through a chemical substance which in this instance is one of their waste products.

Towards the other end of the animal scale we find that the growth rate of frog tadpoles is sharply reduced if they are placed in water in which crowded tadpoles have previously been living. This effect of crowding is a result of the presence in such 'conditioned' water of a substance which is non-dialysable and which will not pass through Whatman No. 1 filter-paper; its property is destroyed by heating or drying it, or by subjecting it to ultra-violet irradiation. The origin of this substance is not understood. It may be that it is a product of micro-organisms growing in the culture (although the property is said to persist in the presence of penicillin and streptomycin), but it is interesting to speculate that it might also be a metabolic product of the tadpoles themselves, adaptively modifying the metabolism of other tadpoles in such a way as to limit their growth while permitting their maintenance.

It has been argued that such chemical interactions are a widespread phenomenon of nature, dependent upon the excretion by organisms of active metabolites, and upon the readiness with which water permits the interchange of these substances, and it may well be, as Lucas has suggested, that they are a basis for far more subtle ecological relationships than those between organisms and their physical environment, or between predator and prey. For example, it is said that the presence of certain carbohydrates

B

in water directly stimulates the pumping action of oysters. The significance of this is obscure, but the substances concerned are thought to be the products of plant metabolism, so that theoretically there is here a means by which feeding activity could be integrated with changes in the composition of the surrounding water and of the organisms in it.

It has been thought, too, that such chemical interactions between organisms may serve to synchronize the spawning of invertebrates. For example, the sperm and testes of male oysters are said to contain some chemical which evokes spawning in the females; these induce spawning in other males which then induce it in other females, so that a chain reaction develops. Similar although less elaborate relationships have been described for worms; thus isolated females of the polychaete *Platynereis dumerilii* will spawn spontaneously, but males will only do so in the presence of females, a situation which, it has been suggested, may depend upon the release of a chemical signal from the latter.

It is well known that such signals operate as part of the regulatory machinery within the body of a single individual, a familiar example being the influence of the carbon dioxide pressure of the arterial blood in controlling the rate of ventilation of the lungs in mammals, but such mechanisms must have been operating before the evolution of vascular systems. Sponges, which lack both blood and nervous systems, must presumably depend upon chemical diffusion from cell to cell for such very limited powers of co-ordination as they possess, and this may still be important in the platyhelminths. The planarian *Dugesia tigrina* occurs in a sexual and a non-sexual strain, and it has been observed that if the anterior third of a member of the sexual one is grafted on to the posterior two-thirds of a member of the other it will induce in the latter the development of testes and copulatory organs. Of course, this might be due, at least in part, to the migration of cells from the sexual portion into the non-sexual one, but the appearance of accessory organs as well as testes certainly suggests that the diffusion of some chemical factor may also be involved.

Such relationships as those which we have been outlining need much more thorough investigation, and the interpretations applied to them are often somewhat hypothetical, but they have been closely studied in vertebrate embryos, where they appear to underlie the phenomenon known as induction. One example is the mesodermal inductor which regulates the form of the more posterior part of the central nervous system of urodele embryos; this seems to be a protein, which can be obtained in solution, and which is reported to be able to produce inductive effects in that condition, although it remains uncertain how far such substances normally exert their effects by diffusion across gaps, or how far they depend upon direct contact of the cells concerned.

That organs, tissues, and cells may remain in communication with each other as part of the general regulatory processes of the fully differentiated body is effectively illustrated by what has been learned regarding the control of the regeneration of the liver. After part of this organ has been removed the remainder will embark upon growth and differentiation until the original total mass has been approximately restored. The regulatory agent concerned here is believed to be a substance, perhaps a protein of the blood plasma, which is released from the liver into the blood stream and which is believed to have an inhibitory action upon the synthesis of fresh intracellular protein. If the total mass of the liver is reduced, so also is the concentration of this substance in the blood stream; thus, with the reduction of its inhibitory influence the liver is freed to increase its own mass until, with the restoration of its normal size, the concentration and inhibitory action of the substance are restored to normal.

This principle is not peculiar to the liver, and such systems of chemical intercommunication and control must be widespread. In this particular instance it forms what is called a feedback cycle, in which the activity of a process is regulated by information that arises out of that activity and is passed back, directly or indirectly, into the originating organ, but systems need not always work in this way. The interactions may be of a more generalized character, or they may involve a direct stimulating action of one organ upon another in what has been called the shot-gun type of relationship. In the latter case the stimulated organ is often referred to as the target organ, a convenient expression which may nevertheless be misleading in creating an unjustified sense of simplicity. We know little enough of the way in which such interactions operate, but it is at least quite likely that the response of the target organ depends upon its possession of a specialized receptor mechanism, which is able to trap the activating substance. That substance, if an analogy is required, might perhaps be compared with a coded missile, the relationships between it and its target becoming one of mutual adaptation. Whatever the exact nature of these interactions may be, however, it is likely that there are few cells in the body which are not involved in them; indeed, it is clear that cells are organized to function in an environment of mutual interaction, as is shown by the way in which they may often lose a great deal of their characteristic metabolic machinery and synthetic capacity when they are cultured *in vitro*.

2. The content of Endocrinology

The study of Endocrinology is concerned, in the classical use of the term, with hormones, which are particular and specialized components of the communication systems which we have been considering. These hormones are regarded as chemical substances which are produced in

particular regions of the body, usually in specialized glands, and are discharged into the blood stream, a process known as internal or endocrine
secretion. They are then carried in the circulation to other parts of the
body where they produce specific regulatory effects. This concept of
hormones arose gradually. The idea of the production of internal secretions
was current in the eighteenth century, and was formulated in clear terms
by Claude Bernard in 1859, for he had realized that the functioning of
certain organs involved the discharge of their products into the blood, and
he had referred to the passage of glucose out of the liver as an example of
this. It has been customary to regard such early speculations as being of
too generalized a nature to be directly relevant to twentieth-century
endocrinology, and they were certainly far removed from current concepts
of the close interweaving of the neural and hormonal components of
regulatory processes. Nevertheless, it will prove helpful to approach those
components as part of the wider system of chemical interrelationships
which we have outlined above.

Thus, it is possible to make some distinction between the regulatory
influence of the nerve cells, precisely localized in space and time, and the
much more diffuse action of hormones, but we shall find that both are
equally products of secretory activity. Indeed, we shall learn that nerve
cells may have specifically endocrine functions, and that they may even
have given rise to the first fully differentiated endocrine organs. It is
possible, again, to make some distinction between the diffuse action of
hormones and the localized action of embryonic inductor substances, but
we shall learn that both of these effects may sometimes be produced by
secretions that are closely similar, if not actually identical. We shall learn,
too, that substances resembling established hormones, or chemically
related to them, are widely distributed in nature, and we shall have cause
to suspect that the evolution of endocrine systems may have involved
the utilization of such substances, so that the tracing of the evolutionary
history of highly specialized secretory products may help us to understand
their nature and their mode of functioning.

We shall, therefore, avoid too restrictive a definition of our subject
matter, but shall concern ourselves not only with hormones in the classical
sense but also with such other aspects of chemical co-ordination as seem
to be immediately relevant to an understanding of them. We shall, in
fact, follow the advice of a modern painter who is reported to have
remarked that to define a thing is to substitute the definition for the thing
itself, for his warning is as relevant to creative science as it is to creative
art. At the same time, and because of this, we shall also treat the subject
from a comparative standpoint, and this also merits a word of explanation, for it is a type of approach which has at times earned some harsh
comments.

3. The comparative method

W. M. Bayliss, in his great treatise on *Principles of General Physiology*, said of comparative physiology that it was 'sometimes apt to become in great part a description of functions peculiar to certain lower organisms, even when they throw no light on the activities of the human body, which are, after all, the most vitally interesting and important problems presented to the physiologist. . . . In treatises on comparative physiology, copious details of alimentary or digestive mechanisms will be found, but no discussion of the general nature of the action of enzymes.' In the present account there will be no room for copious details and, although this is less fortunate, there will be little discussion of hormone action, for our ignorance of this field is profound. What we shall do, however, is to compare hormone with hormone, and system with system, firstly within the mammals, for that group provides at the present time the foundations of our understanding. We shall then extend our analysis to other groups of vertebrates, and to those groups of invertebrates that have been most thoroughly investigated. Our comparisons will therefore be developed on two fronts, the hormonal and the taxonomic, and as a result, brief though some of the treatment will have to be, we shall hope to extract from the variability that is so characteristic of animal life some statement of general principles, which will be reinforced by excursions into evolutionary speculation. Some readers may not necessarily feel that the activities of the human body are the most interesting of biological problems, but we must hope that even those who do will come to feel that the comparative treatment of animal function can contribute to an understanding of human physiology and, indeed, is ultimately essential if that understanding is to be reasonably complete.

Such was clearly the opinion of William Harvey. We can see him still, through the eyes of Aubrey, wearing his dagger, 'as the fashion then was which he would be apt to draw out upon every occasion' (not offensively, as a more recent biographer insists, but merely in the way of gesticulation!), and we can hear him answering those 'who say that I have shown a vainglorious love of vivisections, and who scoff at and deride the introduction of frogs and serpents, flies, and others of the lower animals upon the scene, as a piece of puerile levity, not even refraining from opprobious epithets. To return evil speaking with evil speaking, however, I hold to be unworthy in a philosopher and searcher after truth; I believe that I shall do better and more advisedly if I meet so many indications of ill breeding with the light of faithful and conclusive observation.' Elsewhere, in an Epistle Dedicatory to the 'learned and illustrious the President and Fellows of the College of Physicians of London', he expressed the essence of the matter when he observed that nature was the best and most faithful interpreter of her own secrets; 'and what she presents either more briefly or obscurely in one department, that she explains more fully and clearly in another'.

It is worth examining briefly why this should be so. The issue has been cogently discussed by Pantin who, in reference to the nervous systems of crustaceans, cephalopods, and vertebrates, asks how it is that 'not once but many times a highly complex mechanism to meet the requirement of behaviour has been built up on principles so similar that valid information about the one can be obtained by study of the other?' He finds the answer in the fact that natural selection does not work upon an unlimited range of random variation. On the contrary, animal organization has limitations imposed upon it which are inherent in the properties of the material of which it is constructed. Children playing with Meccano sets may well arrive independently at similar end-results simply as a consequence of the limited potentialities of the constructional units which they are handling. So also in nature, where unrelated groups of animals may, for fundamentally this same reason, develop in the course of their evolutionary history some striking parallelisms of pattern. We shall see many examples of these, and all that we need note about them now is that such parallelisms may transcend the classical definitions of homology and analogy. To quote Pantin again, they constitute 'a morphology with new and unfamiliar rules'. Their analysis needs, therefore, to be approached with a spirit of caution, allowing this to regulate, but not to obliterate, the intellectual exhilaration which flows as naturally from comparative endocrinology as from other branches of contemporary biology.

4. A guide for readers

The themes that we have outlined will be developed in such a way that it is desirable for the book to be read as a whole, and it may therefore be helpful to map the paths that we shall follow through what may seem at times to be difficult territory.

Most of our attention will be given to the vertebrates, and Chapter II begins by considering the digestive hormones of the gastro-intestinal tract, partly because of the exceptional historical importance of the work of Bayliss and Starling, but even more because this subject provides a convenient introduction to the methodology of endocrinology. Moreover, it presents us with an endocrine system which has remained curiously primitive in its organization and which therefore provides a good base line from which to evaluate the more specialized systems that we shall encounter later.

We shall begin to sense the scope of such specialization in Chapter III, for this introduces the concept of hormonal interactions, and we shall see why a hormone, which must have originated, like those studied in the previous chapter, within the alimentary tract, should have become involved in a much more complex physiological system. We shall see, too, something of the significance of the molecular structure of hormones and shall make our first acquaintance with the pituitary gland. So dominating is the influence of this in the vertebrates that before we can proceed further it will be necessary to examine briefly the plan of its structure and organization in mammals, and then, in the remainder of Chapter IV, we shall deal with the function of one of its major components, the neurohypophysis. This will introduce the concept of neurosecretion, and will constitute our first attack upon the problem of the nature of the relationship between the pituitary gland and the brain, while we shall also see some more of the extraordinarily interesting results that are flowing from current studies of molecular structure.

Chapters V and VI deal with some of the problems of hormones in relation to sexual reproduction, a daunting subject, partly because of the richness of the literature and partly because the diversity of sexual practice in the vertebrates makes it very difficult to achieve an elementary statement of general principles. This statement must be achieved, however, because the principles involved are fundamental to so much of the endocrine organization of these animals, and it must be hoped that the situation will be eased by having our attention concentrated largely upon the problems of sexual periodicity. We shall examine some of the biological possibilities of the steroid ring system, but shall be particularly concerned with the analysis of the dominating position that the adenohypophysis occupies by virtue of its relationships with the brain, with the outside world, and with the other endocrine organs. We shall touch, too, upon the special adaptations involved in the establishment of viviparity in mammals, and upon the part played by hormones in development.

Some of the principles established in these two Chapters are applied further in the next four. In Chapters VII and VIII the glands of the pharynx provide further examples of the readiness with which the tissues of the alimentary tract have evolved endocrine activities, and in concentrating upon the thyroid gland we shall see how hormonal functions may apparently change in the course of evolution while the hormones concerned remain unaltered. We shall see, too, how modern techniques have displayed the remarkable precision of the biochemical adaptations which underlie thyroidal biosynthesis, and shall examine one of the ways in which an endocrine gland might have originated.

In Chapters IX and X we break down the adrenal gland into its medullary and cortical components and find that the peculiar relationship of the chromaffin tissue to the sympathetic division of the autonomic nervous system brings to light the importance of another aspect of neurosecretion and extends the field of reference of the endocrinologist. The adreno-cortical tissue shows us more of the possibilities of the steroid ring system and completes our analysis of the tropic functions of the pituitary gland, already developed further in the study of the thyroid. The widespread ramifications of the responses of vertebrates to emergencies and stress also become apparent, but we leave unresolved the problem of the ultimate significance of the relationships between the adrenal medulla and cortex.

In Chapter XI we complete our analysis of pituitary function by considering the physiology of colour change in vertebrates, and, incidentally, are again made aware of the close interaction between neural and endocrine co-ordination. Thus in Chapter XII we are at last free to attempt a synoptic view of the history and functional relationships of the pituitary gland, and we glance also at the circumstances that might have determined its origin.

Chapters XIII and XIV deal with the crustaceans and insects, and in a manner that will be much too brief to satisfy those who research upon those animals or to do justice to the elegance of the results that they have achieved. We are not concerned here, however, with a detailed review of the diversification of the endocrine systems in these two groups but rather with the determination of the main features of their organization. With this as a basis we are then able to consider how far common principles operate in them and in the endocrine systems of vertebrates, how research has benefited by the recognition of such principles, and what degree of caution is needed in applying the classical concepts of homology and analogy in this context. Thus we are led finally to Chapter XV, in which we attempt, in that cautious atmosphere, to draw some threads together and to justify some of the hopes with which we set out.

II. HORMONES AND DIGESTION

1. Neural control of pancreatic secretion

IT is easy to suppose that the introduction of new ideas into the development of a science is a logical and tidy process, arising naturally as older ones are discarded or modified in the light of new discoveries. Biological problems, however, are so complex that too close an application to what appears to be logical reasoning may actually impede the acceptance of new facts, and the result of this is that empiricism and intuition prove to be essential tools for the investigator, provided always that their use is based upon wisely informed experience. The truth of this will be repeatedly brought home to us in our survey of comparative endocrinology, and there is no better illustration of it than the progressive unravelling of the physiological principles that are involved in the regulation of the activity of the alimentary canal of vertebrate animals.

This canal is essentially a tube connecting the mouth with the anus and lined by an epithelium, which both secretes the enzymes required for the digestion of the food and also absorbs the products of that digestion. In the mammals, as is very well known (Fig. 1), it has become highly specialized, so that the food, after some preliminary treatment by the saliva, passes down the oesophagus into the stomach; here proteolytic digestion is initiated by the secretion of hydrochloric acid and pepsinogen from the chief glands, while mucus is added from the lining epithelium and from the glands of the cardiac and pyloric portions. Most of the digestion, however, takes place in the small intestine, the first section of which, the duodenum, receives secretions in part from the liver and pancreas, which have grown out from the wall of the alimentary canal, and in part from Brunner's glands and the crypts of Lieberkühn, which have remained within it. Of these, the crypts are distributed throughout the small intestine, while Brunner's glands are confined to the duodenum and are probably related phylogenetically to the pyloric glands of the stomach. The next part of the small intestine after the duodenum is sometimes distinguishable as the jejunum, but the greater part of it is the ileum, and it is here that the digestive processes are largely completed; water, however, is absorbed through the wall of the large intestine, while a specialized microflora in either the stomach or the caecum has an essential role to play in many herbivorous mammals. We may follow Pavlov in comparing such an alimentary canal with a chemical factory in which food is processed in preparation for its absorption; the necessary reactions take place in stages, sometimes in separate compartments, and usually through the agency of secretions, which are discharged in a co-ordinated way in the right place at the right time and in the appropriate quantities.

At the turn of the present century, and largely as a result of Pavlov's brilliant exploration of the physiology of digestion, it was supposed that

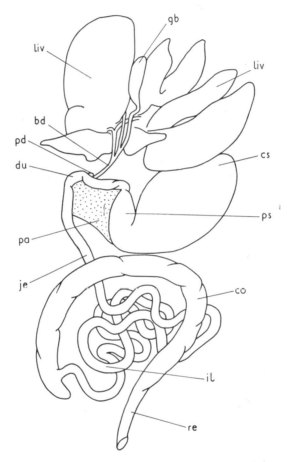

Fig. 1. The alimentary tract of the cat in ventral view (after Mivart). *bd*, bile duct; *co*, colon; *cs*, cardiac region of stomach; *du*, duodenum; *gb*, gall bladder; *il*, ileum; *je*, jejunum; *liv*, liver; *pa*, pancreas; *pd*, pancreatic duct; *ps*, pyloric region of stomach; *re*, rectum.

the co-ordinating machinery for this sequence of events was provided by the nervous system. This was natural enough, for not only was the general importance of this system in the regulation of responses well appreciated, but he was able to demonstrate its direct involvement in the control of the secretion of the pancreatic juice. This demonstration, which he had perfected to the point of carrying it out before lecture audiences, involved the establishment in a dog of a permanent pancreatic fistula, the opening of the pancreatic duct being transferred to the outside of the body so

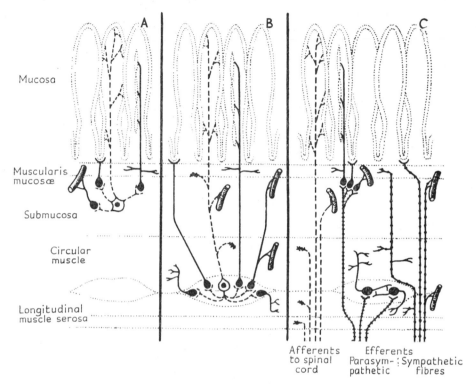

Fig. 2. A diagram illustrating hypothetical nervous pathways in the wall of the alimentary tract.

A. Local reflexes. Ingoing pathway (broken line) from epithelium to Meissner's plexus; outgoing pathways (continuous line) to mucosa, blood vessel, muscularis mucosae, and smooth muscle of villi.

B. Local and spreading reflexes. Ingoing pathway from epithelium to Auerbach's plexus; outgoing pathways to muscle layers, blood vessels, and mucosa.

C. Spinal reflexes. Ingoing pathways to spinal cord; outgoing pathways by parasympathetic and (ortho) sympathetic outflows.

(From Garry, 1952. *Advanc. Sci., Lond.* **9,** 197–206.)

that the rate of discharge of secretion could be directly observed. Then, after prior preparation of the cervical vagus nerve, he was able to show that no secretion was to be seen while the animal was resting, but that if the nerve was stimulated with an induction current (faradic stimulation) a flow of juice began after a latent period of some two minutes and

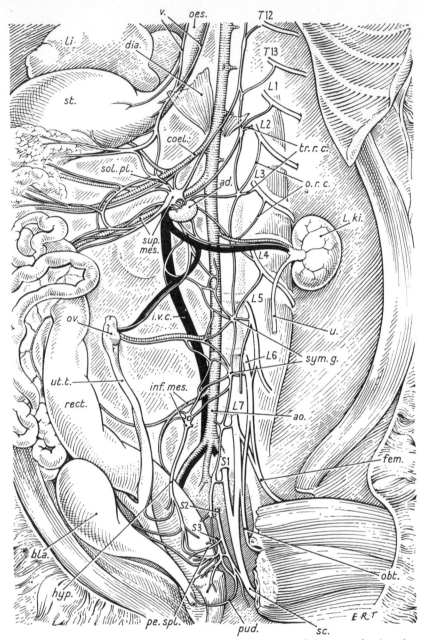

Fig. 3. Dissection of the autonomic nervous system of the cat. *ad.* adrenal; *ao.* aorta; *bla.* bladder; *coel.* coeliac artery; *dia.* diaphragm; *fem.* femoral nerve; *hyp.* hypogastric nerve; *inf. mes.* inferior mesenteric artery and ganglion; *i.v.c.* inferior vena cava; *L* 1–7, ventral rami of lumbar nerves 1–7; *li.* liver; *L. ki.* left kidney; *obt.* obturator nerve; *oes.* oesophagus; *o.r.c.* oblique ramus communicans; *ov.* ovary; *pe. spl.* pelvic splanchnic nerve; *pud.* pudendal nerve; *rect.* rectum; *S* 1–3, sacral nerves 1–3; *sc.* sciatic nerve; *sol. pl.* solar plexus; *st.* stomach; *sup. mes.* superior mesenteric artery and ganglion; *sym. g.* sympathetic ganglion; *T* 12 & 13, thoracic nerves 12 & 13; *tr. r. c.* transverse ramus communicans; *u.* ureter; *ut. t.* uterine tube; *v.* vagus nerve.

(From Young, 1957. *The Life of Mammals*. Oxford: Clarendon Press. Fig. 172, p. 389.)

continued for four or five minutes after the cessation of the stimulus. Thus it appeared, as he expressed it, to be 'definitely settled that the vagus is the secretory nerve of the pancreas'.

What, however, was the normal stimulus which brought the cervical vagus into action? In the search for this, attention was focused on the fact that when the food material enters the duodenum it carries with it hydrochloric acid derived from the gastric secretion. It seemed possible that this acid might serve to signal the need for the release of pancreatic juice, and experiments showed that some such device was, in fact, employed. It was found that if 150 ml of a 0·5 per cent. solution of the acid was introduced into the stomach of a dog with a pancreatic fistula there resulted, after two to three minutes, an increased outflow of secretion from the latter. Pure gastric juice had a similar effect, but an equivalent amount of alkaline water did not, while if the contents of the stomach were neutralized at the height of the normal digestive process, when pancreatic juice was flowing freely, this flow was brought to an end. So, again in the words of Pavlov, it seemed possible to conclude that 'this powerful influence of acids upon the pancreas is one of the most securely established facts in the whole physiology of the gland'.

It looked, then, as though the most likely explanation of the increased outflow of juice from the pancreas during the normal course of digestion might well be that it was mediated through the vagus as a result of stimulation set up by the entry of acid into the intestine, but, even if this were so, it still remained to determine the actual connexion between this stimulus and the discharge of impulses through the nerve, and it was at this point of the analysis that difficulties of interpretation began to appear. Within the wall of the alimentary canal there are two nerve plexuses, an inner Meissner's plexus, lying immediately beneath the mucosa, and a outer Auerbach's plexus lying between the main circular and longitudinal muscle layers (Fig. 2). As with other visceral organs, the nervous regulation of the activity of the alimentary canal is mediated through the autonomic nervous system, in which we distinguish two main divisions, the parasympathetic and the sympathetic. The whole of this system is characterized by the fact that its motor pathways involve two sets of nerve cells, the first, the preganglionic neurones, being situated within the central nervous system and sending axons to synapse with the second, the peripherally situated postganglionic neurones. Preganglionic fibres of the parasympathetic division run to the alimentary canal mainly in the vagus and pelvic nerves (Fig. 3), synapsing in the gut wall with the cells of the plexuses (Fig. 2), which can thus be regarded, at least in part, as the postganglionic neurones of this division. Preganglionic fibres of the sympathetic division run in the splanchnic nerves to the superior mesenteric and coeliac ganglia of the solar plexus, and to the inferior mesenteric ganglia, where they synapse with the postganglionic neurones, which then send fibres direct to the muscles and gland cells of the alimentary canal. The difference in the location of the synaptic relay points in these two divisions, the parasympathetic ones being more peripheral and the sympathetic ones more central, is an important feature to which we shall return later in another context.

For the moment we may note that as regards the functions of the two divisions it is generally held that the sympathetic in mammals is inhibitor to the muscle of the gut wall and motor to the sphincters, bringing about, therefore, closure of the latter. The effect, in the words of one writer, is to secure 'quiet lodgement of the contents', such as may be needed to allow for absorption, or at times when blood must be diverted to other parts of the body, or when pathological influences are at work in the digestive system. As regards the parasympathetic division, defaecation depends upon the integrity of the pelvic nerves, and it has been very generally taught that the rest of the division balances the effect of the sympathetic by being motor to the gut wall and inhibitor to the sphincters, thus facilitating the passage of food through the alimentary canal. This is an attractive generalization, but it would be well to bear in mind that it may be over-simplified; it is said, for example, that both sympathetic and parasympathetic divisions will tend to inhibit the stomach when this is active, and to excite it when it is inactive, and in any case, the generalization is certainly not applicable to fish (p. 35).

2. The discovery of 'secretin'

It was shown by Popielski at the beginning of this century that the stimulating effect of acid upon pancreatic secretion could still be demonstrated even after all of these connexions of the alimentary tract with the central nervous system had been destroyed by section of the vagi and of the splanchnic nerves, together with removal of the solar plexus and destruction of the spinal cord. He therefore concluded that the response must depend upon a peripheral rather than a central mechanism, and that it must be mediated by local reflexes (Fig. 2) operating through the nerve cells associated directly with the pancreas and the intestinal wall. This view was a plausible one as far as it went, and it received support from other workers, although the question how far the neural organization of the alimentary canal actually provides for such local reflexes is still a matter of dispute. In any case, however, a more rigorous analysis of the situation was to show that this was not, in fact, the only possible explanation, and the credit for appreciating this belongs to Bayliss and Starling who, in resolving this particular problem, established one of the major landmarks in the development of the science of endocrinology.

Their achievement in breaking through the established preconceptions that were hindering progress was the more remarkable in that their studies of the movements of the alimentary canal had led them at that time to the view that peristaltic contractions might be mediated by local nervous connexions in Auerbach's plexus. This was, of course, substantially the explanation postulated by Popielski to account for the regulation of pancreatic secretion, but Bayliss and Starling perceived in the literature indications that it was not wholly convincing in this particular context. Wertheimer and Lepage, for example, had shown in 1901 that the introduction of acid into a portion of the jejunum would evoke pancreatic secretion even when this portion was completely severed from both the duodenum above it and from the rest of the intestine below it. It is curious that they did not carry this experiment to its logical extreme by cutting at the same time all the possible nervous connexions, but Bayliss and Starling saw the necessity for doing this and made it the basis for their crucial experiment.

This was carried out on 16 January 1902. Using an anaesthetized dog maintained under artificial respiration in a warm saline bath, they removed the ganglia of the solar plexus, cut both vagi, tied off a loop of jejunum at both ends, and cut the mesenteric nerves supplying it; the loop was thus connected to the rest of the body only by its arteries and veins. (Such an experiment, in which the animal is necessarily killed at the end of it, is referred to as acute, while those in which the animal remains alive, as in the pancreatic fistulae experiments already mentioned, are described as chronic.) With a cannula inserted into the pancreatic duct, and with the blood pressure being recorded from the carotid artery, they introduced 20 ml of 0·4 per cent. hydrochloric acid into the duodenum; this (Fig. 4A) evoked a well-marked pancreatic secretion of one drop every twenty seconds, lasting for some six minutes, after an initial latent period of about two minutes. Such a response merely confirmed previous work, but they went further and introduced the acid into the loop of jejunum, and found that this, too, evoked the discharge of pancreatic secretion. This might have been a result of the acid stimulating the pancreas directly after it had been absorbed into the circulation, but in fact Wertheimer and Lepage had already shown that the injection of acid into the blood stream did not produce a secretory response. Bayliss and Starling therefore concluded that the presence of the acid was causing the jejunal mucosa to discharge some chemical excitant into the circulation, and that it was this that was stimulating the pancreas. To quote the words of C. J. Martin, who was present at the time, 'I remember Starling saying: "Then it must be a chemical reflex." Rapidly cutting off a further piece of jejunum, he rubbed its mucous membrane with sand in weak HCl, filtered, and injected it into the jugular vein of the animal. After a few moments the pancreas responded by a much greater secretion than had occurred before. It was a great afternoon.'

This important experiment (Fig. 4B) was one of the major steps in the evolution of the fundamental concept of internal secretion. As we have

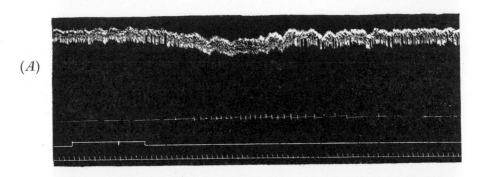

(A)

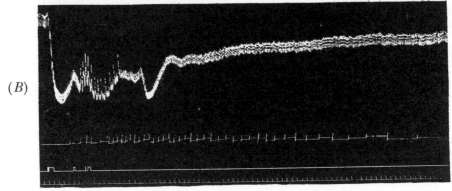

(B)

Fig. 4. Tracings illustrating the discovery of 'secretin' in the dog. Upper curve, blood pressure; uppermost of the three lines, drops of pancreatic secretion; middle line, signal indicating injection; bottom line, time in 10-sec intervals, and level of zero blood pressure. *A*. Effect of injection of acid into duodenum after destruction of spinal cord; a marked flow of pancreatic juice occurs after a latent period of about two minutes. *B*. 'The crucial experiment'—the injection of acid extract of jejunal mucous membrane into a vein; the effect is a considerable fall of blood pressure, followed after a latent period of about 70 sec by a flow of pancreatic juice.

already seen, this was not a new concept at the time, nor is it usual for such a novel idea to arise, as it were, ready made, but Bayliss and Starling were dealing with a particular type of such secretory activity in which a product of one tissue was co-ordinating the functioning of another one by acting as a chemical messenger. To the secretion which they had shown was produced by the intestine they gave the name 'secretin', which we shall continue to place within inverted commas for a reason that will become apparent later. After much search for a general term for such secretions they adopted the name hormone, which had been suggested to them by W. B. Hardy, and which we have already defined (p. 3). This word is less apt than could have been wished, for it is derived from the

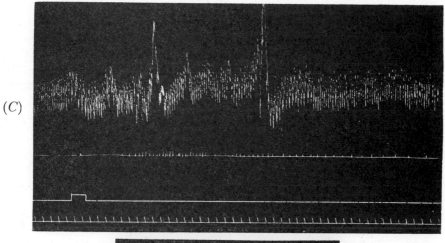

(C)

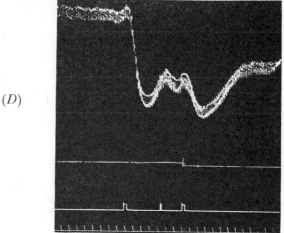

(D)

Fig. 4. Tracings illustrating the discovery of 'secretin' (cont.).
C. Effect of injecting 'secretin' prepared from mucous membrane extracted with absolute alcohol; there is a powerful effect on the pancreas, but no fall of blood pressure. (Blood pressure zero is here 21 mm below the time marker). D. Effect of injecting acid extract of lower end of ileum; there is a fall of blood pressure but no effect on the pancreas.
(From Bayliss & Starling, 1902. *J. Physiol.* **28**, 325–53.)

Greek *hormaein*, which merely means 'to impel or arouse to activity', and Bayliss, in recounting at a later date the history of this event, found it necessary to emphasize that 'although the property of messenger was not suggested by it, it has been generally understood as carrying this meaning'.

3. The hormonal status of 'secretin'

It was natural that these important findings should have been subjected to searching examination and criticism by contemporaries. Indeed, as we shall consider more fully later, the complete demonstration of hormonal action requires the satisfying of certain conditions which may not always be easy to achieve, and so much was this so in this particular instance that it was possible for two workers publishing as recently as 1951, forty-nine years after the appearance of Bayliss and Starling's classical paper, to claim that they had now completed the physiological proof of the existence of this particular hormonal mechanism. It will be instructive, therefore, to consider both the criticisms and the steps by which they have been countered.

Firstly, it was argued that the nervous connexions of the pancreas with the jejunal loop had not, in fact, been as completely severed as the investigators had claimed. This was fair criticism, in so far as it was impossible to be sure that no nerve fibres were reaching the loop in conjunction with the blood vessels that were supplying its circulation, but to this Bayliss and Starling replied that the possibility of such fibres being present did not alter the fact that by assuming their absence they had been led to the discovery of 'secretin', and that the demonstration of such fibres, even supposing that they were present, could not invalidate that discovery. It cannot be denied, however, that such an important new principle would appear in a much more convincing light if all possibility of nervous control were actually eliminated, and this assurance was subsequently given as a result of ingenious surgical procedures that were developed in the United States by Ivy and others, utilizing dogs as experimental animals.

In essence, these consisted of transplanting a portion of the pancreas and its duct, and also portions of the jejunum, into new positions beneath the skin of the same animal, a procedure known as auto-transplantation, since the organs remain within the animal from which they originate. At first these auto-transplants were allowed to retain their original vascular connexions, but after an interval they acquired a new circulatory supply from the cutaneous vessels, and when this had happened their original supply was cut away. They were now vascularized solely from the skin, and there was no possibility at all of their newly developed vessels conveying into them nerve fibres which might connect them with each other or with the organs from which they had been separated. Under these circumstances it was found that when dilute hydrochloric acid was passed through the isolated jejunal loop there resulted a discharge of secretion through the duct of the auto-transplanted portion of the pancreas, a response which could only have been evoked by the transmission of some substance from the loop to the pancreas through the blood stream.

This experiment goes a long way, incidentally, to meet another requirement for the complete proof of hormonal action, and that is a demonstration that the supposed hormone does actually circulate in the blood under normal physiological conditions. To this point attention was given as soon as Bayliss and Starling's first results had been published, and within a year other workers had shown that the transference of blood from a dog with acid in its intestine into another dog would cause the pancreas of the latter to secrete even though no acid was present in its own intestine. It was, however, argued that the amount of secretion so produced was no greater than that produced by the injection of blood obtained from an animal with an inactive pancreas and, in order to meet this criticism, Matsuo devised in 1913 a cross-circulation experiment in which two dogs were placed together head to head with a carotid artery of each connected by glass tubing with a jugular vein of the other, and with separate cannulae inserted into their pancreatic ducts. After this common circulation had been maintained for ten minutes, during which time no secretion was discharged from the pancreas, 30 ml of 0·4 per cent. hydrochloric acid were introduced into the duodenum of one of the animals. In five minutes the pancreas of this dog began to secrete and after another one to three minutes the pancreas of the other began also, both continuing for some fifteen to twenty minutes. This type of cross-circulation has been criticized as unphysiological, but since the mere mixture of the blood of the two animals did not influence pancreatic secretion, Matsuo felt justified in concluding that it was 'beyond doubt that the secretion of pancreatic juice is caused under physiological conditions by some chemical substance which is liberated by the injection of acid into the duodenum or jejunum, enters into the general circulation, and stimulates the cells of the pancreas'.

Another criticism, and one of a different character, was that the effect of the supposed hormone upon the pancreas was not a specific one, produced by one particular secretion which was adapted to evoke one particular response, but was a generalized property of tissue extracts. The basis of this criticism was the well-recognized existence in many such extracts of a component which evoked a complex of symptoms in animals into which they were injected, these including a fall of blood pressure and vasodilation, with a consequent increase in the secretory output of certain organs, included in which was the pancreas. Bayliss and Starling were, of course, very well aware that the injection of intestinal extracts gave a marked lowering of blood pressure, which is clearly seen in Figs. 4B and 4D, but they showed that this effect was much reduced if the extraction was carried out for twenty-four hours with absolute alcohol in a Soxhlet apparatus instead of with acid (Fig. 4C). They also found that the epithelial lining of the intestine was mostly shed if the dorsal aorta was temporarily occluded, and that extracts prepared from these desquamated cells still had a marked effect on pancreatic secretion but only a negligible one on blood pressure.

Moreover, they were able to show that 'secretin' was specific in its site of origin within the body, for it was not present in extracts of a variety of other tissues and, most significantly, it could not be obtained from the mucosa of other parts of the alimentary canal (Fig. 4D). In fact, potent extracts could only be obtained from those parts, the duodenum and jejunum, which were normally acted upon by the acid gastric chyme. Thus the supposition that 'secretin' was no more than a generalized 'vasodilatin' was never very well founded, and the situation was further clarified when Dale showed that a major cause of the vascular effects produced by tissue extracts was the presence in them of β-iminazolyl-ethylamine, later to be known as histamine. Nevertheless, it needs to be remembered that the presence of such contaminants is a factor that has always to be rigorously controlled before it is safe to evaluate the results of injecting extracts of supposed endocrine tissue, and failure to observe this precaution is said to account for early reports of the presence of 'secretin' in nettles and spinach. It is curious to reflect, however, that such reports, even though disproved in this particular case, seem less bizarre now than they probably did when they were first put forward; as we have already indicated, there is an increasing suspicion that the evolution of hormones may sometimes have involved the utilization by organisms of molecules that were already widely spread before they became incorporated into endocrine mechanisms.

The ideals towards which investigations of a particular hormone must be directed include the preparation of it in a highly purified and, if possible, crystalline form, the determination of its chemical constitution and, finally, the synthesis of it in the laboratory, but such aims are not easily achieved, as is clearly shown by the results of more than fifty years of research on 'secretin'. One major line of advance derives from the discovery in 1926 that most of the vasodilator activity present in the initial acid extract could be removed by saturating this with sodium chloride, the 'secretin' coming down to form the so-called 'A precipitate', a putty-like substance, which contains up to 72 per cent. water and a considerable amount of impurities. From this there has been obtained by alcohol extraction, followed by evaporation and precipitation by trichloracetic acid, a highly potent material known as 'SI', which is free of vasodilator activity but is still far from being a pure substance; owing to the ease of preparing it, however, and with its well-defined properties, it has proved an excellent starting point for further purification, although more recently the drying of 'A precipitate' with acetone has been recommended as yielding a stable powder which is relatively free of impurities.

Swedish workers, Hammarsten, Wilander, and Ågren, obtained in 1933 a preparation of 'secretin' in the form of a crystalline picrolonate, derived, after crystallization from pyridine, from a salicylate obtained by an electrodialytic procedure. Later, in 1938, Greengard and Ivy in the United States obtained another crystalline picrolonate, also by the use of pyridine, but it is clear that the two substances are by no means identical. The Swedish preparation has a high molecular weight and liberates a number of amino acids without loss of 'secretin' activity when it is digested by aminopolypeptidase, which suggests that it may well be a complex of 'secretin' and protein. The American preparation, on the other hand, has a relatively low molecular weight and contains a high proportion of picrolonic acid, so that it is probably a much simpler substance. Both, however, must be regarded as complexes of uncertain composition, as may be judged from the fact that X-ray diffraction studies have been said to show that the pattern of the Greengard and Ivy preparation is identical with that of pyridine picrolonate. Evidently the final determination of the exact nature of the hormone, not to mention its synthesis, remains to be achieved, although it has been rather generally assumed that it is a polypeptide, the estimated molecular weight of the Swedish preparation being about 5,000. The use of the material in its present state of purification has proved of some value in clinical studies, although it seems not to have come into general use. By persuading a patient to swallow a lead ball, a silk cord, and a double stomach and duodenal tube, and by waiting for the appropriate portion of the latter to pass through the pylorus, it is possible to aspirate the duodenal contents; study of the composition of the pancreatic juice secreted in response to intravenous injections of the hormone may then make it possible to form an opinion as to the functional condition of the gland.

4. Secretin and pancreozymin

We must now consider in more detail the physiological significance of 'secretin' in the digestive processes of the mammal. From what has been said so far this may seem to be a relatively simple issue, but such issues commonly appear more complex when they are subjected to analysis and the present one is no exception, the initial complication being the established fact that the secretory activity of the pancreas is influenced by the vagus nerve as well as by hormonal action. Pavlov's technique for demonstrating this in dogs has already been mentioned, but it can also be readily shown in acute experiments of the type used by Bayliss and Starling. For this purpose the vagus is prepared for faradic stimulation and a cannula inserted into the pancreatic duct so that the drops of secretion can not only be counted but can also be collected for subsequent analysis, particularly for their enzyme content. It is also convenient to fix a small portion of the pancreas at the beginning and end of the experiment, for by suitable staining of sections (e.g. with Lane's neutral gentian, p. 41) it is possible to demonstrate the stored zymogen granules in the cells and to determine whether there has been any discharge of these into the pancreatic juice.

Now it is agreed that the main effect of vagal stimulation in such experiments is to bring about an extensive discharge of enzymes from the pancreatic cells. This is indicated by their increased concentration in the pancreatic juice, while examination of sections shows that a marked reduction in the granule content of the cells has occurred (see below). On the other hand, the effect upon the volume of secretion is very variable; an increased output in the dog was, as we have seen, clearly demonstrated in Pavlov's experiments, but in the anaesthetized cat there may be little or no increase.

In contrast to this, the main effect of the injection of 'secretin' preparations into the blood stream is to promote a great increase in the volume of secretion, while the juice so produced has at most only a low concentration of enzymes. Indeed, there was for many years disagreement as to whether 'secretin' had any effect at all upon the discharge of the latter. Those investigators who used the 'SI' substance or its derivatives were satisfied that some discharge did occur, but they recognized that it was slight in comparison with that evoked by vagal stimulation. There was in use, however, another substance, which had been prepared in England by J. Mellanby. He employed a method that differed fundamentally from that used in preparing 'SI', the intestinal mucosa being extracted with absolute alcohol, and bile salts being employed to bring about a precipitation of bile acids with the active material adsorbed to them. A potent preparation of the hormone was then obtained by elution. Using this, Mellanby was unable to obtain any evidence at all for any discharge of enzymes, and from this result he developed the view that the enzyme output was entirely under the control of the vagus and that the function of 'secretin' was to bring about the secretion of the fluid in which the enzymes were conveyed down the pancreatic duct into the intestine. In so doing he had moved a very long way indeed from the position first taken up by Bayliss and Starling who had at one time claimed that the hormonal method of control was 'the normal one' and that 'a concomitant nervous process . . . is superfluous and therefore improbable'.

Renewed investigation of these disagreements by Harper and Vass in 1941 showed that the entry of food material into the duodenum of the cat undoubtedly promoted an increased discharge of enzymes from the pancreas, even when all the nerves to the intestine had been severed, so that Mellanby's view could not possibly be correct, yet they were able to confirm his finding that the hormone did not stimulate the discharge of enzymes *if it was prepared by his method*. At this stage Harper and Raper perceived that these difficulties could be resolved if it could be shown that more than one hormone was concerned, one being responsible for the discharge of enzymes and the other for the secretion of fluid, and if the different methods of extraction gave different yields of the two. They were able to show that this was in fact so, and as a result of their work it is now agreed that two hormones are actually secreted by the duodenum.

One of these, secretin *sensu stricto* (which we shall refer to without the use of inverted commas), is responsible for the secretion of the fluid, while the other, to which they gave the name pancreozymin, brings about the discharge of enzymes. With Mellanby's method of preparation the secretin is precipitated with the bile salts, while the pancreozymin remains in solution and can then be obtained by precipitation with sodium chloride. This explains why his material evoked no discharge of enzymes. The 'SI' preparation, however, contains both hormones, so that those who used it were perfectly correct in claiming that their 'secretin' did evoke enzyme discharge. The two hormones can be separated from this material by making the final precipitation with bile salts and acetic acid instead of with trichloracetic acid; both come down

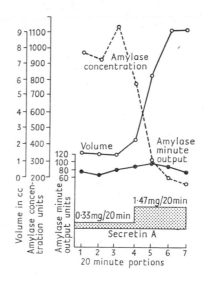

Fig. 5. Effect of increasing the rate of secretin administration on the volume and enzyme content of pancreatic juice in an unanaesthetized dog.
(From Wang *et al.*, 1948. *Amer. J. Physiol.* **154,** 358–68.)

in the precipitate and the secretin can be extracted from this with alcohol, the pancreozymin remaining with the alcohol-insoluble residue. That pancreozymin is actually transmitted through the blood stream has been demonstrated in dogs prepared, in the manner outlined earlier, with a subcutaneously auto-transplanted pancreas; the introduction of food substances into the duodenum through a fistula evokes the discharge of pancreatic fluid and an increased output of enzymes and, in the absence of any nervous connexions, the stimulus must be a hormonal one.

We are now in a position to consider data illustrating the contrasting effect of these two hormones and, in effect, summarizing our present understanding of their mode of action. Fig. 5 presents data obtained from an experiment in which secretin was administered to an unanaesthetized dog, initially at a rate of 0·33 mg per twenty minutes; the volume of secretion and its amylase concentration remain approximately constant and so also, in consequence, does the output of amylase per minute. When the rate of administration of secretin is suddenly increased more than threefold, to 1·47 mg per twenty minutes, the volume of secretion immediately increases but there is a reciprocal fall in the concentration of

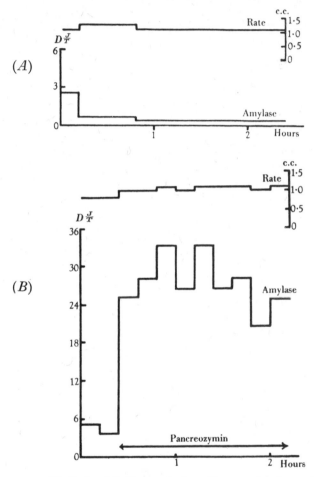

Fig. 6 *A* and *B*. Demonstration of hormonal and neural influences on pancreatic secretion in the cat.

A. Secretin only injected, resulting in a flow of juice of low enzyme content, with no alteration in the granule content of the zymogen cells (cf. Plate I). *B.* The flow of pancreatic juice was maintained by injections of secretin. In addition, during the period indicated by arrows, 9 mg of a pancreozymin preparation was given every 12 min. This resulted in a sustained increase in the output of amylase and a depletion of the granule content of the zymogen cells (cf. Plate I).

the enzyme, so that the output of this per minute remains approximately constant. In other words, the secretin is affecting the rate of output of the fluid but not the rate of output of the enzyme. Actually, there is often a temporary small rise in the latter when the rate of administration is increased, but this is due to the washing-out of accumulated enzyme from

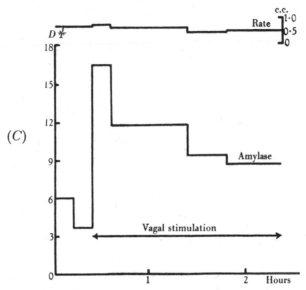

Fig. 6 C. Demonstration of hormonal and neural influences on pancreatic secretion in the cat (cont.). The flow of pancreatice juice was maintained by injections of secretin. In addition, during the period indicated by arrows, the dorsal vagus trunk was stimulated in the thorax. This resulted in an increase in the output of amylase and a depletion of the granule content of the zymogen cells.
(From Harper & Mackay, 1948. *J. Physiol.* **107**, 89–96.)

the pancreatic alveoli, the small cavities into which the cells discharge; a similar effect is usually seen at the beginning of an experiment, when the secretin is administered for the first time, the early samples of juice carrying a high enzyme content which is also a result of such a washing-out.

The effects of secretin and of pancreozymin are contrasted in Fig. 6 (see also Plate 1). The injection of secretin at regular intervals into an anaesthetized cat produces a steady output of pancreatic juice with a low amylase content, and at the end of the experiment there has been no noticeable diminution of the zymogen content of the cells. If pancreozymin is injected in addition, however, there is no change in the volume output but a marked increase in the output of amylase, accompanied by a reduction of the zymogen granules. If, instead of the injection of pancreozymin, the stimulation of the vagus is superimposed upon the secretin treatment, the result is very similar; amylase output is increased (its subsequent decline being almost certainly due to fatigue of the preparation) without any concomitant increase in the volume of the fluid secretion, while the cells again show a marked decrease in their zymogen content (Fig. 6C). In fact, the action of the vagus almost exactly parallels that of pancreozymin except that treatment of the animal with atropine has no effect upon the action of the hormone while it abolishes the secretomotor effect of the vagus as a result of its normal paralysing influence upon the parasympathetic nerve endings.

These reactions can also be readily demonstrated *in vitro*, slices of the pancreas of the pigeon being particularly suitable for the purpose. If such slices are incubated in saline media in Warburg baths it is found that extrusion of preformed secretory granules will take place on the addition to the medium of either pancreozymin or acetylcholine. The latter mimics the effect of vagal stimulation since it is the normal chemical transmitter at parasympathetic nerve endings (p. 224), and its effect is therefore abolished if atropine is also added, since this prevents it from acting upon effector cells. The effect of pancreozymin, however, is uninfluenced by atropine, a clear demonstration of the distinction between the hormonal and the neurohumoral types of action which we shall be discussing later. Another distinction can equally clearly be made by the substitution of secretin for pancreozymin; this shows that the former has no influence upon discharge of the zymogen granules.

So far we have referred to the discharge of hormones by the duodenum as though hydrochloric acid were the only stimulating agent involved; such an assumption is, in fact, often implicit in accounts of the process, but it is certainly not correct, for it is known that gastrectomy (removal of the stomach) and achlorhydria (reduction of gastic acidity) need not affect intestinal digestion. The evidence shows that only a part of the total response of the pancreas can be accounted for by the stimulating effect of the acid that enters the duodenum, and that in dogs the response of the gland to a meal of meat continues even if the duodenal contents are neutralized by the introduction of a solution of sodium bicarbonate. By using an animal with the auto-transplanted pancreas and duodenal loop described above, it has been shown that acid in the latter is a powerful releaser of secretin but that its effect on pancreozymin is much weaker. Peptones and amino acids, on the other hand, are strong stimuli for the release of pancreozymin and are second only to acid in their effect on secretin. Fats and soaps are also effective stimulants, but carbohydrates are not. That these substances act by releasing the relevant hormones and not by direct stimulation of the pancreas is shown by the fact that they have no effect upon that organ when they are injected into the blood stream. It is thus clear that the pancreatic hormonal mechanism does not rely only upon acid, but that it makes use also of the class of stimulants known as secretagogues; these may be defined as substances present in food, or produced by its digestion, which excite the production of digestive secretions either by local action, or by entering the blood, or by causing hormones to be released.

5. Other supposed hormones of the vertebrate digestive system

There is every reason for believing that the control of the secretion of the salivary glands of mammals is regulated through the parasympathetic and sympathetic divisions of the autonomic nervous system. This is understandable, for the requirement here is a rapid and often quite brief response to the presence of food in the buccal cavity, and for this the nervous system is well suited. Elsewhere, however, the situation is more complex, and nowhere more so than in the stomach.

Pioneer observations in this field were carried out by the American Army surgeon Beaumont upon Alexis St. Martin, a French-Canadian trapper who was left with a permanent gastric fistula after unexpectedly surviving the effects of a serious gunshot wound in the abdomen. Much of our later knowledge, however, is drawn from the results of chronic experiments carried out upon dogs with a surgically prepared gastric fistula, or with a gastric pouch, the latter consisting of a portion of the stomach completely or partially separated from the main organ and arranged to open to the exterior. Heidenhain devised a pouch that was deprived of its vagus nerve supply, but Pavlov (aided, it is said, by his ambidexterity) developed a technique for preparing a pouch (Fig. 7) that retained its full innervation. Events proceeding in this Pavlov pouch may be expected to parallel closely the secretory activities of the main stomach, and these can in consequence be analysed by collecting the gastric juice produced in the pouch. An important later development was the introduction by Ivy and Farrell in 1925 of the technique of auto-transplantation, to which reference has already been made in connexion with our analysis of the control of pancreatic secretion. As applied to the study of gastric secretion this technique involves moving a portion of the stomach, with its nerves and blood vessels intact, to a new position under the skin, the mammary region being selected because of its rich vascularization. Here the transplant, formed into a pouch, develops a new blood supply and, when this has occurred, its nervous and vascular connexions with the main organ are severed. Secretion is collected from the pouch through a fistula, and it can be assumed, as with the auto-transplanted pancreas, that stimulation of its secretory epithelium can only be effected through the blood stream.

As a result of the application of such techniques it has been established that the secretory response of the stomach to feeding takes place in two distinct phases. The first of these, known as the nervous or cephalic phase, is controlled reflexly through the parasympathetic division of the autonomic system either in response to the stimulation of taste buds by the ingestion of food (Fig. 8) or, as a conditioned reflex, and with the higher nervous centres participating, in response to stimulation of other receptors such as the eye and the nose. The gastric juice so produced is very rich in

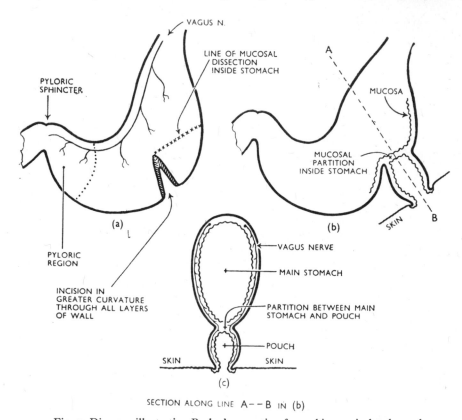

Fig. 7. Diagram illustrating Pavlov's operation for making an isolated pouch of the stomach. Note that the pouch has the same nerve and blood supply as the main part of the stomach.
(From Bell *et al.*, 1956. *Textbook of Physiology and Biochemistry*. Livingstone.)

pepsin, and in agreement with this it is found that faradic stimulation of the vagus will result in depletion of the granules of the chief (peptic) cells, an effect similar to that produced in the zymogen cells of the pancreas.

The nervous phase is followed in mammals by a second stage of gastric digestion, which is known as the chemical phase, and this can be further subdivided into the pyloric and intestinal phases. The pyloric phase is believed to be regulated through a hormonal mechanism, the first evidence for which was obtained shortly after the discovery of 'secretin', Edkins showing in 1906 that the intravenous injection of extracts of the pyloric region of the stomach would evoke gastric secretion. Although, for reasons that we have examined earlier (p. 20), this was far from being a complete proof of the existence of hormonal control, Edkins felt justified in assuming that a gastric hormone was probably concerned, and gave to it, by analogy with 'secretin', the name of gastrin.

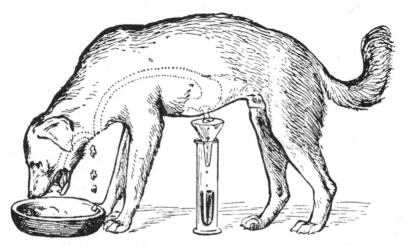

Fig. 8. A demonstration of the nervous phase of gastric secretion, illustrating Pavlov's experimental methods. The food consumed drops out of the open end of an oesophageal fistula without entering the stomach; the gastric secretion evoked by feeding is collected through a gastric fistula, consisting of a tube flanged at each end.
(From Winton & Bayliss, 1937. *Human Physiology*, 2nd ed. Philadelphia: Blakiston.)

This 'gastrin theory' has in the past aroused much criticism on a number of grounds, including, for example, the assertion that the effect is due to secretagogues or vasodilator substances rather than to a true hormone. On the whole, however, it has become strengthened with the passage of time, and particularly convincing evidence for it has been obtained from experiments upon dogs in which, in addition to the preparation of an auto-transplanted gastric pouch, the main stomach has also been denervated and transformed into an isolated pouch. Liver extract placed in the latter pouch will evoke secretion both in it and also in the transplant, but will fail to do so if the lining of the main pouch is first treated with procaine. The inference drawn from this experiment is that the gastric lining will respond to the presence of the liver extract by releasing a hormone into the blood stream, but that it is unable to react in this way if it is first anaesthetized.

Further evidence has come from study of the effects of antrum-exclusion gastrectomy, one of the surgical treatments for duodenal ulcer, in which the jejunum is connected to the proximal portion of the stomach while the distal (pyloric) portion, or antrum, together with the duodenum, are left *in situ* as a blind pocket. Despite this short-circuiting of the pyloric portion, it is certain that a barium meal may sometimes pass into it, and there is reason to suspect that normal food may also do so. Under these circumstances, so it is thought, gastrin may be released from it and may then evoke the secretion of acid, a situation which would account for the formation in certain patients of new ulcers in the jejunum.

It may now be regarded as very generally accepted that either mechanical or chemical stimulation, the latter by means of a variety of substances, including meat extractives, peptone, water, bile, and alcohol, probably do evoke the release of a hormone from the mucous membrane of the pyloric portion of the stomach, but the situation has been much confused by assertions that in this particular instance the hormone is actually histamine. The basis for this belief is the fact that this substance admittedly has a particularly strong stimulating effect upon the acid-secreting (parietal) cells of the stomach, and that it is also found in considerable amounts in the pyloric mucosa. However, it has now become possible to prepare from the latter a histamine-free extract which strongly stimulates the acid-secreting cells, and it thus seems very likely that there is a hormone, gastrin, which is distinct from histamine. It has been suggested that the explanation of the presence of the latter substance in such large amounts in the mucosa may be that it is an agent serving as the final local stimulant of the parietal cells, being itself released by the presence of the hormone.

Evidently the analysis of the pyloric phase of gastric digestion is not yet complete, but the nature of the intestinal phase is very much more obscure. The essential fact is that the introduction of various substances (water, meat extractives, and peptone, for example) into the duodenum through a fistula will evoke secretion in the stomach even if the latter is entirely separated from the intestine. The possibility that this may result from the liberation of an 'intestinal gastrin' has been raised, but there is very little evidence indeed to support such a view, and it seems more likely that the secretory activity may be stimulated in this instance by secretagogues absorbed from the food. In support of this are observations that intravenous injections of amino acids may evoke some small amount of gastric secretion.

We have so far been concerned with hormones that are believed to exert stimulatory effects upon their target organs, but there is, of course, no reason at all why a hormone should not have an inhibitory effect. At one time it was suggested that such a hormone should be distinguished as a chalone, but this term has never come into general use, probably for the very good reason that the effects of hormones are much too complex to lend themselves usefully to such a simple analysis. However, an example of a supposed inhibitory hormone acting within the alimentary system is provided by enterogastrone. It has been known since 1886 that the addition of fat to a meal in man will reduce the acidity of the stomach, for it has some effect upon both the secretory and motor activity of the gastric contents and will also delay the emptying of the stomach. It was later shown that fat only acted in this way when it was in the duodenum, and that no such effects occurred while it was in the stomach. Subsequently it was established with the aid of auto-transplanted gastric pouches that reduction of motility and of acidity occurred in the pouch after feeding through the main stomach with olive oil, even with all the nervous connexions of the pouch severed, so that there was some presumptive evidence for the vascular transmission of the agent concerned, and since the intravenous injection of fatty gastric contents has no such inhibitory effect there was some justification for regarding that agent as a hormone.

There are, however, considerable complications in this situation. Various substances additional to fats can, when present in the duodenum, inhibit gastric motility, and it seems certain that this effect is at least in part mediated through a nervous reflex involving the vagus nerve. Moreover, extracts containing the supposed enterogastrone will only inhibit motility if the stomach retains its vagal innervation, which would not be a necessary condition if the effect were purely hormonal. Pancreozymin, for example, will act on the pancreas even when the vagal innervation of that organ has been paralysed by atropine. While, then, the occurrence of hormonal inhibition of movement remains uncertain, there is somewhat better evidence for hormonal inhibition of gastric acid secretion, for fats are the only activators of this reaction and it can be evoked by intestinal extracts which seem to be free of other intestinal hormones and of active contaminants. It has been suggested, therefore, that the term enterogastrone might be better restricted to a supposed hormone concerned only with the inhibition of secretion, but even so the evidence for the existence of such a hormone requires to be strengthened before it can be regarded as entirely convincing.

As regards the liver, it is very well established that secretin not only influences pancreatic secretion but also increases the rate of secretion of bile. Thus is explained an early observation, dating back to 1880, that the flow of the latter is stimulated by the presence of acid in the duodenum. It has been suggested that the common action of secretin upon the pancreas and the liver reflects the close association of these two organs in their early development, for they arise from adjacent outgrowths of the embryonic intestine, but the simultaneous need for both secretions during the normal sequence of digestive processes has no doubt been at least as significant a factor.

Another consequence of the passage of acid into the duodenum is the evoking of rhythmical contractions of the gall-bladder with the consequent discharge of its contained bile, and that this involves a hormonal mechanism is indicated by the fact that an auto-transplanted gall-bladder will also respond in this way, while the effect is shown, too, in animals connected by cross-circulation. The hormone that is thought to be concerned in this response has been called cholecystokinin. As might be expected from its relationship with the duodenum, it seems to be closely associated with secretin and is present with the latter in duodenal extracts, although the two can be separated by electrophoresis and by alcohol extraction. There are differences, too, in their mode of action. The latent period after intravenous injection is several minutes for cholecystokinin, as compared with about one minute for secretin, while fatty acids and fats are especially potent duodenal stimulants of the release of the former, so that a meal of five egg yolks and half a pint of cream is a powerful promoter of contractions of the gall-bladder in man. It is a matter of interest that this hormone appears to be absent from the horse which also lacks a gall-bladder, but is present in company with the gall-bladder in pigs, sheep, cattle, rabbits, and dogs, as well as in man.

With such good evidence for hormonal control of the secretory activity of the stomach, liver, and pancreas, it is understandable that a search has been made for the existence of similar mechanisms in the intestine, but here the evidence is very much less satisfactory. We have seen that in mammals an important contribution to the intestinal secretion comes from Brunner's glands, situated at the upper end of the duodenum, and it is known that an isolated subcutaneous auto-transplant of this region will secrete in response to the feeding of a meal in the dog, cat, and pig, so that there is here a strong indication of the operation of some hormonal factor. That these glands are the ones that respond, and not the crypts of Lieberkühn, is shown by the fact that the lower portion of the intestine, where the crypts are present but where Brunner's glands are lacking, will only respond if it is subjected to local stimulation. Many of the intestinal extracts that have been used to investigate this matter have been secretin preparations, and it has often been supposed that secretin itself is the operative hormone. It has also been suggested that we may here be dealing with a distinctive duodenal hormone for which the name duocrinin has been proposed, but it would probably be agreed that the existence of this has not yet been substantiated, and it may well be that secretin will prove to be the hormone actually concerned.

Another suggestion that has not yet been confirmed is to the effect that a hormone called enterocrinin, believed to be formed in the intestinal mucosa, is responsible for increasing the volume and enzyme output of the succus entericus, secreted by the mucosa of the small intestine. Apart from the incompleteness of the available evidence, a major difficulty here is that some at least of the intestinal enzymes are believed to be intracellular, which makes it likely that the release of enzymes into the lumen will be much influenced by mechanical stimulation, produced either by motor activity during normal digestion or by friction during the experimental collection of the secretion. Mention may also be made of a substance called urogastrone, which was obtained from urine in 1940 and which appears to inhibit gastric motility and secretion, but there seems to be no good reason for including it as a hormone, while its physiological significance is, to say the least, doubtful. It has been thought, too, that the rhythmical activity of the intestinal villi may be promoted by an intestinal hormone called villikinin, but the passage of twenty years has seen no corroboration of this claim.

6. Requirements for the demonstration of hormonal mechanisms

It cannot be denied that the results of the study of the hormones of the digestive system are less clear-cut than could be wished, and it will be well to consider the reasons for this, since they will help us to determine the type of evidence for which we should seek in endocrinological research. During the sixty or so years in which mammalian endocrinology has been under intensive investigation there has emerged a set of criteria which are collectively held to justify a belief in the endocrine function of a particular organ, and which can be regarded as requirements to be met before its endocrine status is completely established. These are as follows:

Histological and histochemical studies. It should be possible to identify in the supposed endocrine organ such characteristic features as secretory cells, ample blood supply, and the absence of secretory ducts. Secretory products or their precursors should be visible in the cells, and it should be possible to correlate variations in their appearance with variations in the intrinsic activity of the organ or in its relationship with other organs or systems. Such variations might be natural ones, or they might be experimentally induced. Histochemical observations should be correlated with the chemical ones mentioned below.

Deficiency studies. Reduced activity of the organ, or its complete absence, should produce a clearly defined complex of symptoms (technically known as a syndrome), observable clinically in human subjects or in the laboratory in experimentally treated animals.

Replacement therapy. It should be possible to relieve such symptoms by treatment of the patient or animal with suitably purified extracts of the organ, or by introducing implants of the latter. A study of the effects of hyperactivity, as a result, for example, of injecting amounts in excess of the actual requirement, would probably arise out of this.

Chemical studies. These would include the isolation, purification, and characterization of the hormone, followed ideally by the determination of its molecular structure and by its synthesis. *In vitro* studies of its reactions with individual tissues would flow from this with a view to determining how its effects are produced; here, incidentally, arises the need to keep clearly in mind the distinction between the gross physiological effects of the hormone and the means by which these are actually initiated in the cells of the target organs. With the structure of the hormone known, it should be possible also to determine the course of its biosynthesis (i.e. its mode of formation within the gland), its metabolism, and its excretion.

Blood studies. As a corollary of the conception of a hormone as a substance which is transmitted through the blood stream (although we shall have to examine this concept further in due course), it is clearly essential to be able to demonstrate the presence of the active substance in the blood under normal physiological conditions. Ideally, it should be demonstrated to be present in the venous blood leaving the supposed gland of its origin, and, to give complete assurance that it has actually been secreted from the latter, it should be possible to show that its concentration is higher in the venous blood than in the arterial blood entering the gland.

Assay procedures. It is essential to be able to give quantitative expression to the strength of active preparations and extracts before their effects can be usefully analysed or compared, and this may depend either upon direct chemical assay or upon bioassays involving the use of living animals or of tissues removed from them.

The above set of criteria constitutes, of course, something of an ideal, and it is not suggested that the whole of it must be satisfied before the endocrine status of an organ can reasonably be accepted. Nevertheless, the completion of each item in it can be expected to yield valuable information, and we shall see later that in some instances the programme has proceeded a long way to completion. On the other hand, the evidence for the establishment of the existence of hormones of the alimentary canal falls unusually short of this ideal, for the site of their secretion is unknown, except in so far as it can be related to one of the major regions of the canal, so that histological and histochemical evidence is completely lacking. Moreover, deficiency and replacement studies are impracticable because of the remarkably self-centred organization of the digestive system, for the hormones which are believed to regulate the system actually arise within it. These hormones are remarkable, too, for their independence of control by the central nervous system, a peculiarity that we shall be in a better position to appreciate later, and their integration with each other thus depends simply upon their sequential release at successive stages of the passage of the food along the alimentary canal.

7. Some evolutionary considerations

The limitations which thus seem to be inherent in our study of the hormones of the alimentary tract, compared with the much more precise knowledge which is already available for other hormonal systems, suggest that we may be dealing here with an endocrine system that has retained a primitive pattern of organization, and this may well be because it is regulating a sequence of events that are essentially preparatory to metabolism rather than a part of it. However this may be, it seems clear that only a few of the substances that have been thought to act as alimentary hormones can at present be placed in that category, and even then on evidence which is less complete than could be wished. In these we should certainly include secretin, pancreozymin, and cholecystokinin, and probably also gastrin, although the status of the latter is confused by the uncertainty regarding its relationship with histamine.

We have seen, however, that the digestive system does not rely solely upon these hormones, for there are many phases of its activity which in mammals can also be influenced by the nervous system, and this aspect merits closer consideration. It is easy to see an advantage in gastric digestion being divisible into nervous and hormonal phases, for the former makes possible the preparation of the stomach for the reception of food, while the latter maintains control during the later stages when the animal (to judge from our own experience) is no longer conscious of its digestive processes. The secretion produced in this preparatory or nervous phase is often referred to as 'appetite secretion', and the need for promoting it provides physiological justification for beginning a meal with soup or some other light but attractive course. 'Now good digestion wait on appetite, And health on both!' The dual nervous and hormonal control of pancreatic secretion is, however, much more difficult to explain, for rapidity of response would hardly seem necessary, and the two hormones provide in themselves a very complete regulatory system. This is a situation that certainly demands for its interpretation more knowledge than we yet possess of the digestive physiology of the lower vertebrates, for the mode of regulation of the alimentary tract in mammals, like other aspects of their physiology, is the end result of an evolutionary process that must have begun with a much simpler pattern of organization.

For example, the autonomic nervous system in fish does not show the antagonism between the parasympathetic and sympathetic divisions which is so marked in the higher forms, nor do the two seem to overlap so far in their distribution over the alimentary canal. Thus both vagal and sympathetic fibres evoke motor responses in the musculature of the alimentary tract when they are stimulated, and it is by no means certain that the vagus extends further backwards than the pyloric region of the stomach in fish, although it is said to innervate the hinder regions of the intestine in lampreys. As regards secretory activity, the small amount of work that has been devoted to this problem in the lower vertebrates has

(A)

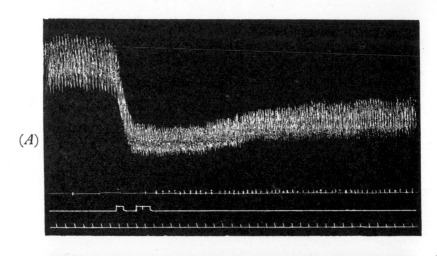

(B)

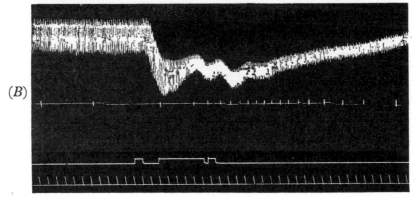

Fig. 9. Effect on pancreatic secretion in the dog of injecting intravenously (A) 15 ml of a 'secretin' solution prepared from the intestine of the fowl, and (B) 5 ml of a 'secretin' solution prepared from the intestine of a dogfish (cf. Fig. 4 for further details).
(From Bayliss & Starling, 1903. *J. Physiol.* **29**, 174–180.)

failed to provide any evidence for either nervous or hormonal control of gastric secretion in selachian fish, and it is remarkable that even in reptiles the effect of vagal stimulation is very slight, despite the fact that the parasympathetic system is a strong stimulator of the salivary glands.

The results of study of the pancreas are more positive, in so far as

Bayliss and Starling showed that the presence of 'secretin' was a wide-spread feature of vertebrate organization, for they were able to prepare active extracts from the intestine of the fowl, tortoise, frog, salmon, dog-fish, and skate. (Fig. 9) The information relating to these lower forms, however, is still very incomplete, although it has since been demonstrated that secretion in rays can be increased by the introduction of acid into the intestine and by the intravenous injections of 'secretin' preparations, which gives at least some indication that the activity of the extracts is of physiological significance. On the other hand, Babkin concluded that there was no parasympathetic or sympathetic control of the secretory activity of the pancreas in these animals, for acetylcholine and adrenaline had no significant effect upon the volume of secretion discharged.

It is impossible to generalize from such fragmentary information, and this is clearly a field where there is a need for new work and for the relating of the results to the physiological and ecological factors which influence feeding and digestion. It is known that even in mammals the pancreas is capable of spontaneous secretion, notably in the rabbit, in which animal it has been reported as continuing after complete denervation of that organ, and even after decapitation and the removal of the whole of the alimentary tract with the exception of the liver and pancreas. It is possible that such a property, together with some degree of modulation by a simple hormonal mechanism, could meet the needs of the sluggish alimentary activity of fish, in which the digestion of a meal may take at least two days for completion. The increasing elaboration of the autonomic system in the course of later vertebrate evolution, associated with increasing mastery of both internal and external environments (p. 228), might then have led to the superimposition of an increasing degree of nervous control, with the result that in the higher forms the digestion of the food can be more closely integrated with its capture and ingestion and can also be regulated with the precision demanded by the increased speed of the digestive processes in homoiothermous animals. We shall see later that the analysis of the physiology of colour change reveals a somewhat analogous inter-weaving of neural and hormonal regulation.

Information relating to comparable problems in the invertebrates is even more fragmentary, and this is particularly regrettable in that investigations in other fields of endocrinology have shown that principles established for one major group of animals are sometimes transferable to other groups with very little modification. At present we can say no more than that there is some evidence for both neural and hormonal control of digestion in the invertebrate groups. As regards the former, it is known that stimulation of the nerves of the body wall of the earthworm will bring about discharge of a proteolytic enzyme from the intestinal epithelial cells. Again the direction taken by the ingested food in mosquitoes depends upon the nature of that food, blood passing to the mid-gut, for example, and sugar to the diverticula, and there is some suggestion that this may be under nervous control and may depend upon the initial stimulation of receptors in the buccal cavity. On the other hand, it is doubtful whether the secretory processes of the mid-gut and caeca in cockroaches (*Blattella* and *Periplaneta*) are regulated by the nervous system, but it has been observed that the injection into a starved individual of blood from a fed one evokes some signs of stimulation of secretion, and that this reaction is not obtained if the blood is taken from another starved animal. Here, then, is some preliminary indication that hormonal factors may be at work in these insects, but a comparison of these data with those that have been so laboriously secured for the mammals is sufficient to show how very much remains to be done before any degree of precision can be attached to such a conclusion. It is to be hoped that our under-standing of this field will grow rapidly, because it is of much more than theoretical interest. The type of information that we are discussing here sheds a light upon the relation between the nature of the food and the digestive capacity, on the powers of adjustment of the digestive system to different types of diet, and so eventually on the degree of limitation thereby imposed on the habits and distribution of the species concerned.

III. HORMONES AND METABOLISM

1. Diabetes mellitus and the pancreas

WE shall now examine the effects of a hormone which, although it apparently originated within the alimentary tract, has come to form part of a physiological system very different from that of the digestive hormones. Diabetes mellitus is a condition arising from profound disturbances of metabolism, the most obvious feature of which is a defective utilization of carbohydrate. This is reflected in an abnormally high concentration of glucose (blood sugar) in the circulating blood (hyperglycaemia) and a reduction in the amount of glycogen stored in the liver and muscle. The affected individual passes a large quantity of urine (polyuria) which possesses a sweet taste as a result of the presence in it of excreted glucose, and it is this circumstance that gives to the condition its name (*diabainein*, to pass through; *mellitus*, sweetened with honey). It is not only the carbohydrates that are affected, however, for protein and fat are called upon to supplement them as energy sources and this leads to an increased excretion of non-protein nitrogen, to wastage of the tissues, and to ketosis, this being the accumulation of ketone bodies (aceto-acetic acid, acetone, and β-hydroxy-butyric acid) in the blood and urine.

So clear-cut are these symptoms that diabetes mellitus has been recognized from ancient times, but its cause was unknown and attempts to control it by regulation of the diet met with only limited success. This, in fact, was the situation up to 1889, in which year Minkowski, at the suggestion of von Mering, undertook removal of the pancreas (pancreatectomy) from a dog as part of their study of digestive physiology. We have already remarked that it is sometimes well not to be unduly inhibited by previous work. Von Mering doubted the practicability of the operation, but Minkowski, happily ignorant of Claude Bernard's statement that animals could not survive total pancreatectomy, found not only that his operation had been successful, but that it had been followed by the development of symptoms of diabetes mellitus. The recognition of this was a result of the dog persistently micturating in the laboratory, a lapse that led Minkowski to examine its urine and thus to find that it had a high glucose content. The importance of this discovery, later described by him as a 'lucky accident', lay not only in the indication that some disorder of the pancreas might be the origin of the diabetic condition, but also in the provision of a technique for its experimental analysis, yet it is doubtful if it could have been exploited so effectively had there not already existed some important information relating to the structure of the organ. We are dealing here in fact, with an endocrinological problem that provides a striking example of the importance of linking experimental studies with histological observations, and it is to the latter that we must first turn.

2. The islets of Langerhans

The digestive secretion of the pancreas arises within secretory alveoli or acini, which discharge into a branched system of ducts, but there is also an endocrine component present and the first step towards the recognition of this was taken when a twenty-two-year-old medical student, Paul Langerhans, published in 1869 a doctorate thesis in which he presented an account of the microscopical anatomy of the organ. He noted the zymogen granules, although since they were blackened by osmic acid he erroneously concluded that they were fat droplets, but he also found small groups of cells that lacked these granules, and which he thought might be associated in some way with the nervous system. The work was left incomplete, to his own regret, and he did not live to associate it with von Mering and Minkowski's discovery, but by 1893 Laguesse had already realized the potential importance of these groups of cells and was referring to them as the islets of Langerhans, a name that they have retained ever since. This was a period in which observations on several organs, and particularly the thyroid gland and the gonads, were beginning to establish the foundations of endocrinology, although the time was not yet quite ripe for the synthesis of the scattered and sometimes confusing data. It was still being suggested that the relationship of the pancreas to the diabetic condition might result from that organ being concerned with the removal of some impurity from the body, but Laguesse was considering the possibility that the islets might be producing an internal secretion, and he seems to have been the first to use in this connexion the terms endocrine and exocrine as descriptive of internally and externally secreting tissue.

It is now well known that the islets of Langerhans (Plate 1) are scattered irregularly throughout the pancreas of mammals and vary greatly in size and number, even within the same species; in the guinea-pig there are said to be from 15,000 to at least 40,000, while in the human pancreas counts ranging up to 2,300,000 have been recorded. It is generally agreed that they arise from the duct epithelium, and they often seem to remain connected with the delicate extensions of this which pervade the whole organ. A feature related to their endocrine function is their very rich blood supply, with capillary vessels or sinusoids lying close against the irregular cords in which the islet cells come to be arranged. As to the possibility of their being innervated, we have seen that the exocrine cells receive sympathetic and parasympathetic fibres, and there is some

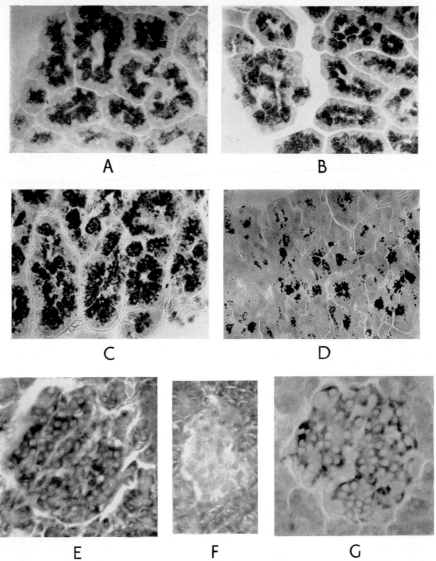

Plate I, *A & B*. Sections of pancreatic tissue of the cat removed before and after stimulation by secretin; there is no reduction in its content of zymogen granules (cf. Fig. 6*A*, p. 24). *C & D*. Sections of pancreatic tissue of the cat removed before and after stimulation by secretin and pancreozymin; there is marked depletion of the zymogen granules (cf. Fig 6*B*, p. 24). (× 500.)

(From Harper & Mackay, 1948. *J. Physiol.* **107**, 89–96.)

E. Islet tissue in a section of the pancreas of the rabbit, stained for sulfhydryl and disulphide groups by the method of Barrnett & Seligman, after fixation in Romeis' fluid, and showing the distribution of intensely reactive sulfhydryl- and disulphide-positive protein in the cytoplasm. *F*. A similar section prepared by the same technique, but two days after the administration of alloxan; no sulfhydryl- or disulphide-positive material remains in the islet cells. *G*. A section adjacent to that seen in *E*, showing B cells stained with aldehyde-fuchsin; comparison of *E* and *G* indicates that the B cells are the ones which are rich in sulfhydryl and disulphide groups. (× 300.)

(From Barrnett, Marshall, & Seligman, 1955. *Endocrin.* **57**, 419–38.)

suggestion that vagal impulses can influence the islet tissue, but it seems doubtful whether this is an important factor in the normal regulation of their secretory activity.

An initial difficulty in relating pancreatic structure to the diabetic condition was that when the islets first came under detailed scrutiny it was impossible to say whether they were an independent tissue or whether they were stages in the development or degeneration of the zymogen cells, and this particular problem was the focus of much of the early histological work. By the turn of the century evidence had accumulated, from the studies of Diamare and Laguesse amongst others, that the islet cells did show distinctive characteristics, and this view was supported by evidence of another type, which was later going to bear unexpected fruit, and which is represented by the experiments of Schulze. He reported in 1900 that careful ligation of peripheral parts of the pancreas of the guinea-pig led to the degeneration of the zymogen tissue while the islets remained unaltered. From this he drew the conclusion that the latter must be independent structures, that they were vascular glands of the same type as the pituitary, and that they might well be involved in some way in the regulation of blood-sugar.

Following upon these pioneer studies, which laid the foundations of current interpretations of pancreatic organization, particularly important advances were made by Lane, in 1907, and Bensley, in 1911. The former introduced the use of so-called neutral stains such as neutral gentian, obtained as a precipitate by adding a solution of orange G to one of gentian violet. With such dyes, and by varying the fixative, he found evidence for the existence in the islet tissue of two distinctive cell types, the A (or alpha) and B (or beta) cells, distinguishable from each other and from the zymogen cells by the reactions of their granular contents. This important concept has had so much influence on later work that it is worth noting that he clearly recognized that these might be two different phases of the same fundamental cell, but he rightly pointed out that even if this were so it would not exclude the possibility of the production of two different secretions. He concluded, in fact, that the islets were discharging into the blood stream 'a twofold substance' with an important effect upon metabolism. These observations were developed much more fully by Bensley, using a greater range of fixatives and stains. He dismissed altogether the possibility of there being any transition between the islet cells and the zymogen tissue and, with similar conclusions drawn from a study of the toad, he firmly established the concept of the pancreas as an organ that seemed likely to be combining exocrine with endocrine functions. The award to him in 1952 of the Banting Medal of the American Diabetics Association was a well-merited tribute to the value of histological studies in the solution of endocrinological problems.

The neutral stains used so successfully by Lane and Bensley in their investigations of the guinea-pig have been found by later workers to be capricious in their effects, particularly when they are applied to other species, the results being influenced, for example, by the pH of the fixative. Much use has therefore been made in more recent years of the Azan technique of Heidenhain, first introduced for this purpose in 1931 by Bloom. This well-known method, which involves staining with azo-carmine and counterstaining with a mixture of aniline blue and orange G, can give results that are both beautiful and at the same time reasonably reproducible. In general, the granules of the *A* cells are stained bright red, and those of the *B* cells orange-grey; a third cell type, the *D* (or delta) cell, distinguished by the presence of blue granules, has also been identified, but its interpretation remains doubtful, while so-called *C* cells are probably stages in the exhaustion or recovery of one or other of the main types.

Equally useful, and even more valuable as a routine procedure, is the chrome-alum-haematoxylin (CAH) method introduced by Gomori in 1941 with the aim of defining more precisely the *B* granules. This technique, usually with phloxine as a counterstain, has since found another important application in endocrine studies (p. 73); as applied to islet tissue in mammals it gives a very sharp differentiation of blue-black *A* granules and bright pink *B* granules, the *D* cells being indistinguishable.

Other methods, including silver impregnation of the *A* granules, and aldehyde-fuchsin (Plate I) staining of the *B* granules, have also been widely used, but Gomori claimed that the Azan and chrome-alum-haematoxylin techniques were adequate for descriptive purposes. It must be said, however, that they suffer from two limitations, which are readily apparent in practice. One of these, which applies particularly to the Azan technique, is that the results depend to a surprising extent upon the careful control of all stages of the procedure, so that there is a markedly subjective element in deciding what constitutes a 'good' preparation, which may mean no more than a preparation demonstrating what the observer expects to find. This, of course, is a difficulty inherent in many such procedures, and it demands the development of a keen critical sense in the user of them. The other limitation, which applies to both techniques, is that the reactions are in no sense specific for any particular component of the cells, so that identity of response needs to be analysed and corroborated by other procedures before it can properly be accepted as evidence for the identity or homology of the cells concerned.

There is probably no serious disagreement at the present time as to the existence of the *A* and *B* cells in mammals, and most students of them would probably feel that they were two distinctive and independent types with the implication that they had separate functions to fulfil. They vary in their arrangement, being sometimes mixed together indiscriminately, as in the guinea-pig, and sometimes segregated, as in the rat and rabbit, where the *A* cells occupy the periphery of the islets. It is rather common for the latter cells to constitute about 20 per cent. of the cell contents of the islets in adult mammals, but this varies to some extent with age. It is certainly also agreed that islet tissue is present in all of the other vertebrate groups down to and including the fish, but although cell types apparently corresponding to the *A* and *B* cells of mammals are often recognizable the interpretation of their functions and relationships is not always clear. Caution is therefore needed in considering the results of staining techniques that have been introduced primarily because of their suitability for mammalian research.

As regards the Cyclostomata, which we might reasonably expect to provide some clues to the evolutionary history of the islets, it is well established that in the ammocoete larva of the lamprey, at the anterior end of the intestine and in close association with the bile-duct, cells grow out from the intestinal epithelium and become arranged in the submucosa in groups, which have been called the follicles of Langerhans. There is no differentiated pancreas in these larvae, but cells that appear to correspond with the exocrine pancreatic cells of higher forms are found in the intestinal epithelium and are concentrated at the anterior end of the intestine, so that they are in the closest possible relationship with the follicle cells. Further, the follicle cells respond to glucose injections in a manner suggestive of islet cells (p. 49), so that there is some presumptive evidence that we have here in recognizable form the exocrine and endocrine components of a pancreas, still separate from each other, and showing their independent origin from the intestinal epithelium. At metamorphosis the follicles give rise to a compact gland-like tissue; the function of this is unknown, but it interdigitates with a blind caecum of the intestine to give rise to a compound structure highly suggestive of a very primitive form of pancreas, while the bile-duct, which in these animals degenerates at this stage of the life-cycle, gives rise to additional follicle cells (Fig. 10).

If the interpretation outlined above is correct, we have evidence that the islet tissue arose very early in vertebrate evolution, and that it must have originated within the alimentary tract, as, indeed, is suggested by its mode of development in the higher vertebrates; its endocrine secretion should, therefore, be classed from this point of view with the gastrointestinal hormones that we have considered in the previous chapter. The important difference is, however, that the latter are concerned with the food before it has been absorbed, whereas the islet secretion has become involved in the regulation of the subsequent metabolism of the digestive products, and it is doubtless because of this that the later evolutionary history of both the islets and their secretion has led them into a complex system of interactions with other endocrine organs.

The existence of a certain uniformity in the organization of the islet tissue of vertebrates is indicated by the fact that the Azan technique gives results in elasmobranch fish which are closely similar to those obtained with mammalian tissue; *A*, *B*, and *D* cells are identifiable, an interesting and presumably primitive feature being that some of these are found in the duct epithelium. In the teleosts the situation has its own peculiarity, as so often in that highly specialized group, in that much of the islet tissue

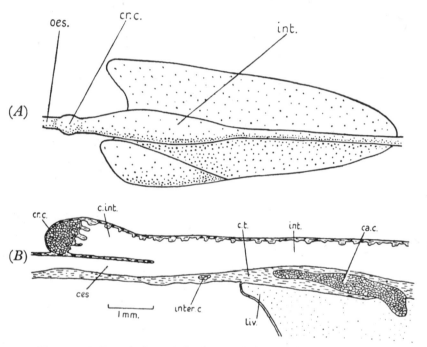

Fig. 10. *A*. Dorsal view of the liver and the associated region of the alimentary canal of the adult lamprey, *Lampetra fluviatilis*. *B*. Vertical longitudinal section of the same, *oes.*, oesophagus; *int.*, intestine; *c. int.*, caecum of intestine; *cr. c.*, follicular tissue derived from the larval follicles of Langerhans; *ca. c.*, similar tissue derived from the bile duct; *inter. c.*, dispersed follicular tissue; *liv.*, liver.
(From Barrington, 1945. *Quart. J. micr. Sci.* **85**, 391–417.)

is often concentrated into a so-called principal islet, which is separable from the rest of the organ; the existence of *A* and *B* cells has, however, been reported, with some evidence for seasonal variation in the proportions of the two types.

In Amphibia and reptiles the situation is somewhat confused. Accounts of urodele islet tissue variously refer to two types and to one type of cell, and it has been suggested that where two do appear to be present one of them may be transitional between the zymogen and endocrine cells. Two types of cell have also been described in anurans, but it has been claimed by some authors, although not all, that these are phases in the activity of one fundamental type corresponding to the B cell. Not the least interesting analysis is an early one of Saguchi, who identified five categories, which he believed to represent a sequence of phases in the activity of one type which was itself derived from the zymogen tissue. It has been customary to dismiss this interpretation on the grounds that it was based upon criteria different from the conventional one outlined above. Had the latter led us to a complete understanding of the organization and functioning of islet tissue in the lower vertebrates such an attitude might be justifiable, but since it has so far failed to do this one may feel that there is room for more, rather than less, non-conformity in the approach to these problems.

As regards reptiles, the early studies of Laguesse on snakes were amongst the first of the investigations of the granular contents of the islet cells. He found two types of cell to be present, but he was led to the view that these were two phases of the same type and, moreover, that the islets arose from exocrine alveoli and later returned to that form again owing to the inability of the endocrine cells to produce their secretion indefinitely. More recently his interpretation, at least as regards the relationships of the islet cells with each other, has found some support, although lizards have been said to possess A and B cells that constitute two distinct types. Finally, birds are said to possess both A and B cells, sometimes together in the same islets and sometimes segregated into separate ones.

It will be apparent that nearly one hundred years of research into islet histology finds us still unable to present any agreed account of the evolution and organization of this tissue in the vertebrates as a whole. No doubt we may conclude that endocrine cells are a common feature of the pancreas of all groups, but if we wish to ask how these cells function, what is the nature of their cytological differentiation, how they are related to each other and to the surrounding exocrine tissue, and what is the likelihood of them producing more than one type of secretion, we are unable to give any very useful answer for most species.

3. Insulin

We have seen how the trend of thought at the end of the nineteenth century was already leading to the view that some secretion of pancreatic islet tissue might be related to diabetes mellitus. The results of transplantation experiments were lending support to this, for it had been shown in 1892 that the diabetic condition resulting from removal of the pancreas was reduced or abolished if a portion of the organ had been previously transplanted under the skin and was allowed to remain there after it had established vascular connexions. If, however, the transplant was removed, following removal of the remainder of the organ, the typical symptoms of diabetes developed. During the early years of the present century many investigators, encouraged by the successes that had been achieved in the preparation of active extracts from the thyroid and adrenal glands and from the 'posterior lobe' of the pituitary, were endeavouring to prepare from the pancreas some extract that would alleviate the symptoms of diabetes mellitus. So convinced were they that the islets were secreting a hormone that in 1909 it was designated insuline (*insula*, island), well in advance of its actual discovery. Even with this unusual abandonment of caution, however, success continued to elude these investigators, although it seems probable that some came very close to it. Indeed, as F. G. Young points out, it is likely that extracts prepared by Zuelzer in 1908 did contain the hormone, but their use was abandoned because of alarming clinical results, a striking warning, this, of the importance of testing new preparations in carefully planned experiments upon animals.

It was not until 1920 that Banting initiated a renewed and intensive attack upon the problem and, in collaboration with Best, finally prepared the long-awaited extract and thereby demonstrated the existence of an islet hormone for which the name insulin, a modification of the earlier suggestion, was immediately adopted. Banting had just settled down to a career of general practice in London, Ontario, but had in addition taken up an appointment as instructor in the Medical School. Those who hold that it is no disadvantage for a university worker to undertake a modicum of teaching will doubtless take encouragement from the fact that the germ of his idea is said to have come to him at 2 a.m. on the morning of 1 November 1920, when he was preparing a lecture on pancreatic function. He was struck by the account of experiments, similar in principle to those of Schulze mentioned above, in which ligation of the ducts had destroyed the zymogen tissue but had left the islets substantially intact, for he saw that by preparing extracts from such an organ it would be possible to avoid the risk of the supposed hormone being destroyed by pancreatic digestion, an occurrence which might well account for previous failures in extraction.

His idea was inscribed in his notebook in the succinct words 'Tie off pancreas duct of dogs. Wait six or eight weeks. Remove and extract.' He was not, in fact, the first to have had this particular idea, nor is it uncommon for investigators to be pursuing the same project quite independently of each other. In 1912 a similar experiment had been started, but the worker concerned seems to have abandoned it owing to the great technical difficulties involved. These were, of course, also encountered by Banting and Best, but in this case they were overcome and after months of concentrated work during the summer of 1921, taking turns at watching and sleeping in order to keep their experimental dogs under continuous

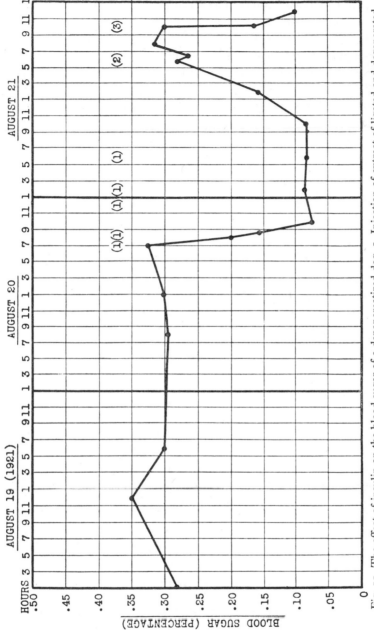

Fig. 11. The effect of insulin on the blood sugar of a depancreatized dog. 1. Injection of extract of ligated and degenerated pancreas. 2. Injection of extract after incubation with pancreatic juice. 3. Injection of extract incubated without pancreatic juice. (From Best & Taylor, 1940. *Physiological Basis of Medical Practice.* Williams and Wilkins.)

observation, they finally obtained extracts that lowered the elevated blood sugar of dogs that had been made diabetic by removal of the pancreas (Fig. 11). The importance of ensuring that the hormone was not destroyed by the digestive secretion during extraction was shown by incubating the active extract with pancreatic juice; after such treatment it was found to have lost its anti-diabetic effect. On 11 January 1922, pancreatic extracts were successfully administered to diabetic patients in the Toronto General Hospital. They had been developed just in time to benefit George R. Minot who, five years later, was to repay the debt by playing a leading part in the discovery of the erythrocyte-maturing factor of liver, which provided a treatment for pernicious anaemia.

It is understandable that a great deal of attention has been given to the purification and characterization of insulin, and this has led not only to its isolation in crystalline form by Abel in 1926, but to the complete elucidation of its molecular structure (Fig. 12), a brilliant achievement, which earned for Sanger of Cambridge the award of the Nobel Prize for Chemistry for 1958, and which has paved the way for the structural analyses of certain other polypeptide hormones. Insulin is a protein of relatively small size, with a molecular weight of about 6,000, and is composed of two polypeptide chains, a shorter A chain of twenty-one amino acids and a longer B chain of thirty. (It may be as well to emphasize that this terminology bears no relation at all to that of the islet cells.) The two chains are connected by two disulphide (-S-S-) linkages, and a third such linkage forms an intra-chain bridge in the A chain.

The importance of such determinations of molecular structure, quite apart from the hope which they hold out of achieving the artificial synthesis of the hormones (an ideal which, in the case of insulin, is far from being attained), is that they should eventually make possible the identification of those structural features that confer upon the molecules their biological activities. In this connexion, studies of variation between different species are important, because it would naturally be expected that such variations would only affect those components of the molecules which were not essential for their activities. As far as insulin is concerned, it has already been established that the B chains of the cattle, sheep, pig, horse, and whale hormone are identical, while the only variations in the A chains concern the three residues within the intra-chain disulphide ring. These are alanine, serine, valine, in cattle, alanine, glycine, valine, in sheep, threonine, serine, isoleucine, in the pig and the whale, and threonine, glycine, isoleucine, in the horse. It thus seems safe to conclude at least that this portion is not biologically active, but it still remains to define more precisely the significance of the remaining parts of the two chains, as is already being done for other much simpler polypeptides.

As to the source of the hormone, there is an abundance of evidence that insulin is secreted by the *B* cells of the islets. For example, if the major part of the pancreas is removed from cats or dogs the *B* cells in the small residual portion become degranulated, and then vacuolated, and finally may degenerate, a consequence of the excessive demands made upon them for the production of insulin in the absence of most of the normal supply of islets. A similar demand, with similar results, can be established by the prolonged administration of glucose into a normal and intact animal, for the consequent rise in blood sugar again stimulates an increased output of the hormone. These can be described as traditional methods, and they

Fig. 12. Amino-acid sequences of the insulin molecule of cattle. (After Sanger, 1960. *Brit. Med. Bull.* **16**, 183–88.)

Glycine	Phenylalanine
*iso*Leucine	Valine
Valine	Aspartic acid—NH_2
Glutamic acid—NH_2	Glutamic acid—NH_2
Glutamic acid	Histidine
┌── Cysteïne	Leucine
Cysteïne —— S —— S —— Cysteïne	
Alanine	Glycine
Serine	Serine
Valine	Histidine
└── Cysteïne	Leucine
Serine	Valine
Leucine	Glutamic acid
Tyrosine	Alanine
Glutamic acid—NH_2	Leucine
Leucine	Tyrosine
Glutamic acid	Leucine
Aspartic acid—NH_2	Valine
Tyrosine	
Cysteïne —— S —— S —— Cysteïne	
Aspartic acid—NH_2	Glycine
	Glutamic acid
	Arginine
	Glycine
	Phenylalanine
	Phenylalanine
	Tyrosine
	Threonine
	Proline
	Lysine
	Alanine

have been widely used, but more recently the recognition that insulin is rich in disulphide has led to the demonstration that a positive reaction for sulfhydryl and disulphide groups in the islet tissue agrees with the distribution of the aldehyde-fuchsin staining of the *B* cell granules, and that the reaction is reduced after removal of the insulin from the tissue (Plate 1).

Another relevant procedure, and one which has a useful application in experimental studies, is the administration of alloxan. This substance, the ureide of mesoxalic acid, was first shown in 1937 to produce extreme hypoglycaemia (low blood sugar) and death when injected into rabbits, but the explanation was not revealed until 1943, when the effect was independently rediscovered by Dunn. On this occasion histological study, which formed no part of the previous investigation, showed that alloxan has a specific destructive action upon the *B* cells, which may show signs of degranulation within five minutes of the intravenous injection of a suitable dose. Ultimately it may bring about complete destruction of these cells, while the *A* cells and the zymogen tissue are virtually unaffected. The result is the establishment of a typical diabetic condition known as alloxan diabetes, and direct assay of the damaged pancreas will confirm its lack of the hormone (Plate I).

The demonstration that insulin is actually present in the circulating blood depends in part upon the fact that plasma from normal animals will lower the blood-sugar levels of normal or diabetic ones, but it should be borne in mind that such methods are not wholly specific. Moreover, they do not prove that the hormone, if present at all, is circulating in the precise molecular form that we have just described, a difficulty that applies to all investigations in which structure is determined from material extracted directly from the gland of origin and not from the blood stream.

Precision has been given to this and other aspects of insulin research by the use of the isolated diaphragm of the rat. This can be incubated *in vitro* in the presence of suitable reagents, and it is then possible to measure, for example, its uptake of glucose from the medium and the extent to which it is synthesizing new protein as reflected in its uptake of amino acids labelled with radio-carbon (Fig. 16). These activities will be influenced by the presence of insulin and certain other hormones in the incubation medium (Fig. 16). Thus, for example, it is possible to make direct measurements of the relative insulin content of different types of plasma by comparing the activity of the diaphragm in these with its activity in a suitable control medium.

A further important development of insulin studies arises from the fact that since this hormone is a protein it is theoretically capable of acting as an antigen and evoking the production of antibodies in the blood sera of animals that are not adapted to the particular form in which it is presented to them. This applies also, of course, to other protein hormones (p. 60), and the study of such immunological reactions, still in its infancy, is of great potential interest; it has obvious bearings on the problem of how far hormones are species specific, and it could contribute to our understanding of the evolutionary history of these substances, while it is to be expected that such antibody formation might be the cause of the rare examples of allergic reactions and insulin resistance which appear in clinical practice. The immunological properties of insulin are well shown in guinea-pigs, which are particularly sensitive to the bovine hormone and readily produce antibodies in response to injections of it. Ox serum will normally, by virtue of its insulin content, promote the uptake of glucose by isolated rat diaphragm, but this effect can be completely abolished by the addition of the guinea-pig antiserum to the medium. Such insulin antibodies are apparently not species specific, but they provide a strikingly precise demonstration of the presence of the hormone in the blood, and it is worth noting that this degree of precision may at times have more than a merely academic significance.

This point is illustrated by a case in which an evidently healthy young woman had been found dead in a bath. The immediate cause of death was drowning, but the absence of any signs of struggle suggested that she was unconscious prior to this, while there were also indications that she had been hypoglycaemic. In the absence of any signs of disease this suggested that she might have been poisoned by insulin and a careful search of the body surface did, in fact, disclose four marks of hypodermic injections on her buttocks. Extracts were accordingly made of the tissues surrounding these marks, but the proof that insulin was present in them had to depend upon biological tests, for there is no way of identifying the hormone by chemical means in a crude protein mixture. The extracts were shown to have a hypoglycaemic action on injection into mice and guinea-pigs, but the biological evidence that probably did most to convict her murderer was the demonstration that they also stimulated glucose consumption by the isolated rat diaphragm, and that this effect was abolished by guinea-pig insulin antiserum.

4. The effects of insulin

We have seen that insulin has a readily demonstrable effect upon the blood-sugar level. This level, in an animal that is not absorbing glucose from its intestine, is the expression of an equilibrium between the utilization of glucose as an energy source and its replenishment by the breaking down of glycogen stored in the liver (glycogenolysis), and the regulation of this equilibrium is a consequence of the balanced action of insulin and certain other endocrine secretions. We are confronted, therefore, with a system altogether more complex than the relatively simple and self-contained organization of the digestive hormones and one which is, in this respect, undoubtedly more representative of endocrine systems in general.

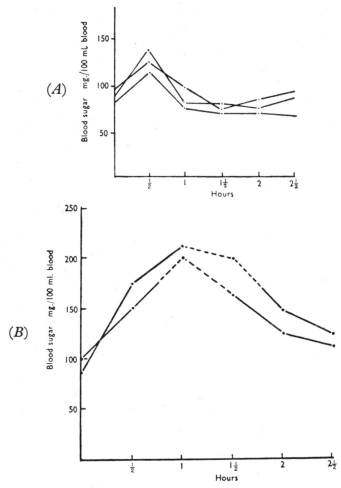

Fig. 13. Glucose tolerance test. *A*. Blood-sugar curves from three normal human subjects after the ingestion of 50 g glucose. *B*. Similar curves from two mildly diabetic patients. The fasting blood-sugar is nearly normal but the response is abnormal, the broken lines indicating glycosuria.

(From Bell *et al.*, 1959. *Text Book of Physiology and Biochemistry*. Livingstone.)

The operation of this regulatory system is seen in the glucose tolerance test in which, for clinical purposes, blood-sugar estimations are made before the drinking of a glucose solution and for a period of two hours afterwards. The glucose content of the blood will normally rise to a peak at about thirty to forty-five minutes (Fig. 13), and will then fall as the carbohydrate is oxidized or taken up into the liver for storage as glycogen. If, however, the supply of insulin is deficient the values will rise to a higher peak and will fall more slowly; this will result in the blood-sugar concentration exceeding the level at which the kidney tubules can re-absorb all of the glucose in the glomerular filtrate (renal threshold), so

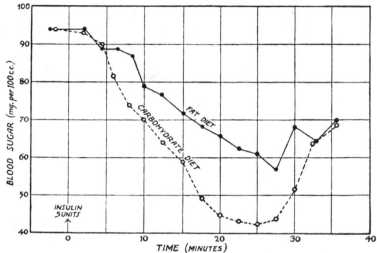

Fig. 14. The effect of the injection of insulin upon the blood sugar of a normal human being after he had been on controlled diets for some weeks. A high fat diet results in a decreased sensitivity to the action of insulin.
(From Winton & Bayliss, 1937. *Human Physiology*, 2nd edn. Blakiston.)

that sugar will appear in the urine (glycosuria) to an extent that will depend upon the severity of the diabetic condition. This accounts for the development of polyuria, for the passage of the glucose demands an increased output of fluid in order to maintain it in solution.

The action of insulin can be demonstrated more directly (Fig. 14) by observing the fall in blood sugar which results when it is injected into normal individuals as well as into hyperglycaemic ones (p. 39). Here the initial fall is a consequence of increased peripheral utilization of glucose, while the recovery phase results from the release of carbohydrate from the liver, and it is agreed that the former is probably due to the direct action of insulin upon the tissues concerned. What is less clear is whether the hormone has any direct action upon the liver during the second phase, but the tendency at present is to ascribe the increased rate of release primarily to the action of those agents which maintain equilibrium by antagonizing the effect of insulin, and which we shall be considering below.

The hyperglycaemia of diabetes mellitus results from increased glyco-genolysis in the liver, and it is evident that this ensures the provision of ample glucose for the peripheral tissues. These, however, are unable to make adequate use of it because in the absence of insulin there is a de-creased capacity for the oxidation of glucose and also a decreased capacity for glycogenesis (the conversion of glucose to glycogen) in the muscles. At the same time there is an increase in gluconeogenesis (the formation of glucose in the liver from non-carbohydrate sources, more particularly from amino acids), so that there is a loss of protein as well as of carbo-hydrate.

While it is possible to state in these general terms the effects of insulin upon carbohydrate metabolism there remains much uncertainty regarding the means by which these effects are brought about. The distinction there-by indicated is an important one, for the overt effects of a hormone, often loosely referred to as its functions, must be thought of as the secondary and perhaps remote consequences of an action or actions exerted at narrowly defined points in the structural or chemical organization of individual cells. Now since the functions of these must be regarded as being dependent upon an organized complex of enzyme-catalyzed reactions it has seemed helpful to many workers to visualize hormones as exerting their influences by controlling the rate of such reactions at some key points. It is well recognized that a central place in the reaction systems involved in carbohydrate metabolism is occupied by the phosphorylation of metabolically inert glucose through the mediation of hexokinase, with the formation of glucose-6-phosphate, and it has been suggested that this might be the key reaction controlled by insulin. This view, however, has not won acceptance, and at the present time attention has turned to other possibilities which derive from recognition of the fact that the sites of hormone action need to be analysed in terms of cell structure as well as of reaction sequences. Thus has arisen the suggestion that the utiliza-tion of glucose is limited by a barrier which determines its rate of entry into the cell, and that insulin may act upon a sugar-transfer mechanism which controls this rate of entry. Such a mechanism might, of course, itself be enzymatic, but Levine and Goldstein have advanced arguments suggesting that it is, in fact, dependent upon physical factors related in some way to the permeability of the cell to sugars.

One major difficulty in arriving at an acceptable account of the mode of action of insulin is that its effects are by no means restricted to the field of carbohydrate metabolism. We have seen that one of the characteristics of diabetes mellitus is the development of ketosis, and it is accepted that this is a consequence of the disturbance of fat metabolism, which is now known to be closely linked with carbohydrate metabolism according to the scheme outlined in Fig. 15. The diabetic animal, in consequence of the decreased utilization of glucose, turns to the metabolism of fat for an increased supply of energy, and this leads to the production of considerable quantities of acetyl co-enzyme A. Normally this should combine with oxaloacetate and then be metabolized by the citric acid cycle, but it is at this stage that a block develops, possibly because the defective carbohydrate metabolism leads to an inadequate provision of oxaloacetic acid.

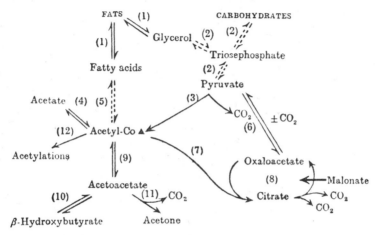

Fig. 15. Outline scheme of the metabolism of fats and carbohydrates. (From Baldwin, 1952. *Dynamic Aspects of Biochemistry*, 2nd edn. Cambridge University Press.)

Whatever the reason, however, the accumulating acetyl co-enzyme A condenses to form acetoacetate within the liver, and from this arise the other ketone bodies. Further, it is known that in the absence of insulin a diabetic animal is unable to convert carbohydrate into fat whereas in a normal rat, for example, as much as 35 per cent. of ingested carbohydrate can be converted in that way. A complete explanation of the mechanisms underlying these diabetic effects is not yet available, although it is possible to see them as consequences of the lack of the stimulating action that insulin normally exerts upon the utilization of carbohydrate.

Finally, we have seen that the diabetic condition is accompanied by a loss of protein. This has often been assumed to be a secondary consequence of the decreased availability of energy from carbohydrate, protein being called upon, like fat, to make up the deficiency. There is, however, some evidence that insulin actually promotes the incorporation of amino acids into peripheral tissues and thus counterbalances the stimulating action of the glucocorticoids (see below) upon protein katabolism; the absence of its counterbalancing influence in the diabetic condition probably accounts for the characteristic increase in nitrogen excretion, which we have already noted. It is evident, therefore, that the metabolic effects of insulin cannot be adequately evaluated without taking into account the effects upon these processes of certain other hormones, the existence of which has already been indicated. The situation will be seen to be a complicated one, and one that is as yet far from being fully understood, and it will be possible here to deal with it only in brief outline.

5. Hormonal interaction: Glucagon and the hormones of the adrenal gland

Belief in the existence of two main types of cell in islet tissue has naturally led to speculation regarding the possibility of more than one secretion being produced by it, and during recent years much attention has been focused upon a substance to which the name glucagon has been given. This has been extracted from the pancreas of mammals in crystalline form, and has been characterized as a protein (polypeptide) with twenty-nine amino-acid residues and with a molecular weight of 3485. It is believed to promote glycogenolysis and thereby to produce a hyperglycaemic condition; using anaesthetized cats, for example, an injection of about 0·07 μg per kg will produce within about twenty-five minutes a rise in blood sugar of 30 mg per cent. (i.e. 30 mg per 100 ml of blood). Glucagon seems to be present as an impurity in many commercial samples of insulin, and it is thought to be the cause of the transient hyperglycaemia which follows the injection of such preparations and which is rapidly succeeded by the hypoglycaemic effect of the insulin. There is evidence, too, that it is present in the pancreas of birds and fishes as well as in that of mammals. Thus extracts of the islet tissue of the teleost *Scorpaena scropha* are said to produce a pronounced hyperglycaemic effect in rats when the insulin present in the extracts has been destroyed by treatment with alkali.

It is suggested that this substance is produced by the *A* cells of the islets, the evidence for this resting partly upon its continued presence in islet tissue in which the *B* cells have been destroyed by alloxan. Certain substances will specifically damage the *A* cells, cobalt chloride, for example, and synthalin A, diethyldithiocarbamate, and *p*-aminosulphonamidoisopropylthiadiazole, so that treatment with these might be expected to eliminate glucagon, but the results obtained with such substances have produced contradictory results, perhaps in part because of the great variation in the extent of the damage that they cause.

The major difficulty in interpreting the significance of glucagon at the present time, however, is that the evidence for its hormonal nature is essentially indirect. There is no clear evidence that the lack of it produces a well-defined syndrome, nor, therefore, that the provision of it can effect anything that could be regarded as replacement therapy. It has been claimed that its secretion into the blood of the dog has been demonstrated in cross-circulation experiments, and we shall see that certain differences in the blood sugar responses of amphibians and reptiles have been accounted for on the assumption that a glucagon-like substance might be physiologically important in the latter group. It would seem, nevertheless, that at present the evidence for its hormonal status stands on quite a different footing from the other examples that we are considering in the present context.

Very clear-cut by contrast are the well-established effects of the gluco-corticoid hormones of the adrenocortical tissue. We shall be dealing with these hormones in more detail later, but we can note here that they appear to influence carbohydrate metabolism in part by inhibiting the peripheral utilization of glucose and in part by promoting the deamina-tion of amino acids and hence the formation of glucose from protein in the liver. In general, then, they may be thought of as being part of the system which opposes the effects of insulin, tending to produce an increase in nitrogen excretion and a rise in blood sugar; prolonged administration of them may, in fact, establish a diabetic condition resulting from damage to the B cells in consequence of the increased demand for the secretion of insulin to antagonize their action.

Hyperglycaemia is also evoked by adrenaline and, to a less extent, by noradrenaline (see Chapter IX), but in this instance by the stimulation of glycogenolysis in the liver, while they also promote the breakdown of glycogen in the muscles (glycolysis), with a consequent increase in the lactic acid level of the blood. There is reason for supposing that these are essentially emergency responses which facilitate the extra activity required when an animal is responding to some stressful stimulus. One such cir-cumstance would, in fact, be a development of hypoglycaemia, such as might result in man or in experimental animals from an overdose of insulin, but these hormones can only produce a rise in blood sugar if there are adequate reserves of glycogen in the liver, and, since these might well be lacking at such a time, a direct supply of sugar would be a more certain remedy than would an injection of adrenaline.

6. Hormonal interaction: Growth hormone

Evidence for the involvement of the 'anterior lobe' of the pituitary gland in the regulation of metabolism derives from studies of its influence on growth in man and experimental animals, and it is now accepted that this influence results from its secretion of a growth hormone.

Gigantism in man is a rare condition which begins in childhood and which is often associated with a tumour (adenoma) of the acidophil cells of the adenohypophysis. It is due to an over-production of the hormone and is characterized by an abnormally high growth rate, which leads in males (which are more commonly affected than females) to a body height of between seven and eight feet, largely resulting from the excessive growth of the legs although various internal organs may also be hypertrophied. Acromegaly is a closely related condition which is also due to hyper-secretion of the hormone but which sets in during the adult stage, after the uniting of the epiphyses. As a result it is impossible for gigantism to develop, but there is an enlargement of the head and extremities and a thickening of the skin and subcutaneous tissue, with protrusion of the lower jaw as a particularly characteristic feature.

The converse condition of hypo-secretion of the hormone may also set in during childhood, and this results in the slowing or cessation of growth and an arrest of sexual development. The affected individuals become either short or actually dwarfed, but they differ from hypothyroid dwarfs in lacking the cretinous appearance of the latter, being in fact well formed, with normal proportions and a youthful appearance. The use of growth hormone preparations in such cases is said to have been unsatisfactory, but the combination of thyroid hormone and androgen has resulted in a dwarfed girl attaining normal height. Oestrogen cannot be used in the early stages of treatment since it promotes early fusion of the epiphyses, but if given at a later stage it can be used to bring the secondary sex characters to development.

These effects of the pituitary gland are not peculiar to man, for it is now established that hypophysectomy (removal of the pituitary gland) in all groups of vertebrates from fishes to mammals will result in retardation of growth, although not necessarily its complete abolition, the retardation in mammals being more marked in adult life than in the young stage. In man, for example, congenital absence of the adenohypophysis (p. 67) still permits of normal growth during the first three or four years of life, but thereafter dwarfism becomes increasingly marked, although growth may never entirely cease. Similarly, the hypophysectomy of a rat during the first few days after birth will exert at first only a moderate retarding effect upon growth, although eventually this will be arrested. By contrast, the hypophysectomy of an adult rat will result at once in a loss of weight which may never be regained.

Direct indications of the existence of the growth hormone responsible for these effects dates from 1921, when Evans and Long showed that saline extracts of the 'anterior lobe' of the pituitary gland of cattle could produce an acceleration of growth when injected into rats, while later, with the application of the classical procedure of replacement therapy, it was shown by Smith that such extracts could restore the growth of hypophysectomized animals. Further developments of these studies date from 1944, when Li and Evans extracted from bovine pituitaries a protein that showed growth-promoting properties. This has a molecular weight considerably higher than that of insulin and it is, of course, out of the question at present to synthesize it, so that its identification as the hormone itself must rest on evidence that it is a homogeneous substance. Applications of the techniques that are available for this purpose, including solubility studies, zone electrophoresis, adsorption chromatography, and counter-current distribution, are considered to have established its homogeneity, and it is therefore accepted that this protein is, in fact, the growth hormone. Wilhelmi has been able to prepare it in a crystalline form by a simplified procedure which is applicable to the pituitaries of teleost fish (e.g. hake and pollack), from which he has been able to obtain 1 mg of crystalline hormone per g (wet weight) of gland. The molecular weight of this fish hormone is estimated at 22,000–26,000, as compared with 44,000–47,000 for crystalline bovine hormone prepared by the same method, and there are differences in their physical properties.

The physiological significance of the hormone in fish has been demonstrated by replacement therapy, and this well illustrates the fundamental uniformity of action of the pituitary secretion in this regard throughout the vertebrate series from fish up to mammals. Growth in length ceases in the teleost *Fundulus* after hypophysectomy, just as in the rat, while the weight changes become irregular and no new circuli (growth rings) are added to the scales. These effects are counteracted by the injection of crystalline growth hormone; nine weeks treatment with this has been reported to increase the weight of such fish by 14·8 per cent. and their length by 4·4 per cent., an average of 3·5 circuli being added during the same period. Nevertheless, the fish hormone is without any effect in rats, whereas the bovine one will promote the growth of both rats and fish, differences which are presumably a consequence of the different molecular structures of the two hormones.

At the present time the growth hormone has also been extracted in a high degree of purity from the sheep, the whale, the pig, the rhesus monkey (*Macacus*), and man, as well as from the ox, and these preparations also show differences in physical and chemical properties, which, like those just described, are accompanied by differences in their physiological activity. Thus the sheep hormone, like the bovine one, is very active in hypophysectomized *Fundulus*, while the hormones of the monkey and man are much less so. Moreover, the bovine and pig hormones are totally ineffective in man and the monkey. It would thus appear that growth hormone has undergone a much wider range of molecular modification than has insulin. The reason for this is obscure, but a relevant consideration is the high degree of protein specificity which organisms develop in the course of their evolution, for the variability of a protein molecule like that of the growth hormone may well be a direct expression of this. As with the insulin molecule, and also with others to be considered later, its biological activity may reside in localized regions which could remain unaffected by such variation.

Having regard to what we have learned of the antigenic properties of the insulin molecule we might well expect the specificities of the growth hormone molecules to be demonstrable in immunological studies. This expectation is, in fact, well founded, and their antigenic properties can be readily shown by such standard methods as the use of precipitin reactions or by evoking anaphylactic shock in guinea-pigs. Growth hormone evokes the formation of antibodies in rabbits, and in one elegant procedure the rabbit antiserum obtained in this way is placed in the central well of an agar plate (Plate 11). Various growth hormones are placed in wells surrounding the central one, and the appearance of localized precipitin lines indicates antigen-antibody reactions between the materials diffusing from the respective wells. In this way it can be shown that rabbit anti-bovine serum reacts with the bovine and sheep hormones but not with the others, so that these two must be closely related antigenically. Similarly, rabbit anti-human serum reacts with human and monkey hormones but not with the others, so that these two must also be closely related. As with insulin, the antiserum will neutralize the biological activity of its specific antigen. For example, the injection into hypophysectomized rats of bovine growth hormone together with normal rabbit serum results in a gain in weight of 18 gm per rat in ten days, whereas the simultaneous injection of the hormone with its rabbit antiserum gives virtually no gain at all.

Growth hormone is often referred to as somatotropin, but objections have been raised to this term on the grounds that it implies a more precise definition of function than is justified by our present knowledge. Undoubtedly a major difficulty in the way of establishing such a definition is the problem of defining exactly what is meant by growth itself. Weiss has well said of this word that it 'covers, like a blanket, a multitude of various things and meanings', but it is no part of our purpose here to strip off the blanket, and it must suffice to point out that growth is the resultant of a diversity of changes in the total amount of organized material in the body. The pituitary growth hormone, then, must be expected to range widely in its influence while other hormones, in so far as they influence metabolic processes, must be expected to interact with it and thus to be, in a narrower sense, growth hormones themselves. With this in mind it is easier to understand why, during the years when only comparatively crude extracts of the 'anterior lobe' of the pituitary were available, it became evident that a variety of metabolic effects could be ascribed to them. There was a tendency to ascribe each of these to distinct hormones, so that references will be found in the literature to such supposed entities as a diabetogenic factor, a hyperglycaemic factor, a ketogenic factor, and so on, but all such

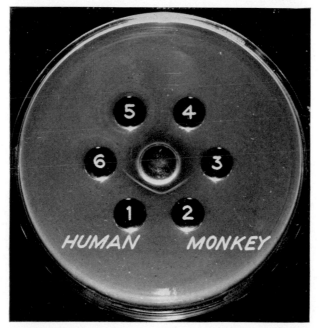

Plate II. *Above*. The interaction of rabbit antiserum to bovine growth hormone (centre well) with purified growth hormones (1, human; 2, monkey; 3, pig; 4, whale; 5, sheep; 6, bovine). Precipitation lines have developed between the centre well and wells 5 and 6 indicating close antigenic relationship between the sheep and bovine hormones. *Below*. The interaction of rabbit antiserum to human growth hormone (centre well) with purified growth hormones arranged in the same numerical order as before. Precipitation lines have developed between the centre well and wells 1 and 2, indicating close antigenic relationship between human and monkey hormones.

The plates were incubated at $20°–22°$ C and were photographed after 44 hours. (From Hayashida & Li, 1959. *Endocrin.* **65**, 944–56.)

effects have more recently been obtained with the purified growth hormone, and it is generally accepted that they represent inherent properties of it.

Appreciation of the influence of growth hormone upon carbohydrate metabolism, and hence of its functional interrelationship with insulin, derives from the classical studies of Houssay, these being of exceptional interest to the comparative endocrinologist since they were initiated on the toad, *Bufo arenarum*. Pancreatectomy in this animal results in hyperglycaemia, just as in a mammal, and Houssay showed that this effect could be diminished by removal of the whole pituitary gland (hypophysectomy, p. 110) or of the pars distalis (p. 70), while implantation of the latter reestablished the condition or even intensified it. The special importance of the pars distalis was shown by the fact that the neuro-intermediate lobe (p. 30) had little or no effect (Table 1). These studies were extended to

TABLE 1

Effect of various combinations of treatment upon the blood sugar of the toad, Bufo arenarum. (From Houssay, 1949. *Quart. Rev. Biol.,* **24,** 1–27.)

	Normal	Hypo-physectomized	Pars distalis removed
With pancreas	64	51	56
Implantation of pars distalis	68	58	69
Pancreatectomy	199	94	94
Pancreatectomy plus implantation of pars distalis	256	228	214
Pancreatectomy plus implantation of neuro-intermediate lobe	199	110	116

mammals, and Houssay was able to show that if hypophysectomy was carried out on a pancreatectomized dog, with the usual symptoms of diabetes mellitus, those symptoms were markedly reduced. So striking is the effect that such a doubly operated dog, known as a 'Houssay animal', can survive for many months without the insulin treatment which is essential for the maintenance of a depancreatized animal with its hypophysis intact. It follows that the pars distalis must be secreting a factor which augments the diabetic disturbances associated with deprivation of insulin and which, therefore, must normally be antagonizing the effects of that hormone, a conclusion that seemed so surprising when it was first announced that one distinguished physiologist declared, according to F. G. Young, that it must be wrong because metabolic control was known to be primarily the function of the 'posterior lobe' of the pituitary gland! As events turned out, however, this discovery helped to gain for Houssay a Nobel prize.

Another aspect of the same phenomenon is the fact, first demonstrated by Young in 1937, that diabetes mellitus can be produced in rabbits and dogs by the injection of extracts of the pars distalis; the condition may be transient, lasting only for the period of treatment, or it may become permanent, showing all of the expected symptoms of diabetes mellitus, including hyperglycaemia, glycosuria, and loss of weight. This does not mean, however, that the pituitary is secreting a tropic hormone which directly affects the islet tissue as, for example, the thyrotropic hormone affects the thyroid gland (p. 202). On the contrary, the evidence is that, although permanent diabetes mellitus established in this way does involve degenerative changes in the insulin-secreting cells of the islets, this, as with the glucocorticoid hormones, is a consequence of the increased demand for insulin set up as a result of the high blood-sugar values, and is not due to a direct action of the pituitary hormone upon the islets.

Some results of such hormonal interactions, as exemplified in reactions of the isolated diaphragm of the rat, are illustrated in Fig. 16. Scrutiny of this will show that growth hormone depresses the uptake of glucose and thus, by restraining carbohydrate metabolism, has an influence opposed to that of insulin; at the same time it increases the incorporation of amino acid into the protein of the diaphragm, as we should expect. Such nitrogen retention can, in fact, be demonstrated in intact experimental animals during a period of administration of growth hormone. Fig. 16 also shows that cortisol (p. 239) resembles growth hormone in restraining carbohydrate metabolism, but differs from it in decreasing nitrogen uptake. It is believed, however, that this is a consequence of its stimulation of gluconeogenesis in the liver, for associated with this is the transfer of protein to the latter organ from the other tissues. Thus the increased wastage of nitrogen in the diabetic animal may be ascribed at least in part to the action of the glucocorticoid hormones.

It will be apparent, even from this brief and selective survey, that the hormonal control of metabolism in mammals is extraordinarily complex, and it should be borne in mind that the thyroid hormones also have a part to play by virtue of their influence on metabolism, at least in the higher vertebrates (see Chapter VIII). The essential subtlety of the regulatory mechanisms can, perhaps, best be sensed by considering what probably happens when insulin is injected into a normal mammal. We have seen that the level of blood sugar is first lowered and then restored (Fig. 14), and that the latter phase is attributed mainly to the action of agents that antagonize the effect of the insulin. We can now define these agents in more precise terms by noting that the hypoglycaemia will evoke the secretion of glucocorticoids, which, by restraining the peripheral utilization of carbohydrates, will tend to counterbalance the stimulating influence of the insulin upon carbohydrate metabolism, while they will also stimulate gluconeogenesis and thereby favour a rise in blood sugar. Meanwhile, growth hormone will join in restraining the use of carbohydrates and, by encouraging nitrogen retention, will tend to counterbalance the influence of the glucocorticoids upon the amino acid metabolism of the non-

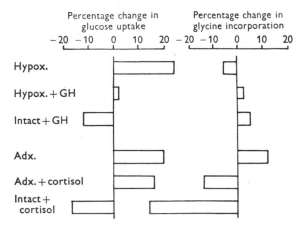

Fig. 16. Summary of the effect of hypophysectomy (hypox.), adrenalectomy (adx.), and treatment with growth hormone (GH) or with cortisol, on uptake of glucose and incorporation of (^{14}C) glycine into the protein of isolated rat diaphragm. Results expressed as the percentage change induced by a particular treatment; comparisons are not quantitatively accurate but illustrate general trends.
(From Manchester *et al.*, 1959. *J. Endocrin.* **18**, 395–408.)

hepatic tissues (Fig. 16). Finally, the hypoglycaemia will also cause an increased output of adrenaline from the chromaffin tissue and this will promote a rise in blood sugar by stimulating glycogenolysis, provided that there are adequate reserves of glycogen in the liver.

7. Homeostasis and blood sugar in the lower vertebrates

The remarkable refinement of control which we have just been reviewing is one aspect of the physiological mechanisms which ensure the constancy of the internal environment of the higher vertebrates. This constancy, or homeostasis, is, in the well-known aphorism of Claude Bernard, an essential condition for the maintenance of their independent life, and we owe particularly to W. G. Cannon the development of this concept in terms of modern physiology. Another aspect of it is to be seen in the mode of functioning of the autonomic nervous system, which, as we have already seen in Chapter II, may exert a regulatory action through the antagonistic influences of the parasympathetic and sympathetic divisions.

It is evident that the hormonal control of metabolism operates upon the same principle, from which it appears that in the course of evolution natural selection has favoured the establishment of antagonistic systems as an effective means of securing precise regulation of dynamic equilibria.

Since there are reasons for thinking that the control exerted by the autonomic nervous system in the lower vertebrates is less precise than in the higher, it is of interest to inquire how far this may be true also of the hormonal regulation of metabolism. Much attention has been given from this point of view to studies of the blood-sugar level, for this is a good indication of the stability of the system under investigation and is at the same time relatively straightforward to measure. As a result of such work we know that this level can fluctuate very widely within normal members of the same species of fish, although unless the method of obtaining blood samples from these animals is very carefully controlled such variation will be artificially exaggerated by partial asphyxia and other stresses of handling, all of which are prone to influence the blood sugar. One illustration which has been reported is given by the toadfish, in which the range is from 20 to 185 mg per cent., with a mean value of 73 mg, and similar results have been reported for other species.

It seems to be agreed that blood-sugar values for Amphibia are low, ranging from 34 to 79 mg per cent. for some frogs and toads, and varying with the season. Indeed, bull-frogs in one set of observations have been reported as having a mean value of only 13·51 mg per cent., with a substantial proportion of the animals giving no reading at all. Studies of the Californian newt, *Taricha torosa*, show levels of much the same order, with a mean value of 28 mg per cent. during the period of reproduction and still lower ones, with a mean of 16 mg per cent., during aestivation.

It is not known how far these low values are correlated with the relatively inactive life of amphibians, but the possibility of such an association is indicated in the substantially higher values found in reptiles and birds. For example, the lizard *Anolis carolinensis* has a mean level of 172 mg per cent., with a minimum value of 110 mg in August and a maximum of 197 mg in February, while the common iguana ranges from 132 to 195 mg per cent., with a mean value of 155 mg. The values obtained for snakes and for the alligator are somewhat lower, although still much higher than the amphibian ones, while those for birds seem to be comparable with the values found in lizards, the pigeon, for example, having a mean level of 150 mg per cent.

Experimental data show that the hormonal mechanism of control of carbohydrate metabolism must have been established early in vertebrate evolution, for already in fish it is possible to recognize the characteristics which we have analysed in mammals, just as we can identify in them a well-differentiated islet tissue. Thus removal of the pancreas produces hyperglycaemia in selachians, as also does removal of the islet tissue from teleosts. Hyperglycaemia and glycosuria have been produced in amphibians and tortoises by removal of the pancreas, but it is difficult to generalize regarding the detailed responses either of these animals or of others of the lower vertebrates. For example, there is evidence that some reptiles and birds are rather insensitive to the action of insulin, and injections of very large doses into lizards are said to produce only a very transient hypoglycaemia, the animals subsequently becoming hyperglycaemic. As compared with this, the urodele *Taricha*, mentioned above, becomes hypoglycaemic after injections of insulin in quantities of only $10\mu g$ per kg.

The reasons for such differences are not yet understood, but Miller inclines to the view that the influence of glucagon may be one factor. The pancreas of birds is said to be very rich in this substance, and hyperglycaemia has been induced by it both in members of this group and also in reptiles. The latter are animals in which the islets are thought to be rich in A cells, whereas, as we have seen, these cells have not been clearly identified in urodeles. It is thus of interest that injections of glucagon have no hyperglycaemic effect in urodeles, a result that might be attributed to the normal absence of this substance, for the A cells are thought to be responsible for its secretion in other groups. The speculative nature of such a hypothesis is sufficiently obvious, for we cannot feel sure either of the function of the A cells or of the hormonal significance of glucagon in these animals, but the facts, limited though they are, constitute an interesting challenge to those who wish to trace the history of the regulation of carbohydrate metabolism in the vertebrates.

There is good evidence that the pituitary gland opposes the action of insulin in all the major vertebrate groups from the fish upwards, as is not surprising in view of the fact that growth hormone is known to be secreted in both fish and mammals. Removal of the pars distalis of the pituitary has been shown to decrease the hyperglycaemia produced by pancreatectomy in dogfish, and the specific nature of this effect is indicated by the observation that only a very slight response is obtained by the removal of the neuro-intermediate lobe. These results are similar to those which have been obtained with toads, and, as we have seen, it was Houssay's demonstration of the diabetogenic action of the pars distalis in *Bufo arenarum* that provided the foundation of our knowledge of hormonal interaction in the regulation of carbohydrate metabolism. The widespread distribution of this pituitary activity has been convincingly shown in experiments in which, for example, extracts from the pars distalis of man, the rat, the whale, and the fowl have been shown to have a diabetogenic action in toads from which both the pancreas and the pituitary have been removed. Finally, the involvement of the glucocorticoids is shown by the hyperglycaemia which is produced in reptiles and amphibians by treatment with cortisol, and which is accompanied by degranulation of the *B* cells, while it is known that adrenaline will induce hyperglycaemia, again accompanied by *B* cell degranulation, in all of the main vertebrate groups.

It will be evident that we are in no position to generalize with assurance from such scattered data as we have been able to review here, but it does seem safe to conclude that the fundamental elements in the hormonal regulation of metabolism in vertebrates must have been laid down very early in their evolution. It seems likely, too, that the operation of this system has been progressively refined during their later history; this is certainly true of other homeostatic mechanisms, such as temperature control, and we may suspect that these became of increasing importance when the vertebrates left the relatively stable medium of water and faced the problems of adaptation to a terrestrial mode of life.

IV. THE HYPOTHALAMIC HORMONES
AND THE NEUROHYPOPHYSIS

1. General organization of the pituitary gland in mammals

OUR discussion in the last chapter of the pituitary gland (alternatively known as the hypophysis) is a foretaste of its central importance in the analysis of the vertebrate endocrine system. From now on we shall be constantly referring to it, so that at this stage it will be convenient to make a preliminary study of its structure, dealing for the present only with the mammalian gland, and leaving until later a comparative survey of its organization in the other vertebrate groups.

The name of the gland (*pituita*, phlegm) derives from a misconception as to its function, for the early anatomists believed that it was concerned with the evacuation of phlegm or mucus from the cavities of the brain. Vesalius supposed that this material was conducted into the infundibulum (Fig. 17, *B*), and that it trickled down from there into the pituitary gland (*A*) below, so eventually reaching the palate and nasal cavities through the ducts *C*, *D*, *E*, and *F*. This sixteenth-century interpretation of the relationship between the gland and the brain may seem to strain credulity, but it is perhaps no more remarkable than the one which has emerged from the results of twentieth-century research, and which we may with some confidence regard as well founded. Curiously enough, it, too, is based upon the conception of a flow of secretion from the brain down into the pituitary gland, so that we shall do well to take warning from earlier centuries, and satisfy ourselves that current views are not vitiated by weaknesses in the evidence such as are symbolized by the imaginary ducts of Fig. 17.

Fig. 17. Vesalius's interpretation of the pituitary gland. (From Singer, 1952. *Vesalius on the Human Brain.* Oxford University Press.)

It is a fact of fundamental importance in regard both to the mode of functioning and to the evolutionary history of the pituitary gland that it is formed of two distinct components, known as the adenohypophysis and the neurohypophysis (Fig. 18). The former arises in the embryo as Rathke's pouch, an outgrowth of the ectodermal lining of the stomo-daeum, while the neurohypophysis arises as the infundibulum, a depression of the floor of the diencephalon, the two rudiments becoming closely applied together and, with further differentiation, forming a complex gland attached to the ventral wall of the brain behind the optic chiasma. The interpretation of the structure of this organ has been confused by the

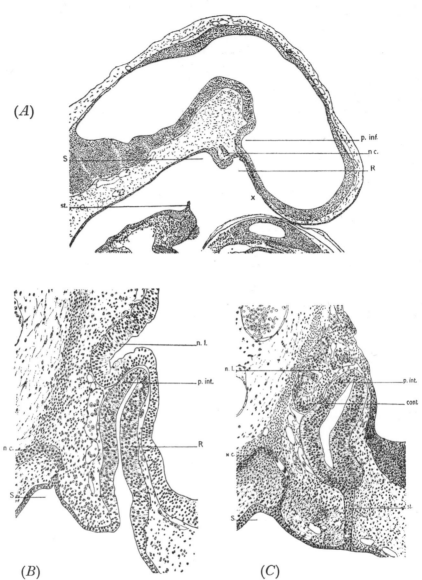

Fig. 18. Development of the pituitary gland of the rabbit, *Oryctolagus cuniculus*. Sagittal sections of *A*, the head end of a ten-day embryo (×50); *B*, the pituitary region of a 13-day embryo, nasal end to the right (×100); *C*, a 15-day embryo (×100); *D*, a 20-day embryo (×75); *E*, a 30-day embryo (at term, ×50). *cont.*, point of contact between neurohypophysis and pars intermedia; *d.m.*, dura mater; *f.*, fossa containing connective tissue; *nc.*, notochord; *n.l.*, neuro-hypophysis; *p.*, process of pars intermedia; *p. inf.*, infundibulum; *p. int.*, pars intermedia; *p.t.*, pars tuberalis; *R*, Rathke's pouch; *r.l.*, residual lumen of Rathke's pouch, separating pars intermedia from pars distalis; *S*, Seessel's pouch; *sphen.*, cartilage of sphenoid; *st.*, remains of the stalk of Rathke's pouch.
(From Atwell, 1918, *Amer. J. Anat.* **24**, 271–337.)

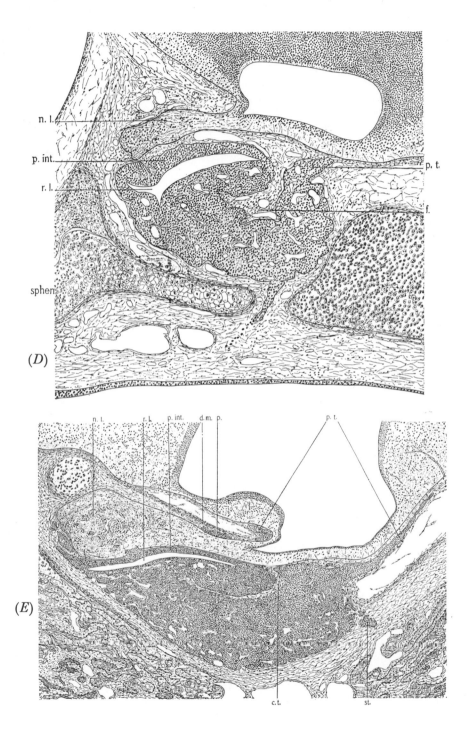

(D)

(E)

fact that in certain mammals it can readily be separated into two portions which it has been customary to term the 'anterior lobe' and the 'posterior lobe', and these have been made the basis for the preparation of commercial extracts. They do not, however, correspond exactly with the above-mentioned regions, and this deceptively simple terminology has therefore been replaced by another which, although more complex, gives more useful expression to the functional organization of the gland.

The adenohypophysis is regarded in this nomenclature (Fig. 19) as differentiated into three regions, the pars distalis, which is the 'anterior

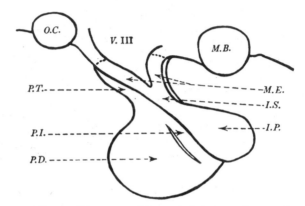

Fig. 19. Diagram to illustrate the nomenclature of the parts of the mammalian pituitary gland. *I.S.*, infundibular stem; *I.P.*, infundibular process or neural lobe; *M.B.*, mammillary body; *M.E.*, median eminence; *O.C.*, optic chiasma; *P.D.*, pars distalis; *P.I.*, pars intermedia; *P.T.*, pars tuberalis; *V.III*, third ventricle.
(From Green & Harris, 1947. *J. Endocrin.*, **5**, 136–146.)

lobe' of the old terminology, the pars tuberalis, which surrounds the infundibular stem (see below) like a collar, and the pars intermedia, so called because it lies between the pars distalis and the neural lobe.

The neurohypophysis is also regarded as differentiated into three regions, the median eminence (of the tuber cinereum), lying in the floor of the diencephalon, the infundibular stem (which, with the pars tuberalis, forms the pituitary or hypophyseal stalk), and the infundibular process, from which develops the neural lobe. The 'posterior lobe' of the old terminology is formed by the infundibular process and the pars intermedia, and it is sometimes separated from the 'anterior lobe' by a cavity which is the remains of the original lumen of Rathke's pouch.

This dual origin of the pituitary gland continues to be reflected in the fully differentiated organ of mammals in certain fundamental features of the organization of the two main components, one of which concerns their blood supply (Fig. 20*A*). The pars distalis is composed of cords of secretory cells which receive a rich vascularization from the internal carotid arteries along two different routes. One of these is a direct one, varying in its details, and sometimes negligible or absent, as, for example, in the rat. The other, which is of much greater significance, is an indirect one, the blood passing first from the internal carotids into the pars tuberalis where it enters a

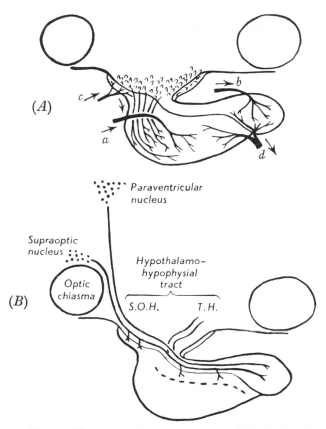

Fig. 20. Diagrams to show some features of (*A*) the blood supply and (*B*) the innervation of the mammalian pituitary gland (cf. Fig. 19).

A. a, vessel from internal carotid to pars distalis; *b*, vessel from internal carotid to neural lobe; *c*, vessels from internal carotid to primary plexus, from which portal vessels drain down into the pars distalis; *d*, venous drainage into surrounding venous sinuses.

B. The supraoptico-hypophyseal tract (*S.O.H.*) and tubero-hypophyseal tract (*T.H.*) innervate the neurohypophysis. A few nerve fibres are shown entering the pars tuberalis and pars intermedia, but it is doubtful if the pars distalis receives any.

(From Harris, 1955. *Neural Control of the Pituitary Gland.* Arnold.)

vascular plexus. Capillary loops extend from this into the median eminence, the whole forming what is called the primary plexus. This drains into portal vessels, which run down the ventral surface of the pituitary stalk to enter the pars distalis where they break up into sinusoids and thereby form a secondary plexus. The whole of this system is called the hypophyseal portal system, and the interpretation of its function is central to the problem of the control of the secretion of the pars distalis.

The neural lobe is also vascularized from the internal carotid arteries, but the distinctive characteristic of a true neural lobe is that this blood supply is completely independent of that of the pars distalis. The median eminence can thus be defined, following Green's suggestion, as that region of the neurohypophysis which receives blood from the hypophyseal portal system or which has a common vascularization with the adenohypophysis, the latter alternative being designed, as we shall see later, to include the conditions existing in fish. The pars tuberalis can then be regarded as that region of the adenohypophysis which forms a bed for the capillary plexus, and it has been suggested that it has no independent endocrine function, although it is not certain that this is actually so.

Another important difference in the organization of the two main components of the pituitary gland lies in their innervation (Fig. 20B). There can be no doubt but that the neural lobe receives a very rich nerve supply, the special characteristics of which we shall consider later. On the other hand, the question whether the pars distalis receives any nerves at all has been much debated, the results of investigations into this problem being confused by the fact that fibres of connective tissue are readily impregnated by the silver methods which are used to demonstrate nerve fibres. This matter cannot be regarded as being finally settled, but it is now rather generally held that such nerves as are found in the pars distalis are composed of vasomotor fibres related to the blood vessels, and that there are no secretomotor fibres supplying the secretory cells of this region. It follows, if this is so, that the latter cannot be under direct nervous control, a conclusion that we shall find to be applicable also to several of the other endocrine glands of the vertebrates and one that clearly raises questions regarding the way in which their secretory activity is actually regulated. To these we shall return in due course, but it will be convenient first to deal with the mode of functioning of the neurohypophysis, for this involves important principles which are operative at all levels of vertebrate evolution.

2. The neurohypophysis and hypothalamic neurosecretion

The organization of the neurohypophysis of the pituitary gland presents some puzzling and unexpected features which have for a long time confused the interpretation of this region. The fundamental difficulty has

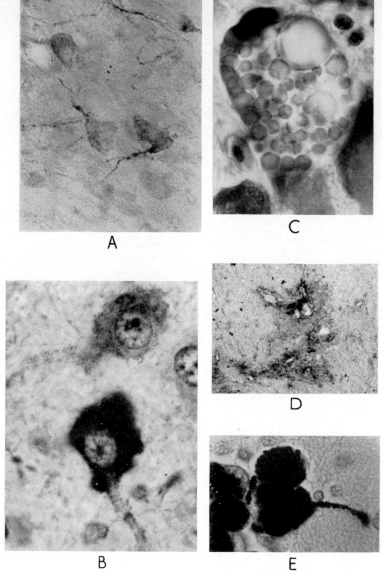

Plate III. *A*. Cells of the supraoptic nucleus of a human aged 55 years; neuro-secretory material is present in the cell bodies and axons. (Performic acid-Alcian blue. × 280.)

(From Adams & Sloper, 1956. *J. Endocrin.* **13**, 221–8.)

B. Neurosecretory cells in the supraoptic nucleus of the dog, showing the presence of neurosecretion in the axons as well as in the cell bodies. (Chrome-alum-haema-toxylin. × 875.)

(From Bargmann, 1957. *The Neurohypophysis,* ed. Heller. London, Butterworths.)

C. Neurosecretory cell in the preoptic nucleus of *Fundulus heteroclitus.* The cell body is filled with red-staining secretory granules. (Zenker-formol; Foot's modification of Masson. × 1,275.)

(From Scharrer & Scharrer, 1954. *Rec. Prog. Horm. Res.* **10**, 183–240.)

D. Neurosecretory material surrounding capillaries of the neural lobe of the dog. (Chrome-alum-haematoxylin. × 95.)

(From Bargmann, *loc. cit.*)

E. Neurosecretory cells in the preoptic nucleus of the minnow, *Phoxinus phoxinus*; note the axon filled with neurosecretory material. (Chrome-alum-haematoxylin. × 700.) Original.

been that whereas the pars distalis has the characteristic secretory and vascular elements of an endocrine gland, the neural lobe has an essentially neural organization, a fact that is not easy to reconcile with the varied activity of extracts prepared from it. A substantial part of its total structure is formed of non-myelinated nerve fibres (as many as 100,000 are said to enter it in man), amongst which are to be found colloidal masses known as Herring bodies, together with many cells. Some of the latter are glial cells, similar to those found in the brain tissue, but many are of a characteristic type, with short branching processes, and are known as pituicytes. These were long regarded as secretory cells, but this view has had to be abandoned, although some authors are still unwilling to believe that their function is simply to provide support.

The nerve fibres of the neural lobe in mammals take their origin in part from the tuber cinereum, passing down the more dorsal region of the pituitary stalk as the tubero-hypophyseal tract. The majority, however, are derived from paired centres in the hypothalamus known as the supraoptic and paraventricular nuclei, and these fibres run down the more ventral region of the stalk as the supraoptico-hypophyseal tract, passing close to the median eminence on the way. Their cell bodies are peculiar in possessing large vacuoles together with granules or droplets of colloidal material. Stainable inclusions of this type were first found in nerve cells by Speidel, who in 1919, following earlier observations of Dahlgren, described granules in cell bodies of the spinal cord of fish (p. 363). The nature of these was not determined, and it was not until 1928 that E. Scharrer drew attention to similar appearances in the cells of the supraoptic and paraventricular nuclei, and of the preoptic nuclei which are their homologues in the lower vertebrates (Plate III).

It was his view that these cells might be concerned in secretion, and the eventual justification of this contention shows very well how the development of a new principle waits upon the availability of suitable techniques, for, while trichrome stains will demonstrate inclusions in these cells (Plate III), it was the introduction into this field by Bargmann in 1949 of a modification of the chrome-alum-haematoxylin (CAH) procedure of Gomori (p. 42) which opened up a phase of intense investigation of the problem. With this method the granular contents of the cells are stained blue-black, and identical material can be seen in their axons and in the neural lobe itself (Plate III). Within the axons it tends to form concentrations which are responsible for the varicosities which had been recognized as a peculiarity of them and which had led to the belief that they might be undergoing degeneration. Stained in this way, however, the material is clearly visible within the fibres, often looking like a string of beads (Plate III), while the Herring bodies are merely larger accumulations of it, usually within the fibres but perhaps sometimes outside them.

Other staining procedures are also effective in revealing the same features, an important one being the aldehyde (paraldehyde)-fuchsin (AF) technique which, like chrome-alum-haematoxylin, was originally introduced by Gomori for the staining of the *B* granules of pancreatic islet cells. Two other methods are the thioglycollate-ferric-ferricyanide technique of Adams and the performic acid-Alcian blue technique of Adams and Sloper; both of these selectively demonstrate a high concentration of cystine in the material, the former by reducing this amino acid to cysteïne and the latter by oxidizing it to cysteic acid (Plate III *A*).

It is now accepted that these cells of the supraoptic and paraventricular nuclei (or, in lower forms, the preoptic nuclei) are specialized neurones of a type referred to as neurosecretory cells, and that they are concerned in the formation of a secretion which is passed down their axons into the neural lobe. It is probable, too (and we shall see the great potential importance of this later), that some is discharged in the median eminence, for we have seen that the fibres pass close to this and some are thought to end in it. The absence from the neural lobe of the characteristic histological features of a gland is thus accounted for by the fact that it acts as a storage depot from which the secretion is released into the blood stream, and that it does not itself actually contribute to that secretion. It belongs, in fact, to a type of organ which we shall encounter again in the crustaceans and insects, and which has been termed a neurohaemal organ, since it provides for the release into the blood of a secretion of neural origin.

The evidence for this interpretation of the hypothalamic nuclei and the neurohypophysis as constituting a single endocrine complex rests not only on the continuity of distribution of the material from the cell bodies into the neural lobe, but also upon the fact that if the pituitary stalk is transected this material accumulates on the proximal (hypothalamic) side of of the cut and gradually disappears on the distal side. This implies that the secretion must pass down the nerve fibres, and such movement, which has actually been observed in living axons obtained from the dog, is naturally prevented by the transection. We are shortly going to relate this visible material to the distribution of hormonal activity, but it should be emphasized now that it is not usually considered to represent the hormones themselves, for it seems more probable that it is a carrier substance, perhaps a cystine-rich protein, to which active substances are attached. Until recently these substances were regarded as hormones of the 'posterior lobe' of the pituitary, and this term is still commonly applied to them. It seems clear, however, that they originate in the hypothalamus and from this point of view it is better to regard them as hypothalamic hormones, a term which, as we shall see, may also include secretions concerned in the regulation of the activities of other parts of the pituitary gland.

The results of electron microscopy are extending our understanding of neurosecretion in suggesting that the secretion of the hypothalamic centres is composed of electron-dense droplets (Plate XII B), about $0.1\ \mu$ in diameter, which can often be seen to be contained within a single membrane about 60 Å thick. The cell bodies of the neurosecretory neurones are well provided with Nissl substance and mitochondria; a Golgi complex is also identifiable, in the sense of an organelle characterized by cavities or cisternae, and it may be within these that the secretory droplets arise. Eventually the droplets accumulate at the endings of the axons, where they are associated with smaller bodies called synaptic vesicles. These, which occur also at the endings of ordinary nerve fibres, are thought to contain chemical transmitter substances (p. 223).

The origin of hormones within nerve cells, their transmission through the axons of these, and their release into the blood stream at neurohaemal organs, are now known to be widespread features of endocrine systems, and they constitute an important extension of the classical concept of hormones as being usually formed and released by specialized endocrine glands (p. 3). This extension, however, need not be a surprising one, for the facts relating to chemical transmission at nerve endings (p. 223) show that secretory activity is as fundamental a property of the nerve cell as is its power of propagating nerve impulses. Moreover, we shall repeatedly find that the close integration of neural and endocrine mechanisms is an essential element of physiological co-ordination; it may well be that the specialization of the secretory capacity of nerves has proved a ready means of securing this, and the mode of production of hormones in invertebrate animals certainly suggests that such specialization must have arisen early in evolution.

The nomenclature attached to this aspect of endocrinology is at present somewhat confused, but it is customary to use the term neurosecretory material or neurosecretion for material secreted by neurones and visible with the light microscope after appropriate fixation and staining. Usually such material will react positively to the chrome-alum-haematoxylin procedure, but this is not a specific method, and it must be emphasized that the mere presence of some stainable material in neurones does not in itself establish the occurrence of secretory activity, and still less does it establish the secretion of hormones. Such material might, for example, consist of the lipofuscins which are particularly common in older cells, but these would normally be confined to the cell body, and an important characteristic of true neurosecretory cells is that their product passes also into the axons (Plates III, XV) where, indeed, some further synthesis may take place, although this is not by any means certain. These cells are often conspicuously large, with nuclei that are also large and have folded surfaces, and they are commonly grouped into neurosecretory systems. Each system has the ends of its axons specialized for the storage and release of the secretion into the blood stream, the close relationship between them and the capillaries (Plate III D) being very similar to that between typical endocrine cells and their vascular supply.

When physiological investigation, combined with cytological study, has established the probability that a particular group of neurones is secreting a neurosecretory material with hormonal activity, that material is some-times referred to as a neuroendocrine material. This, however, can be confusing, for the term neuroendocrine is also used in another sense, to describe a reflex arc in which the pathway is partly neural and partly hormonal, an example being the milk ejection reflex of mammals which will be described below. In practice, the description of a material as a neuro-secretion will commonly be found to carry the implication that it is, in fact, hormonally active. As we have emphasized, however, even where this implication is justified, the material is not necessarily the hormone itself, and to the latter we may apply the term neurohormone, using this also as a general term to include the neurohumours (p. 232) which are secreted as chemical transmitter substances.

3. Properties of 'posterior lobe' extracts

We shall be considering later the consequences of the discovery in 1895 by Oliver and Schäfer of the vasopressor action of adrenal extracts. As a direct result of this work they were also the first to be able to draw atten-tion to a possible specific function of the pituitary gland, for in the course of pursuing similar investigations into the effects of other glands they found that intravenous injections of extracts of that organ also produced a rapid rise of blood pressure which could be maintained for many minutes. As with the adrenal effect, the rise resulted from the combination of vasoconstriction with augmentation of the heart beat, and it appeared to be due to a peripheral action rather than to a central reflex, since it occurred even if the spinal cord was cut or the medulla destroyed. A little later on it was shown that the substance responsible for this vasopressor effect was obtainable only from the 'posterior lobe' of the gland, and that the properties of the extracts were not confined to vasopressor activity. In this connexion Dale has recorded how in 1906 he was comparing the effects of adrenaline and of 'posterior lobe' extracts upon the arterial blood pressure of the anaesthetized pregnant cat and happened at the same time to be recording the activity of the uterine wall; as a result he discovered that the pituitary extract produced a powerful contraction of the uterine muscle, a response which became known as the oxytocic effect.

Meanwhile, Schäfer and others had been studying another property of these extracts, for it had been found that intravenous injection of them into anaesthetized animals resulted in an increased diuresis, an increase, that is, in the output of urine. Now there is found in man a condition known as diabetes insipidus (which has nothing at all to do with diabetes mellitus, p. 39) in which excessive urine production is accompanied by a thirst so tormenting that afflicted individuals have been known to drink as much as thirty litres of water per day; the urine lacks the sugary taste characteristic of diabetes mellitus, and this fact is the origin of the medical name for the condition. Frank in 1912 drew attention to the frequent association of diabetes insipidus with injury to the pituitary gland, and it was at first assumed that such injury, by irritation of the glandular tissue, evoked an over-production by the 'posterior lobe' of a diuretic principle. When, however, investigators came to examine the effect of injecting such extracts into patients suffering from the disorder, there emerged the quite unexpected discovery that they actually alleviated diabetes insipidus, whereas on the above hypothesis the diuresis should, if anything, have been increased.

We now know, as we shall see in more detail later, that the active principle concerned is actually antidiuretic, that diabetes insipidus results from a lack of it, and that the spectacular alleviating effect of 'posterior lobe' extracts is true replacement therapy. The diuretic action of these extracts which had been observed by the earlier workers was probably a secondary and artificial effect, associated with the influence of anaesthesia upon the functioning of the kidney, so that the hypothesis based upon it was unjustified. Nevertheless, it was perfectly reasonable in the light of the knowledge then available, and its real value, like that of all scientific hypotheses, lay in the further experimentation which it stimulated.

These three effects, the vasopressor, oxytocic, and antidiuretic, were at first the only ones thought to be associated with 'posterior lobe' extracts, which it has been customary to separate into two fractions, 'oxytocin', containing the bulk of the oxytocic principle, and marketed as Pitocin, and 'vasopressin', containing the bulk of the vasopressor and antidiuretic activities, and marketed as Pitressin. Later, however, it became apparent that 'oxytocin' also influenced lactation, a process which should be thought of as comprising two main phases, milk secretion, and milk removal. The latter itself also involves two stages, the first being the active ejection of milk from the alveoli and finer ducts of the mammary glands into the larger ducts, as a result of the contraction of the myo-epithelial cells of the alveoli, while the second is the withdrawal of the milk by the act of suckling or by the hand of the milker, and is a purely passive phase as far as the mother is concerned.

The earlier workers, again including Schäfer, had noted that the injection of 'posterior lobe' extracts could evoke active ejection (cf. p. 82), and it was further shown that normal ejection could be abolished in the nursing bitch by anaesthesia and that this inhibition could then be overcome by injection of these extracts (Fig. 21). As has been pointed out by Folley, such evidence would nowadays be regarded as a strong indication that a 'posterior lobe' secretion was involved in the milk-ejection reaction.

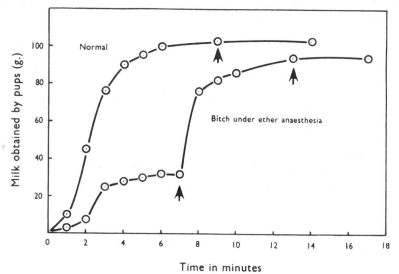

Fig. 21. Milk flow curves from a bitch, under normal conditions and under ether anaesthesia. Arrows indicate injection of 'posterior lobe' extract. (From Cowie & Folley, 1957, in *The Neurohypophysis*, ed. Heller. Butterworth.)

At the time of these observations, however, there was a marked tendency to regard all the actions of 'posterior lobe' extracts as of pharmacological interest rather than indicative of normal physiological activities, and it was not until later that it became recognized that this particular effect fell into the latter category.

This early caution has, in fact, proved well justified, for it still remains doubtful whether the vasopressor effect is of any physiological significance, nor is its hormonal status established, while the interpretation of the oxytocic effect is almost as doubtful. The latter is employed in obstetrical practice, but evidence as to its role during normal parturition is contradictory. Equally uncertain is the validity of the suggestion that uterine contractions evoked by the release of this principle during coitus may aid the ascent of sperm in the female genital tract.

4. Antidiuresis

On the other hand, the evidence for the release from the mammalian neural lobe of an antidiuretic hormone (ADH) acting directly on the kidney

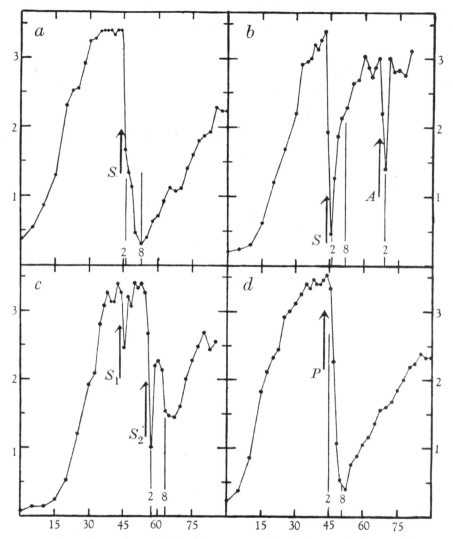

Fig. 22. Two types of inhibition of water diuresis by emotional stress in a normal bitch. Abscissae are minutes after administration of 300 ml of water by stomach tube; ordinates show the rate of urine secretion in ml per minute.

At S in a, b, and c, emotional stress was induced by mild faradic stimulation to the flanks, lasting 30 or 60 seconds; at A in b, 40 μg adrenaline, and at P in d, 1·0 mU post-pituitary extract, were injected intravenously. The vertical lines 2 and 8 are drawn 2 and 8 minutes respectively after the end of the stimulus of injection.

The rapid type of inhibition and recovery after stress in b and c is believed to be due to vasoconstriction in the kidneys resulting from action of the sympathetic nervous system (cf. the effect of adrenaline in b). The slow type of inhibition and recovery in a is believed to be due to the action of antidiuretic hormone (cf. the effect of post-pituitary extract in d).

(From O'Connor, 1947. *Biol. Rev.* **22**, 30–53.)

is quite decisive, and we must now review briefly the basis for this conclusion. Firstly, it is possible to establish an isolated preparation of the heart, lung, and kidney of the dog. If this is perfused with blood there results a considerable diuresis, and this can be inhibited by the addition to the perfusing fluid of 'posterior lobe' extract. It can be shown that this inhibition is not accompanied by any significant reduction of the rate of flow of blood through the kidney, so that the extract must be exerting a direct and specific action upon the kidney itself rather than upon its blood supply. Further, inhibition can also be produced by including the head of the dog in the perfusion circuit, the implication being that the inhibition is here a result of the addition to the blood of the secretion released from the neural lobe.

Analogous experiments have been carried out on live dogs. The introduction of water into the stomachs of these animals results in considerable diuresis which can be inhibited by emotional stress induced, for example, by faradic stimulation or by auditory stimulation from a klaxon horn. One type of response, illustrated in Fig. 22, is a rapid one, diuresis reaching its lowest level in about three minutes and recovering in ten, and this is thought to be a result of vasoconstriction brought about through the action of the sympathetic nervous system and the chromaffin tissue (p. 220). The evidence for this rests upon the fact that similar responses can be obtained by intravenous injection of adrenaline, while the inhibition caused by stress can be eliminated by denervation of the kidney and section of the splanchnic nerves, which, as we shall see later, eliminates the influence of the sympathetico-chromaffin complex upon that organ.

If, however, such an animal, with its kidneys and chromaffin tissue denervated, receives either a faradic stimulus or an injection of 'posterior lobe' extract, a response is obtained which differs from the previous one in being much slower (Fig. 22), diuresis reaching its lowest level after seven to ten minutes with a correspondingly slower recovery. This second type of response is considered to be due to the discharge of antidiuretic hormone from the neural lobe, and corroboration of this is given by the fact that it is abolished by removal of that lobe. Such evidence provides a very satisfactory demonstration that a hormone is released from the neural lobe as a physiological response in the intact animal. Combined with the other facts mentioned, in particular the antidiuretic activity of the extracts and the successful use of these in the treatment of diabetes insipidus by replacement therapy (in man by inhalation as a form of snuff), we find that many of the classical criteria of hormonal action are satisfied, while we shall see later that the characterization and synthesis of the hormone have also been achieved.

Our understanding of the mode of action of the hormone and its interrelationship with the mineralocorticoid secretion of the adrenocortical

tissue (p. 247) is less complete. A current view of the mode of functioning
of the mammalian nephron is that active reabsorption of sodium occurs in
the proximal convoluted tubule (Fig. 23) and is accompanied by a passive
diffusion of water; these processes are thought to be unaffected by the
antidiuretic hormone. In the distal convoluted tubule and in the ascend-
ing limb of Henle's loop there is a further active reabsorption of sodium,
but the amount of water absorbed there, and
perhaps also in the collecting tubule, is variable,
and is thought to be regulated by the action of
that hormone upon cell permeability, the resultant composition of the urine reflecting the
state of water balance of the animal. These two
types of water reabsorption are referred to
respectively as obligatory and facultative; it has
been suggested that the latter may also take
place in the first (descending) limb of Henle's
loop and in the collecting tubules, and that at
these sites too it may be regulated by the
antidiuretic hormone. The operation of the
facultative reabsorption is well seen if a
hypertonic solution is injected into the carotid
artery of an experimental animal. This brings
about an antidiuresis, which is supposedly
evoked by the release of the hormone. This release, it is thought, may be a consequence of
the stimulation of osmo-receptors in the fore-
brain, as Verney has argued, or may perhaps
result from the direct response of the neurosecretory cells to the osmotic composition of
their blood supply.

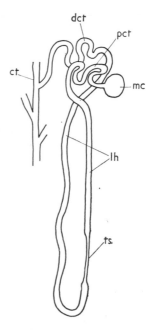

Fig. 23. Diagram of a
nephron from the cortex of
a mammalian kidney. *ct*,
collecting tubule; *dct*, distal convoluted tubule; *lh*,
loop of Henle; *mc*, Malpig-
han corpuscle; *pct*, proximal
convoluted tubule; *ts*, thin
segment.

We have now reached a stage at which we
can consider how far the distribution of visible
neurosecretion can be correlated with physiological activity. This correlation, is, in fact, a
close one, for typical 'posterior lobe' activity
can be detected also in the hypothalamus and in the pituitary stalk,
while if the latter is transected it can be shown that the accumulation
of neurosecretory material at the proximal side of the incision (p. 74) is
paralleled by an increase in the yield of activity at the same point. Moreover, conditions such as deprivation of water or heavy salt intake, which
result in the discharge of antidiuretic hormone in experimental mammals,
can be shown to be accompanied by a discharge of neurosecretory material
from the neural lobe. Thus if a rat is caused to drink 2·5 per cent. salt

solution for thirteen days its pituitary will be completely devoid of the material at the end of that time; if the demand for antidiuretic hormone is then reduced by allowing the animal to drink tap water the neurosecretory material will rapidly reaccumulate and will reach a more or less normal condition in a few days.

We have seen that there is reason for believing that the hypothalamic neurosecretion is composed of granules or droplets contained in vesicles. Evidence that hormonal material is released from these comes from the observation that empty profiles of similar size, but devoid of dense contents, are identifiable in electron micrographs of the neural lobe of dehydrated rats. Neurosecretory droplets have occasionally been observed within the blood vessels of the neurohypophysis, and it is possible that the material is released in its entirety and broken down into its active constituents in the blood stream. Whether the release takes place as the result of the transmission of nerve impulses along the axons is not clear, but there seems no reason why this should not be so, and it is possible that the response is mediated by the discharge of a chemical transmitter substance from the synaptic vesicles (p. 75).

5. Milk ejection

We have already noted that earlier work gave indications of an influence of the 'posterior lobe' upon the mammary gland, but it was not until 1941 that Ely and Petersen showed that the application of the normal milking stimulus to a cow would bring about ejection from a denervated half of an udder as well as from the other half which retained its normal innervation. It was further shown that ejection of milk could be evoked from an isolated udder when this was perfused with blood taken from a cow which had itself been stimulated by milking. The hypothesis suggested by these results was that the milk-ejection response was dependent upon the stimulation of receptors during suckling or milking, the resulting nerve impulses being transmitted to the brain and bringing about the release of a hormone from the neural lobe. Such a pathway is often called a neuroendocrine reflex arc (p. 76), and in this instance it provides a means by which the mother can become conditioned to various external stimuli with which the milking process is normally associated.

We have already touched upon the earlier evidence relevant to this hypothesis. Amongst the later is the fact that if a female rat is deprived of its neurohypophysis her young are unable to obtain milk from her teats and will die of starvation, whereas if 'oxytocin' is injected into her they can secure the milk and can be reared at almost the normal rate. It has been shown, too, that milk ejection can be evoked in cows by the injection of 'oxytocin', and in ewes and goats by electrical stimulation applied through electrodes implanted in or close to the supraoptic nuclei.

Andersson has demonstrated the hormonal nature of the response by showing that it can be obtained from a denervated half-udder (see above), while the presence of the hormone in the blood is indicated by the obtaining of milk ejection from a lactating animal when it is injected with blood taken from a goat that had been subjected to this electrical stimulation. Similarly, Cross and Harris, using an experimental technique which we shall discuss later, have shown that milk ejection can be evoked in lactating rabbits by electrical stimulation through an electrode implanted into the supraoptico-hypophyseal tract or median eminence (Fig. 24), and that the response closely resembles that resulting from the injection of 'oxytocin'. Lastly, injury to the tract will not only inhibit these responses,

Fig. 24. Tracings of kymograph records of milk-ejection responses to electrical stimulation of the median eminence and infundibular stem in an anaesthetized rabbit. The stimuli were applied for ¼ min in the vertical plane of the median eminence; the figures give the depth of the electrode tip below the surface of the skull (cf. Fig. 39). A moderate response is obtained at 2·0 and 2·1 cm depth, but none at 1·8, 1·9, and 2·2 cm. Stimulation of the infundibular stem (S) gives a greater response which is similar to that following the injection (I) of 50 mU of whole pituitary extract.
(From Cross & Harris, 1952. *J. Endocrin.* **8**, 148–61.)

but will also prevent the young from obtaining milk by normal suckling unless the mother is injected with the extract.

6. The polypeptide hormones of the hypothalamus/neuro-hypophysis complex

It will now be appreciated that while the early investigators of neuro-hypophyseal activity tended to analyse the situation in terms of vaso-pressor and oxytocic effects, later work has concentrated on antidiuresis and milk-ejection, but the question remains whether one or more hormones are involved. It has for some time been possible to separate the extracts into two fractions (p. 77), but there have been two opposing views as to the significance of this, one holding that it was the consequence of the existence of two distinct secretory products while the other considered that the chemical procedures had broken up an originally single substance which carried all the activity.

This problem was resolved from 1949 onwards by the success of du Vigneaud, another Nobel laureate, in isolating from the pituitary glands of cattle two pure hormones to which have been given the old-established names of oxytocin and vasopressin, which were originally applied to the crude fractions (p. 77). With the pioneer studies of Sanger as an example, it proved possible to determine the molecular structure of

Fig. 25. Amino-acid sequences of oxytocin, vasopressin, and arginine vasotocin (8-arginine oxytocin).

Oxytocin

$$S \text{————————} S$$
Cysteïne—Tyrosine—Isoleucine—Glutamic acid (NH_2)—Aspartic acid (NH_2)—Cysteïne—Proline—Leucine—Glycine (NH_2)

Arginine vasopressin

$$S \text{————} S$$
Cysteïne—Tyrosine—Phenylalanine—Glutamic acid (NH_2)—Aspartic acid (NH_2)—Cysteïne—Proline—Arginine—Glycine (NH_2)

Lysine vasopressin

$$S \text{————} S$$
Cysteïne—Tyrosine—Phenylalanine—Glutamic acid (NH_2)—Aspartic acid (NH_2)—Cysteïne—Proline—Lysine—Glycine (NH_2)

Arginine vasotocin (8-arginine oxytocin)

$$S \text{————} S$$
Cysteïne—Tyrosine—Isoleucine—Glutamic acid (NH_2)—Aspartic acid (NH_2)—Cysteïne—Proline—Arginine—Glycine (NH_2)

these, and they were shown to be octapeptide amides of closely similar pattern, each being formed of a cyclic pentapeptide with a tripeptide amide side-chain. The composition of the two molecules is shown in Fig. 25, from which it will be seen that they have six amino acids in common, cystine (represented in the Figure by its two cysteïne components), glycine, glutamic acid, aspartic acid, proline, and tyrosine. Vasopressin differs from oxytocin in having phenylalanine replacing isoleucine at position 3 in the ring, and arginine replacing leucine at position 8 in the side-chain. In this form, known as arginine vasopressin, it has been identified in the camel, cat, macaque, man, ox, rabbit, and sheep; in the pig, however, it occurs as lysine vasopressin, with lysine replacing the arginine in position 8, and it is of interest that the same form of the hormone is probably also present in the closely related hippopotamus.

Studies of the properties of these pure hormones have made it clear that rat oxytocic and rabbit milk-ejection effects are mainly the property of oxytocin, and that rat vasopressor and dog antidiuretic effects are mainly the property of vasopressin; in addition, oxytocin shows a small amount of vasopressor and antidiuretic action, amounting to 1–2 per cent. of the activity of pure vasopressin, while the latter hormone shows a small amount of oxytocic and milk-ejection activity. It is a matter of great interest that arginine vasopressin and lysine vasopressin differ in their properties, the pressor/antidiuretic potency ratio being 1:1 in the former and 6:1 in the latter. This fact, together with the differences between the actions of oxytocin and the vasopressins, clearly shows the influence of molecular structure upon biological activity, and this has been further demonstrated by studies in which the pharmacological properties of the natural hormones have been compared with their synthetic analogues. For this purpose use has been made of various properties of neurohypophyseal extracts additional to those already mentioned, including the lowering of blood pressure in the fowl (fowl vasodepressor effect), the production of contraction in the oviducts of the fowl and turtle (fowl and turtle oxytocic effects), the production of antidiuresis in the fowl, and the acceleration of the passage of water through the wall of the isolated bladder of the frog. This latter property, and the water relationships of amphibians generally, are of particular importance in this context, and it is these that we must now examine.

7. Water balance in Amphibia

Although the relationship of the neural lobe to the hypothalamus in the lower vertebrates is essentially similar to that in mammals (Chapter XII), the ecological and physiological situations are clearly very different. Thus the water balance of Amphibia is determined by the relationship between uptake of water through the skin and loss of water by evaporation and excretion, while the latter process is affected by the fact that they are unable to produce a hypertonic urine.

Frogs and toads, but not the completely aquatic *Xenopus*, have a remarkable capacity for increasing the uptake of water through their skin in response to desiccation. The first indication that the neurohypophysis was involved in this emerged from the work of Brunn, who showed in 1921 that if 'posterior lobe' extract was injected into the lymph sac of a frog or toad, and the animal kept in water, the result was an increase in weight which might amount to as much as 20 per cent. in five to ten hours. It is now thoroughly well established that this 'Brunn effect' is a result of the accumulation of water, which is mostly retained in the lymph spaces, and that it depends in part upon the action of the extract in promoting the uptake of water through the skin, accompanied, as we now know, by the active uptake of sodium. Because of the latter phenomenon the name 'natriferin' has been suggested for the supposed hormone concerned, but we shall see below that it is probably identical with a substance that is already known and chemically characterized. Since this uptake can be demonstrated in the isolated tissue as well as in the intact animal, it was at first thought that the 'Brunn effect' was mediated solely through the skin, and that it might not, therefore, be at all closely comparable with the results of the action of the antidiuretic hormone in mammals, but it subsequently became apparent that this was not so.

By cannulating the cloaca of a toad it can be demonstrated that the uptake of water which follows the injection of 'posterior lobe' extract is accompanied by a reduction in the rate of flow of urine, so that the skin and the kidney must both be cooperating in building up the excess of water. As for the mechanism of this, we have seen that in mammals the antidiuretic effect is believed to be brought about mainly by the action of the hormone on the distal segment of the nephron. Similarly, in amphibians it is believed that the extracts increase tubular reabsorption, but there is evidence that they act in addition by constricting the afferent arterioles of the glomeruli, thereby reducing the amount of fluid available for filtration. Another peculiarity of the water-balance system of these animals is the use they make of the bladder as an organ for the storage of water, a property that is of particular importance in those that are exposed to the risk of severe dehydration. This, also, seems to be under the control of the neurohypophysis, as can be shown by tying off the cloaca of a frog and then leaving the animal in water for some hours. During this time it will gain in weight because water will enter the body through the skin and will be unable to escape; it will, in fact, accumulate in the bladder, and the amount of urine found there will be approximately equivalent to the water taken in. If, however, 'posterior lobe' extract is injected at the end of this period and the animal left for another two hours it is found

that the water content of the bladder has decreased. This must presumably be due to the passage of the water through the wall of the organ,
for it is known that neurohypophyseal extracts can accelerate this in the
isolated bladder of the bull-frog.

It appears, then, that the secretion released by the neurohypophysis
can regulate the loss of water from amphibians by action at three points,
the glomeruli, the kidney tubules, and the bladder, and that it can further
regulate the absorption of water by its action on the skin. There can be
no question but that this represents a complex of adaptive mechanisms
which are of the greatest importance to the group in the terrestrial phase
of its life. So long as the animals are in water their main problem is to get
rid of the excess that enters as a consequence of the osmotic pressure of
their body fluids, but on land they are faced with the problem of desiccation and this becomes increasingly acute as they become increasingly
terrestrial in habit. It is in this context that the adaptive value of their
water-balance responses becomes strikingly clear, for different genera vary
in the intensity of their responses and these variations can be seen to be
related to their mode of life.

For example, the highly terrestrial toad shows a much greater degree
of water uptake after 'posterior lobe' injections than does the less terrestrial
frog, while the fully aquatic *Necturus* shows the least of the three. Again,
the fully aquatic *Xenopus* is unable to increase its water uptake after
dehydration and shows virtually no antidiuretic response to neurohypophyseal extracts. The evidence indicates that such adaptations depend
in part upon variations in the sensitivity of the target organ, the skin of
the frog being, for example, less sensitive than that of the toad, but it is
possible that there may also be differences between the hormones of the
different species.

In the earlier investigations of water balance in amphibians it was
impossible to decide whether or not the active agent was, in fact, identical
with one or other of the known neurohypophyseal hormones of mammals.
Heller took the view that it could not be, for he established in 1941 that
the effect of extracts of frog pituitaries on the uptake of water was not
proportional to their antidiuretic (Fig. 26*A*), oxytocic (Fig. 26*B*), and
vasopressor activities, and he therefore concluded that an entirely separate
'water-balance principle' must be concerned. More recently we have
learned that either pure oxytocin or lysine vasopressin can evoke water
reabsorption from the bladder of *Rana pipiens*, and that the former is the
more potent of the two. Yet it is difficult to see how oxytocin could be
identical with the 'water-balance principle', for large doses of it are
required in comparison with the small amounts of frog pituitary extract
which will produce similar responses. In other words, it has become
necessary to postulate the existence in the latter of a substance with

pharmacological characteristics quite different from those of the mammalian hormones, and it is here that the study of their analogues has proved of extraordinary interest.

One of these is arginine vasotocin (8-arginine oxytocin), so called because

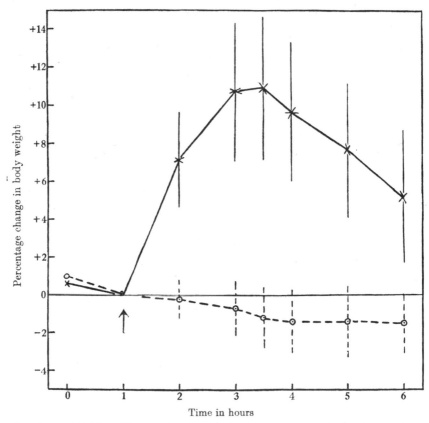

Fig. 26*A*. The difference between the mean percentage changes in weight of twenty frogs produced by the injection into each of the extract of a single frog pituitary gland (X——X) and of 10 mU pitressin (O- - - -O). Injections at the time marked by arrow. Vertical lines indicate the standard errors. The pitressin (*A*) has no effect, although the maximum antidiuretic activity of a frog pituitary gland had been found to equal only 5 mU pitressin.

the vasopressin side-chain is here combined with the oxytocin ring (Fig. 25). As might be expected, such a substance shows the properties of the natural mammalian hormones but in quite different ratios, and these agree so closely with those required of the 'water-balance principle' that it now seems likely that the latter is, in fact, arginine vasotocin, this being the only synthetic analogue so far studied which shows the necessary high ratio of frog-bladder activity to oxytocic activity. This conclusion, which implies that this substance is the postulated 'natriferin' to which we have already referred, has been supported by chromatographic studies.

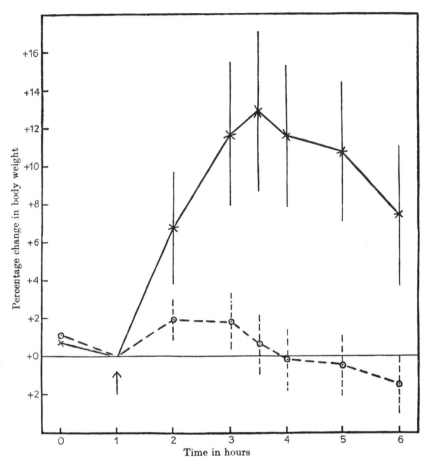

Fig. 26B. An experiment similar to that illustrated in Fig. 26A, but with 40 mU pitocin substituted for 10 mU pitressin. The pitocin has little effect, although the oxytocic activity of a frog pituitary gland had been found to be considerably less than the equivalent of 40 mU pitocin.
(From Heller, 1941. *J. Physiol.* **100**, 125–41.)

Ideally, it needs to be substantiated by extraction of arginine vasotocin from the pituitaries concerned; if this can be done we shall have the remarkable situation of a hormone being first discovered and characterized as a synthetic product in advance of its isolation from biological material.

8. The hypothalamic polypeptides and vertebrate evolution

The interest of arginine vasotocin is by no means restricted to amphibian physiology, for Sawyer has provided evidence that the ratio of frog-bladder activity to oxytocic activity is also high in extracts of the pituitaries of *Petromyzon marinus*, *Pollachius virens* (pollack), *Bufo americanus*, *Rana catesbeiana*, and *Chelonia mydas* (green turtle), and is approximately

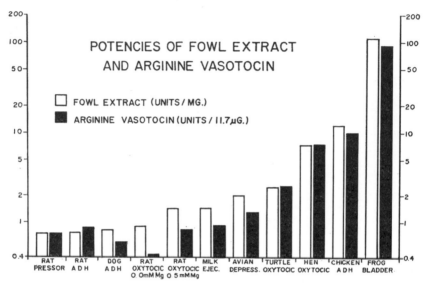

Fig. 27. Potencies of fowl neurohypophyseal extract and arginine vasotocin in eleven different assays. The potencies are plotted logarithmically, with scales adjusted to approximate pressor activities.
(From Munsick *et al.*, 1960. *Endocrin.* **66**, 860–71.)

what would be predicted on the assumption that they all contain this polypeptide. Nor does this exhaust its interest, for the pharmacological properties of extracts of the neurohypophysis of the domestic fowl (*Gallus domesticus*) are not what would be expected from a combination of the two mammalian hormones, and it appears that these properties, too, can be accounted for on the assumption that the hormones actually secreted in this animal are chiefly oxytocin and arginine vasotocin. The evidence for this depends partly on direct chemical studies of the extracts and partly upon a comparison of their pharmacological properties with those of the latter substance. The results of such a comparison are shown in Fig. 27, and clearly indicate a close correspondence between the fowl extract and arginine vasotocin, the differences in the cases of rat oxytocic, milk-ejection, and fowl vasodepressor potencies probably being due to the presence of oxytocin in the extracts, although this is probably less abundant than the arginine vasotocin.

It is not yet clear how far such results are applicable to other species of birds, but there is already sufficient evidence to show that the different groups of vertebrates are by no means uniform in the make-up of their hypothalamic hormones. We have seen that arginine vasotocin may well be present in the marine lamprey, and this may account for the whole of its oxytocic activity, for this animal is thought to have little or no oxytocin. Both hormones are probably present in teleosts, amphibians, and reptiles, as far as can be judged from the few species studied, but they are absent from elasmobranchs, which are believed to secrete a polypeptide different from the others so far described.

If the evidence for these conclusions can be strengthened by investigation of a wider range of species the results will have an important bearing upon the problem of the evolution of endocrine systems, for it has often been debated whether this has involved the evolution of hormones or of their actions. The hypothalamic polypeptides certainly provide an example of the evolution of the molecular structure of hormones, but on present information it is not easy to correlate this with changes in the adaptive responses that they mediate. Arginine vasotocin, for example, serves as the water-balance hormone of amphibians, but is not confined to that group, while oxytocin, although concerned in lactation, is not confined to the mammals. It would appear, therefore, that changes in the mode of functioning of these hormones must have occurred independently of the changes in their molecular structure, presumably as a result of modifications in their relationships with their target organs.

It will become apparent, as our analysis proceeds, that some hormonal molecules, such as the thyronines and the steroids, remain relatively constant during long periods of evolutionary history, while their functions become diversified in relation to changing demands. Molecular variation, on the other hand, is particularly characteristic of the protein and polypeptide hormones, and we have already noted in our review of the growth hormone that this may be in part a consequence of the protein specificity which characterizes living organisms. Other possibilities, however, must not be excluded. Single amino-acid substitutions like those that we are considering here may well be the result of single gene mutations, and, on current evolutionary theory, we should expect the survival of these to be associated with adaptive advantages. Such advantages might, for example, consist of improvements in the mutual relationships of hormone and target organ, or they might be related to hormonal functions that have not yet been detected by our experimental methods.

These issues will not be resolved until information is available from a much wider range of species. It seems likely, however, that once balanced relationships between hormones and target organs are established in any one group there would be strong counter-selection against any mutations tending to disturb them, and the history of the hypothalamic polypeptides, as far as our present knowledge goes, provides some support for this supposition. These hormones seem to have preserved a remarkable constancy in the mammals, apart from the appearance of lysine vasopressin, while fish presumably inherited arginine vasotocin unchanged from the Agnatha (although the situation in elasmobranchs is at present difficult to interpret from this point of view). Oxytocin might then have arisen in fish by the substitution of leucine for arginine in the side-chain, and have remained throughout the subsequent history of vertebrates, although it is not clear that it has any physiological activity in non-mammalian forms. Arginine vasotocin has also remained, but at some stage in the evolution of mammals it must have been replaced by arginine vasopressin. At present our only clue to when this change might have occurred is provided by a few pharmacological tests. These have shown, according to Sawyer, that arginine vasopressin may be present not only in the placental mammals but also in the opossum (*Didelphis virginiana*) and the echidna (*Tachyglossus aculeatus*), which would suggest that the replacement may have occurred in the extinct synapsidan reptiles. This would be in line with our general conception of the history of mammals, for it is well known that those reptiles gradually established a wide range of mammalian skeletal features, and it is accepted that physiological features characteristic of mammals must have been evolving at the same time.

Our consideration of the functions of the hypothalamic polypeptides has made it evident that the hypothalamus/neurohypophysis complex must have played a very important part in the adaptation of vertebrates to terrestrial life, and it is of interest, even with our present limited knowledge, to enquire how far its functions were already established before the vertebrates embarked upon this adventure. We know that oxytocic, vasopressor, and antidiuretic properties are present in extracts of teleost pituitaries when these are tested on higher vertebrates, so that it is natural to look for an involvement of the neurohypophysis in the water balance of these fish, but so far it has been difficult to establish this point, although some depletion of neurosecretory material is said to result from exposure of *Callionymus lyra* and *Ammodytes lanceolatus* to hyper-osmotic conditions. An illustration of the apparent contradictions that arise here is the fact that extracts of the 'posterior lobe' of salmon bring about uptake of water in frogs but are without effect when injected into carp, and that this is so even if the injected fish have been previously subjected to partial dehydration by immersion in saline solution. Actually, of course, freshwater fish such as carp are not normally subject to water deprivation, and it is desirable to test this issue thoroughly on marine fish which, being hypotonic to the external medium, are continuously losing water to it.

Clearly we cannot abstract these problems from those associated with the action of the adrenocortical steroids on water and salt-electrolyte metabolism, but in addition we need to relate them to current interpretations of the origin and early history of the vertebrates. It has been very widely taught that these animals first arose in fresh water, a view that is largely based upon the conclusions drawn by Homer Smith and Marshall as to the history of the kidney. As is well known, the functioning of this organ depends upon a process of ultrafiltration at the glomerulus, the result being the production of a protein-free filtrate which is subsequently modified in composition in its passage down the tubule. It has been argued that this is a freshwater adaptation which permits the removal of a large volume of water, and that it would not, therefore, have evolved in the sea, but this interpretation has since come under serious and cogent criticism. Palaeontological evidence suggests that the earliest known vertebrate remains are marine in origin, and, with this in mind, Robertson has pointed out that marine invertebrates, such as crustaceans, have excretory organs that function in fundamentally the same way as the vertebrate kidney tubule, with filtration followed by reabsorption and secretion, despite the fact that they are in isosmotic equilibrium with the sea water. There is certainly no question of these animals having had a freshwater ancestry, and it seems likely that this type of excretory organ is of value to marine animals in helping them to maintain their body fluids in ionic equilibrium with the external medium. It follows that the glomerular kidney, on this view, might well have evolved under marine conditions, and that it may subsequently have proved a valuable pre-adaptation which would have greatly facilitated the penetration of the early vertebrates into fresh water.

Of particular interest here is the unique position of the myxinoid cyclostomes, which alone among vertebrates have a salt concentration in their body fluids equivalent to that of the sea, but which also have a glomerular kidney. It seems possible that these animals may be preserving today the osmotic relationships of the earliest vertebrates, and it is certain that an analysis of their water metabolism would shed a great deal of light on the evolutionary history of the neurohypophyseal hormones.

The evolution of the vertebrate freshwater fauna was evidently accompanied by an adaptive change in the composition of the body fluids which, while lowering their osmotic pressure, still left them hyperosmotic to the medium. Under these conditions there is an inflow of water and presumably little need for antidiuretic control. Of the fish which returned to the sea, the elasmobranchs restored the isosmotic condition by building up a high concentration of urea, while the teleosts retained the salt content that was established during the freshwater phase and are thus hypo-osmotic to the medium. They alone, then, lose water in considerable amounts to the outside, but this is a steady and continuous loss which they counter by swallowing sea water and excreting the surplus salt; although, therefore, they might be expected to have some mechanism controlling desiccation, their position, like that of the elasmobranchs, is not one that would seem likely to create sudden demands for antidiuretic action.

With terrestrial forms, however, the situation is very different, for the permeability of the skin of amphibians exposes them to frequent and irregular hazards of desiccation, which increase as their terrestrial habit increases; at this stage, then, the regulation of the uptake and conservation of water takes on a new importance for the vertebrates. It seems possible that the control of water and salt-electrolyte metabolism in fish may demand primarily a mechanism controlling the exchange of ions with the external medium, and that the adrenocortical steroids might have a more important part to play in that regard than the hormones of the hypothalamus. In the amphibians, as Sawyer points out, the latter seem to predominate in the regulation of water metabolism, and the adrenocortical steroids in the regulation of salt-electrolyte metabolism, so that we may perhaps think of the functional relationships of these two groups of hormones as becoming increasingly close in the course of vertebrate evolution.

It must be emphasized that these arguments are largely speculative, and that they are developed here primarily to illustrate the type of evolutionary analysis which needs to be employed as a background to experimental research. It will be evident, however, that they at once raise the question whether these polypeptide hormones of the hypothalamus may have some other functions in the lower vertebrates, and to this possibility we shall return later.

V. HORMONES AND REPRODUCTION

1. Introduction

IN dealing with the problems of reproduction we enter a field which is central to the study of endocrinology, and one in which it is particularly easy to allow detail to obscure general principles. It will probably be agreed, however, that periodicity constitutes a particularly striking single aspect of reproductive activity, and it is to the endocrinological problems presented by this that we shall mainly devote our attention, for the analysis of these has been the foundation of much of our present understanding of hormonal interactions in the vertebrates and of the unique status of the pituitary gland.

The existence of sexual cycles arises in part from the fact that the production of germ cells, and the behavioural adaptations that are essential to ensure successful insemination, are physiologically exhausting and will often necessitate a relatively quiescent period for recovery, but this by itself would not result in all sexually mature members of a population passing through the same phase of the cycle at about the same time, as they very often do. The need for this arises from the fact that conditions favourable for reproduction and, in particular, for the rearing of the young, will commonly be restricted to a limited period of the year, determined by the nature of the climatic variations which the species encounters, and we may therefore expect to find that these cycles are of a highly adaptive character.

Sexual periodicity, then, has a dual basis, and this is reflected in the physiological mechanisms by which it is controlled, for these depend in part upon endogenous factors (arising within the body) and in part upon exogenous ones (arising in the outside world). Important amongst the former are the gonadal hormones secreted by the ovary and testis, while the latter include a variety of stimuli such as those provided by temperature, daylight, rainfall, and the presence of other individuals, the relative importance of these depending upon the mode of life of the species concerned. Further, it is now accepted that the pituitary gland is of central importance in effecting the coordination of these endogenous and exogenous factors, and we shall find that this is a consequence of its being related to the outside world through the nervous system and receptors and to the rest of the endocrine system by a complex pattern of hormonal interactions. In attempting an analysis of this situation we shall begin by considering the mammals, for it is research on that group which has so far provided us with the most complete data. We shall then turn to review some aspects of sexual periodicity in other vertebrates with the aim of judging how far the principles established for mammals can be regarded as of general applicability throughout the group.

2. The mammalian ovary

The ovary of mammals (Fig. 28, and Plate v) is formed of an outer cortex and an inner medulla, the latter small in extent and possessing large blood vessels. The cortex contains follicles in all stages of development, the

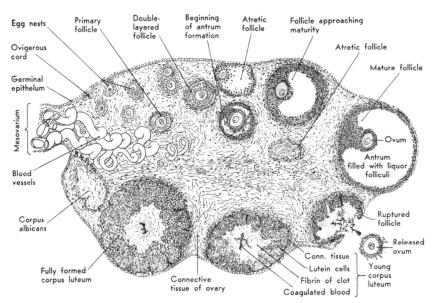

Fig. 28. Schematic diagram of a mammalian ovary showing the sequence of events in the origin, growth, and rupture of the Graafian follicle, and the formation and retrogression of the corpus luteum. Follow clockwise around the ovary, starting at the mesovarium.
(From Patten, 1958. *Fundamentals of Embryology*. McGraw-Hill.)

smallest consisting of a single layer of flattened epithelial cells surrounding a primary oocyte; between these extends a dense stroma containing spindle-shaped interstitial cells. Externally the cortex forms a dense tunica albuginea, composed of muscle cells and connective tissue, and externally to this again is the germinal epithelium, continuous with the peritoneal epithelium and formed of more or less cubical cells.

Far more follicles are formed than will ever complete their development, and many undergo a regression called follicular atresia. Those that do complete it undergo immediately prior to ovulation an enormous enlargement, brought about by proliferation of the follicular epithelium and by the accumulation of fluid. Initially the cells become cubical or columnar and multiply to form several layers, while a zona pellucida appears around the oocyte, perhaps by transformation of the cell membrane, and the surrounding stroma becomes organized into a theca. Later the follicle becomes vesicular as a result of the increasing accumulation of fluid amongst its cells, and it thus becomes transformed into the mature Graafian follicle.

In its fully developed form this consists of a peripheral layer, several cells thick, called the membrana granulosa; the latter encloses a cavity, the antrum, filled with the fluid, or liquor folliculi, into which projects a thickening of the granulosa. This thickening, the cumulus oöphorus, contains the much enlarged oocyte, the cells immediately surrounding this being the corona radiata. Externally to the membrana granulosa the theca has differentiated into the theca externa and the theca interna; the former is fibrous and seems to be primarily a supporting tissue, but the large cells of the latter contain lipids which give the histochemical reactions of steroids (p. 243). For this reason it seems likely that this tissue is the source of the ovarian hormone that we shall discuss below, but, while it is accepted that this almost certainly does originate in the mature follicle, there is not complete agreement as to whether it is actually secreted by the theca interna or by the granulosa cells, despite the fact that the latter contain little lipid. The interstitial cells are another possible source, particularly since there is some evidence that these may actually be derived from the cells of the theca interna. Quite apart from this, however, the corresponding cells of other vertebrate groups, where the follicles are of a simpler nature, may well function in this way.

When the oocyte has been discharged from the ovary, usually after the first maturation division, its follicle becomes transformed into the corpus luteum. This involves an enlargement of certain of the granulosa cells, these assuming a polygonal shape while lipoid droplets and lipochrome pigments accumulate in them; in this way they are transformed into the characteristic luteal cells, and it may be that the theca interna also makes a contribution to these. A supporting framework is formed around the cells by connective tissue and blood vessels which extend inwards from the theca interna, and perhaps also from the theca externa, and this completes the development of what we shall find to be an important endocrine gland, the essential features of which are already established in the Monotremata (Fig. 29). Its function will be considered below, but we may note now that when its period of duty is ended it degenerates into a whitish body, the corpus albicans, which sinks deeper into the ovarian stroma and eventually disappears.

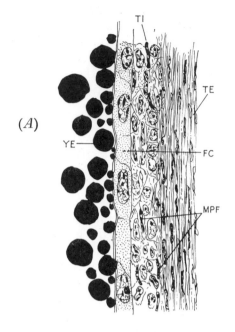

(A)

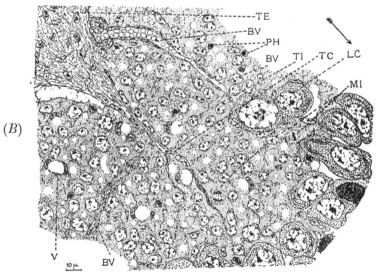

(B)

Fig. 29. The ovarian follicle of the platypus (*Ornithorhynchus*).
A. Follicular wall of oocyte, about 3 mm in diameter. B. Portion of wall
of corpus luteum. *BV*, ingrowing capillary; *FC*, follicular epithelium; *LC*,
differentiating luteal cell; *MI*, cells in mitosis; *MPF*, nuclei of fibroblasts;
TC, ingrowth of theca externa; *TE*, theca externa; *TI*, theca interna; *V*, vacuole
in theca interna cell; *YE*, yolk spheres of oocyte.

(From Hill & Gatenby, 1926. *Proc. Zool. Soc. Lond.* **2**, 715–62.)

3. The ovarian hormones

Brown-Séquard is said to have been the first to suggest, in 1889, that the ovary might be an internally secreting organ. It was at about this time that the therapeutic value of thyroid extracts was becoming established, and, following his suggestion, extensive use was optimistically made of extracts of ovaries, but the attempts were premature and the results highly variable. Later and more successful developments may be said to derive from the studies of F. H. A. Marshall and Jolly on the reproductive system of the dog, as a result of which they expressed in 1906 the view that 'the ovary is an organ providing an internal secretion which is elaborated by the follicular epithelial cells or by the interstitial cells of the stroma. After ovulation, which takes place during oestrus, the corpus luteum is formed, and this organ provides a further secretion whose function is essential for the changes taking place during the attachment and development of the embryo in the first stages of pregnancy.'

With this and other work as a foundation, the concept of the ovary as an endocrine organ won increasing acceptance during the early years of the century, but the turning-point in the investigation of its secretory activity came with the development by Allen and Doisy in 1923 of a simple and reliable bio-assay method. We have already noted the important place which such procedures must have in endocrinological research, and the development of this one owed much, as Dodds has pointed out, to the fact that the association of these two investigators brought biological and biochemical experience into association. It is, in fact, another good example (p. 73) of the way in which biological research often waits upon the development of the proper tools, for, coupled with the large expansion of research after the First World War, it initiated an intense concentration upon sexual endocrinology.

The method of Allen and Doisy depends upon the fact that the sexual activity of most female mammals is based upon the recurrence of an oestrous cycle (*oistros*, gadfly). In rats and mice the successive stages of this are characterized by clearly defined changes in the vaginal epithelium, so that by taking samples of this from the living animal, and by studying vaginal smear preparations made from them (Fig. 30), it is possible to follow the whole course of the cycle. What is more important, however, is that this cycle is absent from sexually immature animals or from those which have undergone ovariectomy (removal of the ovaries) so that by injecting test substances into them and examining their vaginal smears it is possible to determine which of the substances can evoke the cycle, those which have this property being termed oestrogens (estrogens in the U.S.A.).

Such oestrogenic activity was readily demonstrable in ovarian extracts

prepared with lipid solvents, but for a time investigators were still handi-
capped by the extreme difficulty of purifying this material. Another
important advance, however, was made in 1927 when Aschheim and
Zondek showed that there was a large concentration of activity in the
urine in pregnant women, for extracts obtained from this abundant

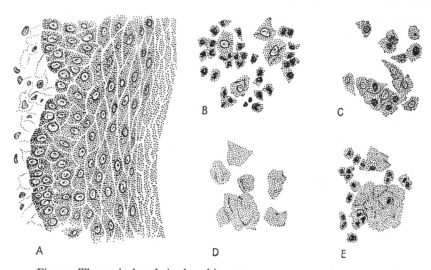

Fig. 30. The vaginal cycle in the white rat.
   A, Vaginal wall at oestrus; the cells of the inner surface (right) are cornified
and without nuclei. *B*. Vaginal smear at dioestrus, containing epithelial cells
(pale nuclei) and leucocytes (dark nuclei). *C*. Just before oestrus the epithelial
cells swell. *D*. Smear at oestrus, showing cornified cells as in *A*. *E*. After oestrus
the leucocytes return and the cornified cells disintegrate.
   (From Young, 1957. *The Life of Mammals*. Oxford: Clarendon Press.)

source, and later from the urine of stallions and of pregnant mares, lent
themselves much more satisfactorily to chemical processing. A third and
equally important advance was the establishment by Rosenheim and King
in 1932 of the correct structural formula of cholesterol, for this settled the
problem of the basic formula of sterols without which, again to quote
Dodds, the discovery of the constitution of the sex hormones would have
been indefinitely delayed. King has told how, at the time when the formula
deduced by Wieland and Windaus was proving to be unsatisfactory, he
said to Rosenheim on the spur of the moment 'Why don't you take ring II
in the Windaus-Wieland structures and put it on the other side of ring I
so as to produce a potential chrysene structure?', and how Rosenheim
took the problem home and returned the next morning to exclaim
excitedly 'It fits, it fits'.
   The accepted formula of cholesterol is shown in Fig. 31. Its characteristic
feature is that it is based upon a four-ring system known as the perhydro-

*cyclo*pentenophenanthrene nucleus and the name steroid has been used since 1936 for all compounds in which this system is present. For descriptive purposes the carbon atoms receive a conventional numbering which is shown in the figure; the group attached at C-17 is referred to as the side-chain, and it will be noted that methyl groups are attached in the

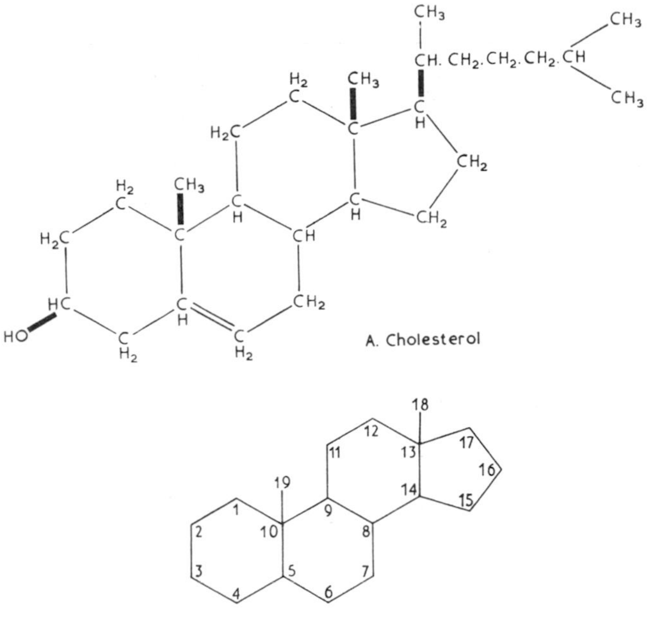

A. Cholesterol

B. The steroid nucleus

Fig. 31.

angles at C-10 and C-13, although these are not necessarily always present in steroids. Side-chain carbon atoms are numbered from 20 onwards.

The nomenclature of these substances is determined by an international agreement, the principles of which are fully explained by Klyne (see Bibliography). The hormones with which we shall be concerned are regarded as being derived from one or other of three parent substances, oestrane, androstane, and pregnane (Figs. 32, 37, 35). These are modified by the incorporation of double bonds and substituent groups which are referred to by the prefixes or suffixes given in Table 2, the position of these being indicated by stating the carbon atom with which they are associated. Thus 1:3:5 (10)-triene indicates the presence of double bonds between C-1 and C-2, C-3 and C-4, and C-5 and C10, both numbers being given when the two atoms concerned are not consecutively numbered. Only one kind of substituent group in each compound is indicated by a suffix; the

TABLE 2

Some prefixes and suffixes used in steroid nomenclature

Group	*Prefix*	*Suffix*
olefinic double bond, C:C		ene
hydroxyl, OH	hydroxy	ol
carbonyl (keto), C:O	oxo	one

di, tri, tetra, penta = 2, 3, 4, 5

remainder are designated by prefixes, the decision as to which of the groups shall be selected for the suffix being determined by agreed convention.

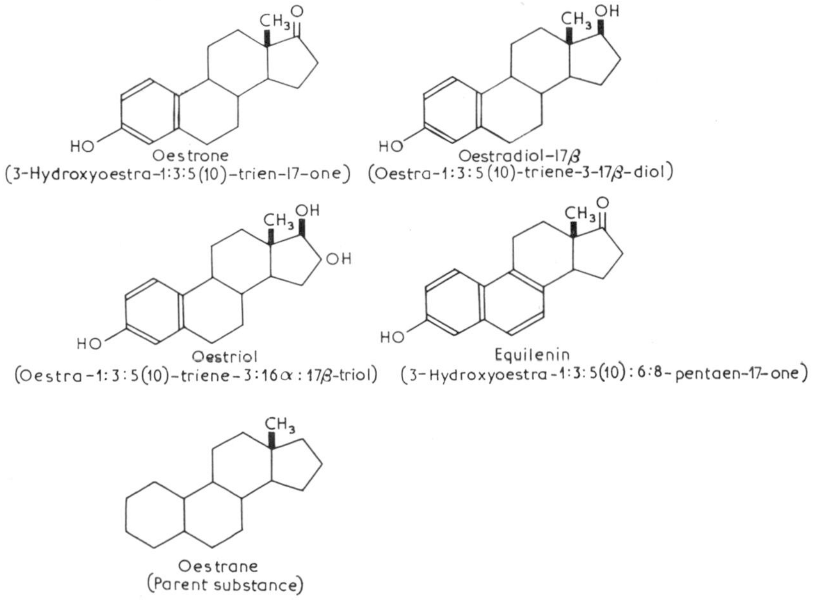
CH3
O
HO
Oestrone
(3-Hydroxyoestra-1:3:5(10)-trien-17-one)
CH3
OH
HO
Oestradiol-17β
(Oestra-1:3:5(10)-triene-3-17β-diol)
CH3
OH
OH
HO
Oestriol
(Oestra-1:3:5(10)-triene-3:16α:17β-triol)
CH3
O
HO
Equilenin
(3-Hydroxyoestra-1:3:5(10):6:8-pentaen-17-one)
CH3
Oestrane
(Parent substance)

Fig. 32. Oestrogens.

The stereochemistry of the molecule is an important aspect of its interpretation, for since there are eight asymmetric carbon atoms (at positions 3, 5, 9, 10, 14, and 17) it can theoretically exist in 256 (i.e. 2^8) stereoisomeric forms. In our analysis we shall be concerned with only a few of these, but it is well to remember that this complication greatly adds to the difficulty of synthesizing the steroid hormones. For graphical representation the nucleus is regarded as being planar and as lying in the plane of the paper; those groups which then lie below this plane are called α, and their bonds are drawn as broken lines, those, including the angle methyl groups, lying above this plane are called β, and their bonds are drawn as heavy continuous lines, while a wavy line shows that the configuration is unknown. The configuration of the substituent groups is indicated by the appropriate Greek letter placed before the term indicating their nature, while C-5 is always represented as 5α or 5β, unless there is a double bond at this point, because the stereoisomerism at C-5 is particularly variable. Thus the systematic name for pregnanediol (Fig. 35) becomes 5β-pregnane-3α:20α-diol, but in practice it is usually more convenient to refer to the steroid hormones by their trivial names, for the commonest of these are internationally accepted; to avoid confusion, however, it is well to quote the systematic name once in each article in which reference is made to a particular hormone.

In producing steroid hormones in their gonads and adrenocortical tissue the vertebrates are making use of a molecular structure that is widely distributed in nature, a fact in itself of no little evolutionary interest. Thus the perhydro*cyclo*pentenophenanthrene nucleus is present in ergosterol, the precursor of vitamin D_2 (p. 358), while it is found also in the bile acids, in toad venom, and in plant glycosides known as sapogenins and cardenolides, the latter being of value in cardiac therapy and in the making of arrow poisons.

The first oestrogen to be identified was oestrone, the isolation of which in pure crystalline form was announced independently by Doisy and Butenandt in 1929, while a second, the less active oestriol, was isolated by Marrian in 1930. Both were obtained from human pregnancy urine, and are now thought to be excretion products, but in 1935 Doisy obtained some 12 mg of a much more potent oestrogen from four tons of pig ovaries, and this substance, which is called oestradiol-17β, has been accepted as the principal ovarian hormone. It is one of the essential factors in the regulation of the oestrous cycle, in many mammals it increases the spontaneous activity of the uterine muscle, and it also promotes the development of the ductules of the mammary glands (p. 114). In general, it may be regarded as responsible for the maintenance of the organs that are involved in sexual activity, and, according to one interpretation, its fundamental effect may be thought of as the stimulation of cell division, the uterus, vagina, and mammary glands being the organs which in mammals are the most responsive to its influence.

In discussions of such sex characters it has been customary in the past to make distinctions in both sexes between the primary sexual characters (the gonads themselves), the accessory sexual characters (those, such as the male and female duct systems, which are of obvious and direct value in reproduction) and the secondary sexual characters (those, such as colour, plumage, antlers, hair distribution in the human, and, indeed, a whole range of features extending from the red belly of the stickleback to the leg elevation of the urinating male dog, which were thought at one time to have no obvious reproductive significance). However, it is now well recognized that these secondary characters frequently play a vital part in bringing the sexes together, in co-ordinating their sexual activity, and in ensuring successful fertilization, so that the distinction between accessory and secondary is largely a false one, and it is not surprising, therefore, to find that they are commonly subjected to similar hormonal control through the gonads, although there are exceptions to this general rule, (p. 130).

The structural formulae of the three oestrogens mentioned above are shown in Fig. 32. They contain eighteen carbon atoms and are therefore referred to as C_{18} steroids, and all are characterized by the fact that ring A is aromatic, the angle methyl group being absent from C-10, while the substituent hydroxyl group at C-3 is phenolic. Oestrone is a phenolic ketone, with a carbonyl (C=O) group at C-17, and the reduction of this group gives rise to oestradiol. This reduction produces asymmetry at C-17, and the formula shown is oestradiol-17β, a substance which, owing to earlier confusion as to its stereo-chemistry, is still referred to as 'a'-oestradiol; oestradiol-17α, a much weaker oestrogen, is still referred to as 'β'-oestradiol (the quotation marks showing that α and β are here used in a trivial sense). The ovary and the urine of females are not the only sources of these substances, for they are also secreted to a varying extent in the testis; thus oestrone has been isolated from the urine of men, while the testis of stallions is of all tissues the one which is richest in oestrogens, a situation which has aptly been described as an eccentricity of equine biochemistry. The function of these substances in males is obscure, if, indeed, they have any at all, but we shall see that the gonadal hormones of the two sexes are chemically very closely related, and in fact, some androgen (p. 109) is secreted in the ovary. It may be, therefore, that the biosynthetic activities of the cells can readily be deflected into pathways that lead to the production of steroids with biological properties considerably different from those of the substances with which they are primarily concerned, a situation that certainly seems to obtain in the adrenal cortex (p. 251). Unfortunately, comparatively little is known about the biosynthesis of the gonadal hormones, although it is reasonable to suppose that they could be derived from cholesterol by degradation of the side-chain and modification of ring A. Some indication that this may actually occur is given by the fact that after administration to a pregnant woman of cholesterol labelled with deuterium it has been possible to isolate from the urine some pregnanediol (an excretory product of progesterone, p. 106) which also contained deuterium and which must presumably have been derived from the administered cholesterol.

Oestrogens occur in plants as well as in animals, oestriol having been obtained from willow catkins and oestrone from palm kernels, but it is important to appreciate that oestrogenic activity is not necessarily associated with the steroid nucleus, a point that is well illustrated by *Pueraria mirifica*. The tuberous roots of this Thailand plant have a remarkable reputation as rejuvenators and are capable, according to local tradition, of prolonging human life to as much as 280 years, but such value as they may have is probably dependent upon their considerable oestrogenic potency. The active substance, now known as miroestrol (Fig. 33), has been obtained in a pure form and chemical studies have shown that it is not a steroid. The reason for its activity is not clear, but it has been suggested that it may be a chance consequence of some feature of its molecular pattern, the distance from 3-OH to 18-OH being very similar to that from 3-OH to 17-OH in the oestradiol molecule. However, this cannot always be the explanation of such a situation, as is shown by consideration of the compounds of the stilboestrol series (Fig. 34), originally synthesized by Dodds.

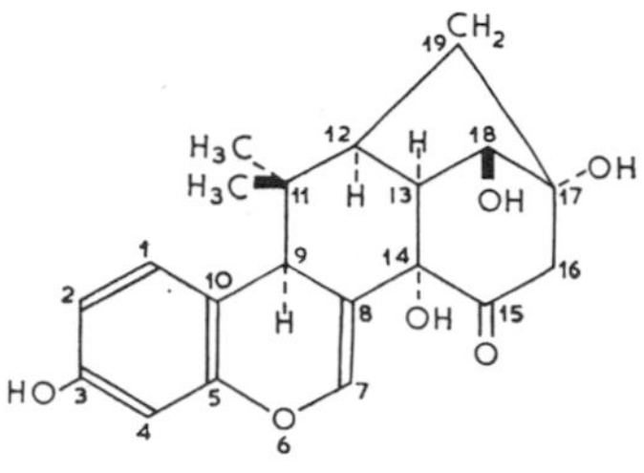

Miroestrol
(From Cain, 1960. Nature 188, 774)

Fig. 33.

These are artificial oestrogens in the sense that they have the biological activity of oestrogens but do not occur under natural conditions. Unlike the naturally occurring hormones, they are highly active when taken by mouth, so that they have been extensively used for clinical treatment, particularly in the control of cancer of the prostate. They have also been

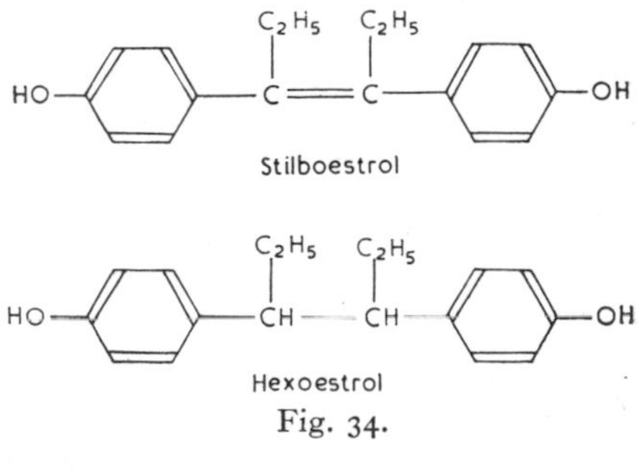

Stilboestrol

Hexoestrol

Fig. 34.

used by the livestock industry owing to the fact that administration of them to poultry, by the insertion of a pellet under the skin, evokes changes in lipid metabolism; associated with these is an increased deposition of fat in the breast muscle and a bleaching of the flesh which combine to make old capons much more acceptable to the housewife. A different effect results from the addition of the substance to cattle feed, for this leads to stimulation of protein anabolism, with accelerated gain in weight and increased efficiency of feed conversion.

The molecular structure of the stilboestrols is substantially different from that of the steroids, and the explanation of their oestrogenic properties remains uncertain. There is no doubt, however, of the reality of these, for they were sufficiently illustrated by the enlargement of the breasts and the sexual impotence which developed in male workers who were inadequately protected from the inhalation of contaminated dust when the commercial manufacture of stilboestrol was first introduced. It is probable that these effects, like the influence on the prostate, result in part from an interaction of this substance with the pituitary gland (p. 122). Their occurrence, together with a possible risk of carcinogenic action, has led to strict supervision of the use of artificial oestrogens in livestock production.

We have seen that after ovulation the Graafian follicle of the mammalian ovary becomes transformed into a corpus luteum, and that from early in this century it had been suspected that this structure was concerned in some way with the preparation of the uterus for the implantation of the fertilized egg. Its function as an endocrine gland is now well established, but it was not until 1934 that four different laboratories were able to announce almost simultaneously the isolation of its hormone from sows' ovaries. This hormone, now known as progesterone (Fig. 35), is a C_{21} steroid and a diketone, with carbonyl groups at C-3 and C-20, the former being described as $\alpha\beta$-unsaturated. (It should be noted that this use of Greek letters has nothing to do with the stereoisomeric convention mentioned earlier; in this context they refer to the position of the relevant carbon atoms, the α atom being next and the β atom next but one to the carbon atom of the ketone group.) Although progesterone was not itself obtained from urine, it is now known that the inactive steroid pregnanediol, which was isolated from that source in 1929, and to which some reference has already been made, is a metabolic derivative of it, formed by reduction in the liver.

This hormone is responsible for promoting proliferation of the endometrium of the uterus in preparation for the implantation of the embryo, for inhibiting ovulation during pregnancy, for stimulating the growth of the mammary glandular tissue in preparation for lactation (p. 114), and also for the actual maintenance of pregnancy, so that in the mouse, for example, total ovariectomy at any stage of gestation is followed by abortion. In many species, however, the placenta is an important source of the hormone during the later stages of pregnancy (p. 148), so that fully functional corpora lutea may not then be present and total removal of the ovaries will only cause abortion if it is carried out during the earlier stages before the endocrine functions of the placenta have become fully established.

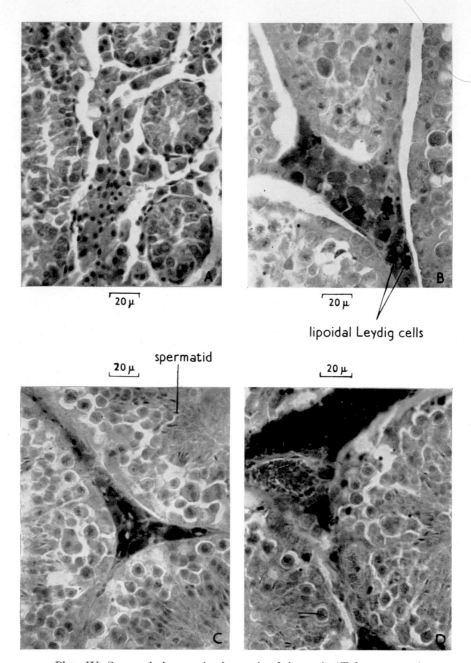

lipoidal Leydig cells

spermatid

Plate IV. Seasonal changes in the testis of the mole (*Talpa europaea*); this species is monoestrous, with a limited breeding season (in England) at the end of March.

A. Section of testis in early January; seminiferous tubules regressed, Leydig (interstitial) cells non-secretory. *B.* Testis in February; spermatogenesis has begun and Leydig cells are beginning to accumulate lipid droplets (coloured here with Sudan black). *C.* Testis in March; expansion of the tubules has constricted the interstitial tissue. *D.* Testis in April; spermatogenesis is at its height and the Leydig cells are densely lipoidal.)

(From Lofts, 1960. *Quart. J. micr. Sci.* **101**, 199–206.)

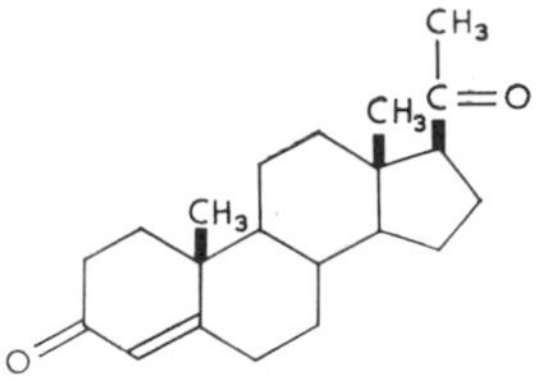

Progesterone
(Pregn-4-ene-3:20-dione)

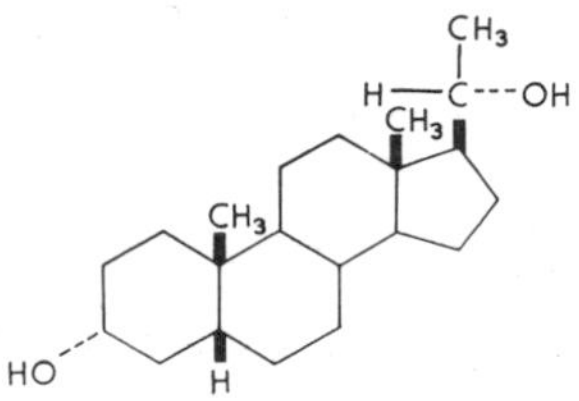

Pregnanediol
(5β-Pregnane-3α:20α-diol)

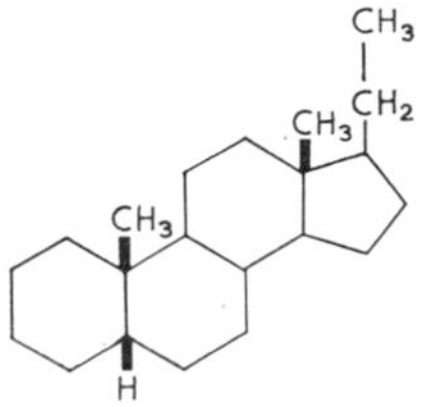

Pregnane
(Parent substance)

Fig. 35.

4. The mammalian testis

The outer wall of the mammalian testis is formed of a tough connective sheath, the tunica albuginea, which is covered on the outside by a mesothelium of the scrotal sac and which is continuous internally with a vascular layer, the tunica vasculosa. The main substance of the organ is formed of the much convoluted seminiferous tubules which open through the rete testis into the epididymis and through this into the vas deferens. The tubules are lined by the germinal epithelium which is composed of two cell types, the spermatogonia and the Sertoli cells. The former give rise by maturation divisions to the sperm, while the latter, which contain lipids and glycogen, are to be regarded as nutritive cells, although from time to time it has been suggested that they may be involved in endocrine secretion.

This function is, in fact, carried on by the interstitial or Leydig cells, which are seen, singly or in groups, lying as large polyhedral cells in the interstices of the tubules. They have a characteristic content of lipoid droplets (Plate IV), which give the various reactions associated with the presence of steroids (p. 243), and there is good reason for regarding this as indicative of the biosynthesis of the steroid male hormone, although the histochemical reactions by themselves are not sufficiently specific to prove this. Further evidence, however, is the fact that it is possible to establish over a wide range of vertebrate groups a close correlation between the state of development of this tissue and the sexual condition of the animal. One example of this correlation is seen in Plate IV, and another is the fact that in man the interstitial tissue is well developed at birth, supposedly as a result of the action of maternal gonadotropins (p. 147); it soon reverts to fibroblast-like cells, and then develops once again at the onset of puberty.

5. Androgens

The remarkable effects produced in mammals by the removal or degeneration of the testes have long been familiar in a variety of uses as, for example, in the modification of the qualities of domestic livestock or in the production of the male sopranos who, despite the penalty of excommunication associated with the operation of castration, became such a characteristic feature of the operatic stage and church choirs of eighteenth-century Italy. John Hunter recognized that the state of development of the male accessory glands was correlated with that of the testes, but the credit for first recognizing that these organs must be discharging a secretion into the blood is due to Berthold. He showed in 1849 that it was possible to transplant a testis into the abdominal cavity of a capon (castrated cock) and that as a result of this the bird would re-develop the characteristics of a male bird, with well-developed comb and wattle, vigorous crowing, and a lively interest in hens.

Substances that show these masculinizing properties are known as androgens (*andros*, male), for while they stimulate the general growth of the body and encourage nitrogen retention, their chief action is the promotion and maintenance of the male sexual characters which (e.g. penis, prostate, seminal vesicles), like those of the female, will usually atrophy in the absence of the gonads. They are steroids, closely resembling the naturally occurring oestrogens, and are now very well characterized, although little progress was made in their study until the remarkable developments in steroid chemistry which we have already noted.

It was shown by McGee in 1927 that injection of extracts of lipoidal material prepared from the testes of bulls would promote the growth of the reduced comb of the capon (Fig. 36), a response that became the basis of a much-favoured bio-assay procedure, and subsequently Butenandt isolated two androgens from the urine of human males, androsterone in 1931 and dehydro*epi*androsterone in 1934 (the term '*epi*' indicating the inversion of the configuration at C-3). It was realized that these might be excretory products, and indications that there were differences between the androgenic activity of urine and of bull testis extracts then led Laqueur in 1935 to the isolation of testosterone from the testis; this has proved to be the most potent natural androgen and in some species may well be the only male hormone actually produced in the organ, the others being metabolic products of it. The molecular structure of these three principal androgens is shown in Fig. 37. It will be seen that they have angle

Fig. 36. *Left*, the head of a capon. *Right*, the head of the
same animal after 22 daily injections of androsterone.
(After Parkes, 1935. *Biochem. J.*, **29**, 1422.)

methyl groups at C-10 and C-13, and an oxygen substituent instead of a
side-chain at C-17; they are therefore C_{19} steroids, and the two with a
carbonyl group at C-17 are referred to as 17-oxosteroids (formerly 17-
ketosteroids). Like the oestrogens, they are largely inactive when given
by mouth, but methyl testosterone can be absorbed from the buccal
mucosa.

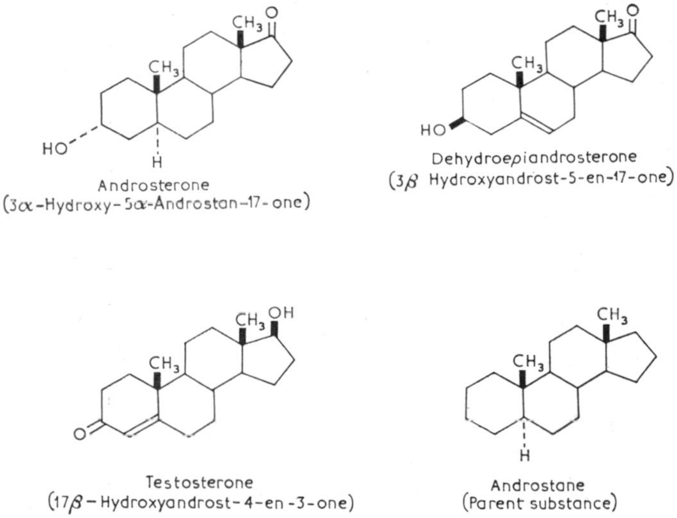

Androsterone
(3α-Hydroxy-5α-Androstan-17-one)

Dehydroepiandrosterone
(3β Hydroxyandrost-5-en-17-one)

Testosterone
(17β-Hydroxyandrost-4-en-3-one)

Androstane
(Parent substance)

Fig. 37. Androgens.

Many other androgenic steroids are known, however, in addition to
these three, derived either from natural sources (usually urine) or by
synthesis. Included amongst them are a number (probably at least five)
which have been isolated from the adrenocortical tissue (p. 251), and we

shall see that over-production of these has an important bearing upon the development of sexual abnormalities. The clear-cut nature of the results of castration, however, show that these adrenocortical steroids cannot normally act in substitution for the male hormone secreted by the testis.

6. The pituitary gonadotropins

The effect of a hormone is rarely an island, entire of itself, and in the regulation of sexual periodicity the pituitary gland has a part to play no less important than that of the gonads. The first step in the analysis of this was taken with the discovery, dating from 1910 and now thoroughly well documented, that while the 'posterior lobe' of the mammalian pituitary could be removed without adverse effects upon breeding, the removal of the 'anterior lobe' was followed by regression of the gonads and reproductive organs. (It is proper to refer to these two operations respectively as neurohypophysectomy and adenohypophysectomy, but it should be remembered that the pars intermedia will usually be included with the 'posterior lobe'. Hypophysectomy should strictly refer to the removal of the entire pituitary gland, although it is also used more loosely, with the extent of the operation left to be inferred from the context.)

The effect of hypophysectomy in mature male rats, for example, is a marked atrophy of the testes; spermatogonia persist and may show mitoses for some months but no mature germ cells are formed, while the interstitial tissue becomes inactive so that the accessory organs regress. In mammals such as the ferret, in which reproduction is restricted to a limited season, the effect depends upon the time of the year at which it is carried out; in winter the testes merely retain their inactive condition, but in the breeding season they regress in the same way as in the rat.

In females comparable changes are found (Plate v *A*); the ovary of the rat atrophies and the larger follicles degenerate at about the stage of antrum formation, although some growth of oocytes and primordial follicles can continue, a fact which indicates that these earlier stages are not under pituitary control. We have seen that classical endocrinological procedure, following the demonstration of the consequences of removal of a gland, is to carry out replacement therapy, and from 1926 onwards it was, in fact, repeatedly shown that implants of 'anterior lobes' could alleviate the above effects in hypophysectomized rats and mice, or could induce precocious puberty in immature animals. Complete success is not always attained, but the testes of the hypophysectomized rat can be restored in this way to more or less normal activity, while ovulation can be induced in immature females and some degree of luteinization in hypophysectomized adults.

Such results made it reasonably certain that the 'anterior lobe' was influencing the gonads through one or more endocrine secretions which are now referred to as gonadotropic hormones or gonadotropins (*trope*,

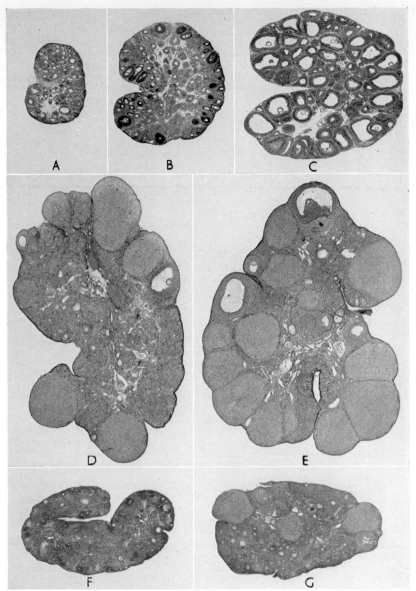

Plate V. *A* to *C*. Ovaries of rats hypophysectomized at 26–28 days, 10–12 days after the operation; all three photographs are at the same magnification. *A*. Untreated control. *B*. ICSH treatment for 3 days; note that interstitial repair is the only result. *C*. FSH treatment for 3 days; note the development of many follicles to medium and large size in the presence of deficient interstitial tissue. (Haematoxylin and eosin. × 13.)

(From Simpson, 1959. In *Reproduction in Domestic Animals*, ed. Cole & Cupps, vol. 1. New York: Academic Press.)

D to *G*. The influence of pituitary transplantation upon ovarian activity in the rat; all four photographs are at the same magnification.

D. Ovary of a normal rat at pro-oestrus. *E*. Ovary after re-transplantation of pituitary from renal capsule to a site under the median eminence; regular oestrous cycles have been resumed. *F*. Atrophic ovary after retransplantation of pituitary from renal capsule to a site under the temporal lobe of the brain; note absence of corpora lutea. *G*. Atrophic ovary after transplantation of pituitary to the renal capsule; the small corpora lutea are the result of transplanting during pro-oestrus. (× 15.)

(From Nikitovitch-Winer & Everett, 1958. *Endocrin.* **63**, 916–30.)

turn). The names refer to the orientation of the pituitary influence towards the gonads and are used here in preference to the alternative, gonado-trophic hormones or gonadotrophins (*trophe*, nourishment), which carry an implication of a nutritive relationship. In reviewing these it must be remembered that their investigation has presented chemical problems of the greatest difficulty, the reason for this being that they appear to be complex proteins, or, to put the situation in another way, that gonado-tropic properties are found to be associated with certain purified proteins of high molecular weight which have been separated out from pituitary extracts. Thus we encounter here in an acute form the problem, already mentioned, of deciding whether the biologically active materials separated in the laboratory are actually released from the gland in the same degree of isolation, or whether they are secreted as more complex substances which unite such properties in a common molecular structure. With these reservations in mind, it can be said that it is now rather generally held that two, or perhaps three, gonadotropins are secreted by the pars distalis, which is the portion of the 'anterior lobe' with which we are actually concerned.

The study of these hormones as distinct entities began with the dis-covery by Aschheim and Zondek in 1927 that after the menopause or ovariectomy there was present in human urine a substance that promoted growth of the follicles in the ovaries of immature rats and mice. It was later shown that similar activity was present in aqueous extracts of the 'anterior lobe', and that the material concerned could be separated into two fractions. One of these, known as follicle-stimulating hormone (FSH), will promote the partial development of multiple follicles in the ovary of immature or hypophysectomized rats (Plate v C), but these will not reach the stage of luteinization, nor will they secrete oestrogen (as evidenced by vaginal smears) unless very high doses of the preparation are used. The function of this hormone in the male is less certain, but it is believed to promote the development of mature sperm (cf. Plate vi C and D); no effect, however, is produced in the interstitial tissue, so that the accessory organs are unaffected.

After hypophysectomy the interstitial cells of both ovary and testis undergo a very characteristic shrinkage, and they are then known as 'deficiency cells'. One effect of the second of the gonadotropic fractions (Plate v B) is to restore this tissue in both sexes, for which reason it is known as interstitial cell-stimulating hormone (ICSH). It is possible that in the male it may be the more important of the two pituitary hormones, for the restored interstitial tissue comes into secretory activity, with consequent growth of the accessory organs, and there is some evidence that once androgen is being secreted this gonadal hormone is able by itself to maintain spermatogenesis. In the female, on the other hand, such accessory

structures as the vagina are unaffected by ICSH treatment, which is understandable on the assumption that oestrogen is secreted by the follicles
rather than by the interstitial tissue of the ovary, for ICSH by itself has
no effect upon follicular growth. For this reason it exerts no gonadotropic
effect upon immature rats, but what it does do in the female is to evoke
ovulation and luteinization in those follicles that have reached the appropriate stage; because of this, it is often known alternatively as luteinizing
hormone (LH). Priority can, in fact, be claimed for this name, as it was
introduced in 1931, six years before the name ICSH was suggested in
recognition of its action in the male. Despite this, there is now a tendency to prefer the later designation, since it refers to an action exerted in
both sexes rather than merely in one.

It is evident that these two hormones must normally act in close conjunction, and it may well be that neither is ever operative without at least
some participation by the other, although the difficulty of securing complete chemical purification of the two makes it difficult to establish this
with certainty. However, it is clear that the effect of FSH, as expressed in
terms of follicular growth, is increased if ICSH is administered at the
same time, despite the fact that the latter fraction is unable by itself to
stimulate that growth; the two together, therefore, produce an effect
greater than the sum of their individual effects, a phenomenon known as
synergism. (This term is also used merely in the sense of interaction in
the same direction, irrespective of whether the total effect is equal to or
greater than the sum of the two single effects. If the former, the result
would be described as summation, but if the latter, one hormone, in this
case ICSH, would be said to potentiate the other.) Because of this relationship it is at least possible that the simulation of oestrogen secretion
by very high doses of FSH is due to the admixture of an appreciable
quantity of ICSH. It follows that tests of the effects of these hormones
must always be carried out on immature or hypophysectomized animals,
for in normal adults both of them will already be circulating in the blood.

Purification studies of FSH and ICSH are still in progress, but they
have each been isolated as preparations which are referred to as hormones
since they behave as single homogeneous proteins (p. 59) under electrophoretic and ultracentrifugal examination. One feature of their constitution which, as we shall see, is of great importance in the analysis of
the functional differentiation of the pars distalis is that carbohydrate
components in the form of hexose and hexosamine are firmly bound to
the peptide molecules. The proportions of these components vary, but
they are present respectively to the extent of 1·2 per cent. and 1·5 per
cent. in the FSH of sheep, and 4·4 per cent. and 5·8 per cent. in the
ICSH of the same animal. The FSH of the sheep is therefore a glycoprotein, which we may define following Meyer as a substance in which

hexosamine-containing polysaccharide is firmly bound to a peptide, the whole containing less than 4 per cent. hexosamine. The ICSH, by contrast, is a mucoprotein, a similar type of substance but containing more than 4 per cent. hexosamine. The molecular weights of the FSH and the ICSH of the sheep are respectively 67,000 and 31,000–40,000; corresponding figures for those of the pig are respectively 29,000 and 100,000, so that in these, and in many other properties, there are differences between the gonadotropins derived from different sources. The difficulties mentioned earlier obviously make it impossible to say how far these reflect differences in the biologically active parts of their molecules.

In addition to these two gonadotropins, the existence of which is generally accepted, there is some reason for believing that a third one is operative at least in the female rat. We have already seen that oestrogens and progesterone promote the growth of the mammary glands, and that oxytocin plays an essential part in the final ejection of the milk. In between these two phases comes the actual secretion of the latter, which we can regard, following a definition proposed in 1951, as the synthesis of milk by the secretory cells of the alveoli and its passage from them into the alveolar lumen (cf. p. 77). It was for some time supposed that this process followed automatically either upon the completion of the growth phase or as a consequence of the physiological changes accompanying parturition. In 1928, however, it was shown by Stricker and Grüter that 'anterior lobe' extracts could bring about secretion in pseudopregnant (p. 123) rabbits which, although they possessed fully developed mammary tissue, would not normally pass into this phase.

The hormone concerned (prolactin, lactogenic hormone, mammotropin) has been obtained in a pure form as a crystalline protein with a molecular weight lying (for the sheep's hormone) between 24,200 and 26,500; it contains no bound carbohydrate, so that it is not a muco- or glycoprotein. In the female rat prolactin will also prolong the functioning of the corpus luteum if it is injected at the end of oestrus, and it has therefore been suggested that it is responsible for promoting and maintaining the secretion of progesterone after the formation of the corpus luteum has been completed under the influence of ICSH. If this is so, it clearly merits designation as a third gonadotropin, and it has received for this reason the alternative name of luteotropin or luteotropic hormone (LTH, which should not be confused with luteinizing hormone, LH). It is not clear, however, whether it has gonadotropic functions in any other species, nor is it known to have any such function in the male rat.

On the other hand, its function in lactation in the mammals generally is well defined, but in this respect its relationship with other hormones is an elaborate one, for it seems to act here as the primary member of a hormonal complex. Indeed, the same might also be said of the mammary

854108   I

action of oestrogen and progesterone, if we follow the analysis of Lyons, Li, and Johnson of the situation in the rat. Oestrogen, secreted under the stimulus of FSH and ICSH, co-operates with growth hormone and the corticosteroids (themselves secreted under the stimulus of corticotropin, p. 250) to induce the growth of the mammary ductules. Prolactin next stimulates the corpora lutea to secrete progesterone, and the full development of the alveoli results from the combined action of prolactin, growth hormone, oestrogen, progesterone, and the corticosteroids, with the co-operation of placental hormones (p. 148). The secretion of the milk takes place under the dominating influence of prolactin and the corticosteroids, the influence of oestrogen and progesterone diminishing at this stage. Finally, the ejection of the milk occurs as a result of the action of oxytocin. Thus some ten or more hormones may be said to cooperate in the production of milk, at least in the laboratory rat! No doubt this is in part a consequence of the complex hormonal interactions that are involved in the regulation of metabolism, for the synthetic activity of the mammary glands is bound to be influenced by this, but, as Lyons points out, these glands came late upon the evolutionary scene and it is understandable that their direct hormonal control would become enmeshed in the complexity that is so characteristic of the endocrine organization of the higher vertebrates.

In any case, it seems certain that prolactin was not evolved in the first instance as a mammary hormone, for it is known to function also in birds. In pigeons it promotes the secretion of the 'milk' which is formed in the crop glands of both sexes and which is fed to the young by regurgitation, the effect being so well defined that the resultant increase in weight of the crop is the basis of a standard method for the bio-assay of the hormone. It is also believe to be a factor in the development of the naked and richly vascularized brood-spots which form in many species of birds at incubation time, and there is good evidence that it evokes the appearance of brooding behaviour in the domestic fowl. It is by no means agreed, however, that it has a similar function in other species, and it has been suggested that its increased output during incubation may be associated with its influence upon various aspects of metabolism.

Even more difficult to interpret, but of great interest from the evolutionary standpoint, is some evidence for its action in certain lower vertebrates. Thus melanocyte-stimulating hormone (p. 259) promotes the proliferation of melanocytes in the teleost *Fundulus*, and it is said that prolactin enhances (potentiates) this action. Furthermore, although prolactin is unable by itself to stimulate actual proliferation of the pigment cells, it is thought to be able to promote melanin synthesis.

Another unexpected action of this hormone is exerted upon the immature terrestrial stages of the newts *Triturus* (*Diemyctylus*) *viridescens* and

Triturus alpestris. Administration of it to hypophysectomized animals will induce within a few days a migration to water (the so-called water-drive effect), although it is said that if the preparations are highly purified they will not evoke the full complement of pigmentary and morphological changes which are normally associated with this change of habit. Since extracts of the pituitaries of late spawning carp (*Cyprinus carpio*) and pre- or post-spawning *Fundulus* also produce this response there is some possibility that the hormone may be present both in fish and amphibians. Obviously, however, such evidence is both meagre and indirect. The mere presence of some activity in extracts affords no information regarding the chemical nature of the substance concerned or its possible physiological significance, while the fact that a mammalian hormone evokes a particular response in fish is not in itself evidence that that hormone is a normal secretion of the recipient species. These results therefore require a good deal of amplification, but they certainly suggest the interesting possibility that we may have here an example of a hormone that has persisted during vertebrate history while its effects have undergone considerable evolution (p. 91).

7. Neural regulation of gonadotropin secretion

The unique importance of the pituitary gland in the regulation of sexual periodicity in vertebrates lies in the fact that it is functionally related not only to the gonads but also to the nervous system and through this to the external environment. The next step in our analysis, therefore, must be to inquire into the paths by which these relationships are maintained. In the elucidation of the connexions with the nervous system particular attention has been given to the rabbit, for in this animal ovulation normally occurs only after coitus, and after a well-defined time interval of some ten hours. This is a clear example of reproductive activity being influenced through the nervous system after the application of a specific stimulus, and it is accepted that the response is mediated by the reflex release of ICSH from the pars distalis, the time interval being required for the mobilization of a concentration of the hormone adequate for evoking rupture of the follicles.

An important step in the elucidation of the pathways involved in this response was taken in 1936, when Marshall and Verney showed that ovulation and pseudo-pregnancy could be produced in the rabbit if the animal was first etherized and electrical stimulation was then applied either to the brain or to the spinal cord. They had, therefore, evoked from the pars distalis an output of gonadotropin which would normally result from the stimulus of coitus, the only difference being that the time interval was seventeen to twenty-four hours instead of ten; this they reasonably ascribed to the slower output of hormone under the artificial conditions of the experiment. They dismissed the possibility that the nervous system was transmitting a signal directly to the ovaries because it was known that post-coital ovulation could occur even when these had been auto-transplanted to abnormal positions where they were completely deprived of any possible innervation; and in any case it is now accepted that the secretory tissue of the gonads does not receive a secreto-motor nerve supply. They therefore felt justified in concluding that they had 'proved that nervous stimuli can act upon the anterior pituitary and change the functional activity of that organ and the character of its secretions in such a way as to alter and control certain of the phases of the oestrous cycle.'

In later investigations designed to define more precisely the pathway by which this nervous control is exercised, particular attention has been given to the hypothalamus, and for this there are several good reasons. For one thing, we have seen that certain regions of this are directly related to the neural lobe of the pituitary gland, but this is actually only one aspect of the wide-ranging importance of this region in the regulation of visceral function. It is, in fact, the main co-ordinating centre of the auto-nomic nervous system, and, by virtue of its integration of visceral responses with the somatic reactions that must necessarily accompany them, it is able to evoke complex patterns of activity based upon such fundamental aspects of animal life as feeding, drinking, reproduction, and sleep. The component parts of these activities are represented within the hypo-thalamus by localized regions, which have been mapped by Hess, using the technique of stimulation by implanted electrodes; examples of the types of response elicited by activating different areas of the hypothalamus of the cat in this way are shown in Fig. 38.

We have abundant evidence that the endocrine system is involved in many of the responses that are controlled by the hypothalamus, in de-fensive reactions, for example (p. 228), or in visceral responses generally, and it would be reasonable to suspect that this system, as well as the autonomic nervous system, might be subject to hypothalamic regulation. Other considerations that strengthen this suspicion are the intimate association of the adenohypophysis with the floor of the diencephalon, the wide-ranging control that the former exerts over other endocrine organs (of which we shall see examples later), and the fact that while it apparently has no secreto-motor nerve supply it is connected by the hypophyseal portal system with the median eminence, for the latter is itself in close relationship with the hypothalamus (p. 74).

The implications of this argument have been subjected to experimental analysis by Harris, adapting for this purpose the above-mentioned tech-nique of electrical stimulation by remote control. His method (Fig. 39) has been to insert into a rabbit a small secondary coil, placed so as to lie between the scalp and the skull; this carries an indifferent electrode also lying beneath the skull, while a fine stimulating one passes downwards to the pituitary. This procedure has the very great advantage that a rabbit can live normally with the apparatus embedded in it, so that repeated experiments can be carried out on the same animal, and without

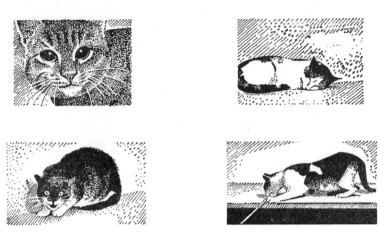

Fig. 38. Reactions induced in cats by electrical stimulation in the hypo-thalamus.
(From Young, 1957. *The Life of Mammals.* Oxford: Clarendon Press.)

the disturbing effects of injury. The stimulation is applied through a small primary coil, with the animal fastened in position, or, if it is desirable to avoid the stress of restraint, a large coil of three feet diameter can be used and the animal left free to move in its cage.

We have already seen the results of applying this method to the analysis of the regulation of milk ejection. In the present connexion, Harris was able to show that ovulation could be brought about in the rabbit by as little as three minutes of stimulation provided that this was applied to the tuber cinereum, the most sensitive area being in its anterior wall, above the anterior region of the median eminence. In contrast to this, direct stimulation of the pars distalis, pars intermedia, and infundibular stem were all without effect.

Thus we have evidence that the release of a gonadotropin can be determined by the activity of a localized region of the hypothalamus, and we may expect to obtain confirmation of this from a study of the effects of establishing localized lesions there. The guinea-pig and the dog are amongst the animals that have been examined from this point of view, and it has been shown that lesions in or near the infundibulum will result in general atrophy of the gonads, presumably because of a diminished output of gonadotropins. There is some suggestion in these experiments that it is possible to distinguish in the hypothalamus an area concerned with FSH control from another concerned with ICSH. Thus, lesions at the anterior end of the median eminence of the female guinea-pig establish a state of continuous oestrus; this suggests an inhibition of ICSH production, and

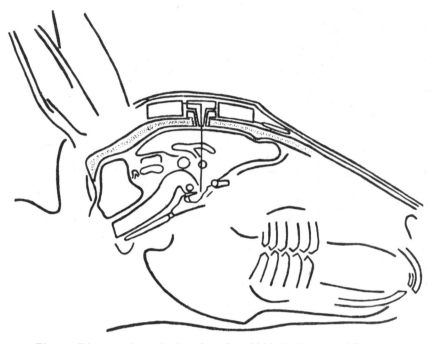

Fig. 39. Diagram of a sagittal section of a rabbit's head prepared for remote-control electrical stimulation. The stimulating electrode, insulated to the tip, is shown descending from the secondary coil unit through the corpus callosum and anterior commissure into the region of the tuber cinereum.
(From Harris, 1947. *Phil. Trans. Roy. Soc.* B, **232**, 385–441.)

the area concerned agrees with that defined by Harris in the rabbit. Lesions located more posteriorly, in the region of the infundibular stem, result in diffuse atrophy of the gonads, and they are presumably associated with inhibition of FSH secretion; the evidence does not, however, establish a complete separation of the two areas, nor do these experiments define any particular groups of nerve cells as being the controlling agents.

We may, then, regard it as well established that the hypothalamus exerts some regulatory control over the secretory activity of the pars distalis, but we have still to determine the pathway by which this control is exerted. In the search for this attention has been increasingly focused on the blood vessels of the hypophyseal portal system, not only because of the apparent absence of a secreto-motor innervation of the pars distalis

but because of the realization of the widespread importance of neurosecretory activity as one of the elements of endocrine co-ordination, the
assumption being that the portal system might convey into the adenohypophysis a chemical regulator substance originating in the hypothalamus
and passed through the median eminence.

The most obvious experimental approach to the problem, and one
which has attracted many investigators, is the study of the effect of interrupting the portal circulation by cutting the pituitary stalk, but the
results of such work have been extraordinarily discordant. To take only
one animal as an example, the effect of this in the rat has been reported
on the one hand to produce atrophy of the gonads and on the other to
produce normal or lengthened oestrous cycles. It seems certain that much
of this confusion results from the fact that regeneration of the portal
vessels readily occurs after stalk section, and Harris has emphasized the
importance of checking this possibility by scrupulous examination of
serial sections of the whole region, prepared after injection of the vessels
with Indian ink. He himself found that out of twenty-three female rats
in which the stalk had been sectioned, only one remained anoestrous until
it was killed, the others showing either regular or irregular cycles. Post-
mortem examination of serial sections showed that there was some degree
of regeneration of the portal vessels in all the animals, and that the degree
of this could be approximately correlated with the extent to which reproductive activity had been retained. In an attempt to prevent this
regeneration he therefore inserted a sheet of paper between the cut ends
of the stalk in a group of nineteen animals; eight of these developed either
regular or irregular cycles and were subsequently found to have achieved
some degree of regeneration of the portal vessels, while the other eleven
remained anoestrous, with atrophy of the ovaries, and showed no regeneration at all.

Conclusive though such results appear to be, the importance of the role
thereby attributed to the portal vessels is so fundamental that it is right
that they should be subjected to rigorous criticism. It is proper, therefore,
to emphasize that section of the stalk must deprive the animal's pituitary
of much of its normal blood supply, and it is difficult to be sure that this
does not in itself depress the activity of the gonadotropic cells, for we do
not know enough of their cytological characteristics to be able to determine
with certainty that they remain perfectly normal after this treatment.
From this point of view great interest attaches to the results of another type
of experimental approach, in which the adenohypophysis of the rat is
removed and transplanted to some distant site such as the eye or kidney,
the purpose of this being to remove the gland from its normal vascular
connexions. It is found that under these circumstances the secretion of
FSH and ICSH is largely abolished (although the luteotropic activity of

prolactin is retained) and that the ovary therefore undergoes regression. Everett has shown, however, that if the pituitary is then grafted back on to its original site, in such a way as to make possible the regeneration of its normal portal blood supply, ovarian function is restored and oestrous cycles are resumed (Plate v). This is a striking result, which goes a long way to justify the belief that the functioning of the pars distalis depends upon the maintenance of its vascular connexion with the median eminence. Nevertheless, the situation is not yet entirely clear, for there is some evidence that transplantation of the pituitary to a remote site does not always result in the complete elimination of the activity of the gonads, particularly when the animals concerned have been maintained in this condition for long periods. For example, male rats with transplants in the anterior chamber of the eye have shown at least partial maintenance of the testis and have been able to sire litters.

In due course we shall have to examine this problem from the standpoint of the regulation of thyroidal and adrenocortical function, but as far as reproduction is concerned it seems safe to conclude from all the available data that severing of the portal vessels does greatly reduce the gonadotropic output of the pars distalis, and that this provides powerful support for the view that these vessels serve as a path for the vascular transmission of chemical regulator substances. These, it is supposed, are released in the hypothalamus in response to a particular pattern of excitation, which is determined in its turn by a particular pattern of exogenous or endogenous stimulation. It is admittedly difficult to reconcile this fully with evidence that some limited degree of gonadotropic activity can still persist in pituitary transplants. If this does occur regularly, however, one possible explanation would be that it results from the liberation of these regulator substances into the general circulation; here they might still be able to influence the transplants, although in a more dilute concentration than would be found if they were released directly into the portal vessels, and thus with a consequent weakening of their effect.

The nature of these supposed chemical transmitter substances has still to be determined, but one view is that they may be polypeptides related to oxytocin and vasopressin. It has, indeed, been claimed that under certain experimental conditions these latter can themselves evoke gonadotropic activity in the pars distalis, and it has even been suggested that oxytocin may normally function in this way as a gonadotropic regulator. This view has been disputed, but another possibility is that a number of polypeptides may be secreted in the hypothalamus, and that those concerned with the control of the pars distalis resemble oxytocin and vasopressin sufficiently closely to enable the latter to emulate their effects under certain experimental conditions. Some authors have been impressed with the way in which certain of the neurosecretory fibres of the hypothalamic tracts enter into close relations with the median eminence (p. 74), and hence with the primary plexus of the hypophyseal portal system, for this suggests that some, at least, of these chemical regulators may be transmitted within those fibres and released from them into the vessels of the eminence. These are still matters for speculation, but they raise issues of the greatest importance in the interpretation of the organization and evolution of the vertebrate endocrine system, and we shall return to them later in other contexts.

8. Reciprocal relationships of the pars distalis and the gonads

Finally we must consider the nature of the relationship existing between the pars distalis and the gonads. The influence of the former upon the latter is amply demonstrated, not only by facts which we have already noted but by many others which we shall encounter later, and we have seen that this influence is exercised by the discharge of gonadotropins into the circulation and their transmission to the ovaries or testes. Equally important, however, is the reciprocal influence which the gonads exert upon the pars distalis, and which can be demonstrated in various ways. It is known, for example, that if oestrogen is administered to immature female rats there results a development of corpora lutea which are clearly functional since proliferation of the uterine endometrium also occurs (p. 106). This can only mean that the oestrogen is stimulating the pars distalis to discharge ICSH, but such experiments also show that this effect falls off with prolonged administration, from which it is concluded that a continuation of oestrogen stimulation will eventually reduce ICSH output. In addition, oestrogen also inhibits the secretion of FSH, as is indicated, for example, by the well-established fact that ovariectomized women, and women who have passed the menopause, have an increased concentration of gonadotropins in the blood and urine; both FSH and ICSH are involved in this, and it appears that the secretion of these has increased with the withdrawal of the restraining influence of oestrogen.

Androgens and progestins exert a similar influence, and experiments in which rats are joined together in parabiotic union provide very convincing evidence for this. For example, a normal female united with a castrated male will develop an hypertrophied ovary, indicating that the output of gonadotropins from the latter animal has increased in the absence of the restraining influence of its androgenic hormone. The injection of oestrogen, or, in larger doses, androgen or progesterone, into the castrate will abolish this effect by inhibiting the secretion of its gonadotropins, while the destruction of these gonadal hormones within its body will prevent them from passing into the parabiotic female and exerting any such inhibitory effect upon her. This reciprocal action, then, can be regarded as amply demonstrated and, to take one other example, it probably underlies the beneficial action of stilboestrol in the treatment of cancer of the prostate (p. 106). We shall also see in due course that the effect of increased gonadotropin secretion resulting from castration is very clearly reflected in the appearance of certain of the secretory cells of the pars distalis, and that this provides a useful clue in the analysis of the histological differentiation of that region (p. 285).

9. Sexual periodicity in female mammals

Our discussion has been a wide-ranging one, and this is a measure of the complexity of the issues involved, but we are now in a position to attempt some causal analysis of the sexual periodicity of mammals. In the great majority of species this is dominated by the oestrous cycle of the female, a cycle which involves a series of changes in the reproductive system and which culminates in oestrus or heat, the period in which alone the female will permit insemination by the male. It will be convenient to consider first the situation in rats and mice, since these have been intensively analysed and have formed the material for so much experimentation. Here the mature unmated female exhibits a four- to six-day oestrous cycle which continues throughout the year, interrupted only by pregnancy; she is therefore said to be polyoestrous all the year round. Following the terminology originally proposed by Heape, this cycle can be divided into four phases:

(1) Pro-oestrus (lasting for 18 hours) is essentially a period of preparation, during which the ripening follicles grow and the output of oestrogen increases. Under the influence of this hormone the wall of the uterus becomes hydrated and its cavity distended by fluid, while the vaginal epithelial cells multiply to form a thick layer from which the outermost cells are delaminated, so that the vaginal smear (p. 99) characteristic of this stage is composed of nucleated cells without any leucocytes. (A preliminary stage of some four hours during which these cells are not found in the smear is sometimes distinguished as pre-oestrus.) In the later stage of their growth, but not, apparently, in the earlier ones (p. 110), the follicles are being stimulated by FSH, probably potentiated by ICSH in small quantities.

(2) Oestrus (lasting for about 28 hours) is the period of sexual receptivity or heat which results from the fact that the secretion of oestrogen reaches a climax during this phase. As the output of this hormone increases it is thought to inhibit FSH output and to increase the output of ICSH; the latter then evokes ovulation, and the secretion of oestrogen diminishes. As a result of these interactions, the ova enter the oviducts at a time best calculated to ensure a good prospect of fertilization. During oestrus the uterine lumen remains distended, but there is some degeneration of its epithelium, while increasing cornification of the vaginal epithelium results

in the vaginal smear consisting of cells which are cornified and non-nucleated (Fig. 30). In addition, those follicles which will be ovulated at the next oestrus begin their growth, while there are abundant mitoses in the germinal epithelium, although it is by no means agreed that this represents, as some have thought, the production of a new supply of oocytes. On the interpretation of oestrogens as mitotic stimulants, it has been suggested that this effect may be evoked by the high concentration of hormone present in the ovary and released from the follicular fluid at ovulation.

(3) Metoestrus (lasting for about 8 hours) is marked by a heavy invasion of the vaginal epithelium by leucocytes so that these predominate in the vaginal smears, although they are accompanied by some cornified and some nucleated cells. The uterus meanwhile becomes reduced in size towards the resting stage that will be characteristic of dioestrus, and there is by now a marked reduction of oestrogen secretion.

(4) Dioestrus (lasting for about 53 hours) is a stage marked by the appearance of both nucleated epithelial cells and leucocytes in the vaginal smear (Fig. 30), and by the formation of corpora lutea. These, however, are virtually functionless in the rat and mouse and begin to degenerate at three days after ovulation, which accounts for the short duration of the oestrous cycle in these animals. In effect, the cycle in the unmated female of these species is a purely follicular one, determined by the time required to ripen a new set of follicles, but the influence of a luteal phase is seen if the animal is mated, the extent of the influence depending on whether or not pregnancy ensues. Without mating, however, dioestrus will be followed by the pro-oestrus of a new cycle, with FSH secretion increasing again as a result of the reduction of oestrogen output; this simple type of cycle is thus visualized as depending upon the reciprocal interaction of pituitary and ovarian secretions.

Pseudopregnancy (lasting for fourteen days in the rat) is the phase which results in the rat or mouse if copulation occurs without being followed by pregnancy; it is essentially a prolongation of dioestrus, with corpora lutea coming into function under the influence of prolactin (luteotropic hormone). It can be evoked by various artificial procedures which simulate the effect of coitus, such as mechanical or electrical stimulation of the cervix uteri, a single electric shock during late pro-oestrus or oestrus being sufficient for this purpose. The progesterone that is secreted during this phase stimulates proliferation in the glandular lining (endometrium) of the uterus, and if this is now irritated, by the insertion of a thread, for example, it will respond by local growth which results in the production of nodules called deciduomata, a reaction which normally assists the implantation of the fertilized ovum. As we have seen, progesterone also prevents ovulation and hence the inception of a new oestrous cycle or the

occurrence of superfoetation (the establishment of more than one generation of embryos in the uterus).

Pregnancy lasts for twenty-one to twenty-two days in the rat and, as
already mentioned, the presence of the corpus luteum is needed to ensure
its maintenance in this and certain other mammals (p. 106).

There are many variants of the oestrus cycle, and we can here mention
only a few of these. The guinea-pig, like the rat and mouse, is polyoestrous all the year round, but its normal cycle corresponds to the pseudopregnant one of the latter. It includes, in other words, a functional luteal
phase during which deciduomata can be induced in the uterus and it is
not modified by sterile mating, so that while in this animal the period of
oestrus usually lasts for less than twelve hours the whole cycle extends
over some sixteen and a half days.

The cow and sheep have several oestrous cycles during a restricted
period of the year, this being followed by an inactive period called
anoestrus; they are therefore said to be seasonally polyoestrous. For cows
the modal length of the cycle is twenty-one to twenty-two days and for
sheep sixteen and a half to seventeen and a half days, oestrus lasting for
less than one day in the former and for perhaps thirty to thirty-six hours
in the latter. In contrast to these, the wild fox has only one oestrous cycle
during the year, in the spring, and is described as monoestrous, with
proestrus and oestrus lasting about two weeks.

In man, apes, and monkeys the characteristic menstrual cycle is determined
by a sequence of events which is not fundamentally dissimilar from those
governing the oestrous cycle (Fig. 40), but which falls into three phases:

(1) The follicular or proliferative phase is accompanied by follicular
growth and oestrogen secretion under the influence of FSH, the uterine
endometrium meanwhile becoming greatly thickened and its glands
enlarged. Ovulation is believed normally to occur towards the end of this
phase, at about the middle of the cycle; at this time the oestrogen content
of the blood is at its highest and it is supposed that this checks the output
of FSH with a consequent increase in the output of ICSH.

(2) The progestational or luteal phase sets in at about one or two days
after ovulation. Secretory droplets containing glycogen are discharged
from the uterine epithelium, the enlarged glands become filled with
secretion, while the endometrium becomes increasingly thickened and
oedematous. At this time the organ is being maintained by progesterone
in readiness for the implantation of an embryo.

(3) Menstruation terminates the progestational phase, and involves the
discharge through the vagina of extravasated blood, fluid, and mucosa
resulting from the collapse of the uterine endometrium, possibly
because of a decline in the output of progesterone. Rapid regeneration follows, and leads to the inception of the next cycle.

In all of the above examples ovulation occurs spontaneously, in the absence of an external stimulus, as part of an endogenous rhythm, but in certain species, including the rabbit (p. 115), ferret, and cat, it will not take place without an exogenous stimulus supplied by coitus (or an artificial substitute for this), this being needed, as we have already seen,

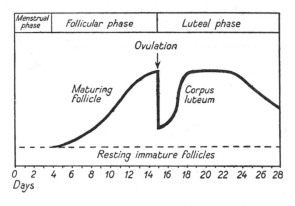

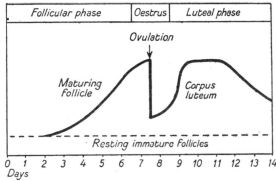

Fig. 40. Comparison of an oestrous cycle (*below*) with a human menstrual cycle (*above*), as reflected in the changes in size of the ovulating follicles.
(From Bullough, 1951. *Vertebrate Sexual Cycles.* Methuen.)

to evoke the release of ICSH. In the absence of this stimulus the cycle is arrested at a period of prolonged oestrus which in the cat is followed by a quiescent phase and this in its turn by another period of heat. In the rabbit the female may remain in heat for up to five weeks in the absence of the male.

It will be apparent from this survey that the oestrous cycle of the female mammal depends upon an alternating ascendency of oestrogen and progesterone in those species in which the corpora lutea are active, and that one of the functions of the latter hormone is to induce what is in effect a temporary sterility. With this fact, and with the availability of synthetic steroids, which can be given by mouth, we have the basis for the development of orally-administered contraceptives, and in one set of trials carried out in Puerto Rico use was made for this purpose of a synthetic analogue of progesterone mixed with an oestrogen, the latter being added in order to reduce the incidence of premature menstruation which had been found to result from the use of progesterone alone. The results showed that a strict adherence to a regular régime of tablet-taking gave a 99·8 per cent. chance of protection against conception, and that the occurrence of pregnancy increased in proportion to the number of tablets that were missed.

This remarkable adaptive modification of a reproductive cycle is, of course, dependent upon the unique cultural evolutionary mechanism of the human species, but the adaptive character of sexual cycles in general is clearly seen in the modifications that the reproduction of other mammals may undergo in special circumstances. For example, the breeding season for Scotch black-faced sheep living in the Highlands may be restricted to only six weeks of the year, whereas Merino sheep in Australia, living in a much more favourable environment, are said to be able to breed throughout most of the twelve months. Presumably these differences reflect selective breeding working upon genetic variations, and again controlled by man, but one may suppose that in the absence of his influence such variations would be either encouraged or suppressed by the operation of natural selection. Thus the young of the red deer are commonly born in June, and it has been observed that those which for some reason or other are born later, in September or October, will often be unable to survive their first winter.

The influence of artificial conditions is well illustrated by the hyper-sexuality which, as Hediger has pointed out, is so often found in animals living in captivity. This is shown by excessive sexual activity in the pursuit of the female by the male, or by an extension of the oestrous period, and is probably due to a variety of circumstances, including the regular provision of food, the confined quarters, and the lack of diversionary interest. Whatever the precise cause, however, the results are certainly striking. Wild sows, for example, which are normally in heat from November to January and which give birth to young in April or May, have been known in captivity to have their litters in January or February, at a time when the young inevitably die of cold. The results may not always be so disastrous, and because of this the existence of hypersexuality is a well-known feature of domestication. Thus the dog is monoestrous but differs from the wild fox (p. 124) in having two cycles, one in early spring and one in autumn, these being separated by a period of anoestrous which lasts for an average of seven months. Again, the domestic rabbit can breed throughout most of the year under favourable conditions, while the wild one is restricted mainly to a period extending from January to June, and the domestic cat may have several breeding periods during the year while the wild cat reproduces mainly during the spring, with perhaps another oestrous period later in the year.

These facts, implying as they do a subtle combination of rigidity and flexibility in reproductive cycles, emphasize the crucial importance of the pars distalis in acting as the intermediary between the exogenous and endogenous factors upon which these cycles are based. A few examples must serve to illustrate the mode of its operation. It is well known that if sheep are transferred across the equator from the northern to the southern hemisphere they show a reversal of their reproductive cycle so that they continue to breed at the appropriate season. There is good reason for believing that this is a result of the declining autumnal photoperiod (i.e. the length of the daylight period during a single solar day) initiating the onset of the cycle, for the same effect can be obtained under experimental conditions by exposing sheep to increased illumination during the winter and decreased illumination during the summer. Other mammals appear to be stimulated to reproduction by the increasing photoperiod of early spring. An example is the ferret, and here also the importance of such photostimulation is convincingly demonstrated by the fact that this animal can be brought into reproductive activity during winter, when it is normally sexually inactive, by exposure to increasing periods of artificial illumination during autumn.

During the prolonged anoestrus in such a monoestrous animal the output of oestrogen is low, a situation which in the rat would result, as we have seen, in an increased output of FSH and the inception of a new oestrous cycle. Here, however, the gonadotropin output also remains low, and it is supposed that this is determined by some form of neural inhibition in the hypothalamus. On this interpretation the effect of the increasing photoperiod is to remove this inhibition, with a consequent rise in the output of gonadotropin, and some support for this view is to be found in the observation that electrolytic lesions in the anterior hypothalamus of the anoestrous ferret will actually promote the precocious development of oestrus, presumably because they have removed the inhibitory influence.

It should not be supposed from these examples that light is the only operative stimulus, although it is probably the principal one; various factors such as temperature and the presence and behaviour of other individuals play their part in different species, and we shall see further examples of this in other groups. For the present, however, these facts serve to reinforce our earlier conclusion that reproductive cycles are controlled through the nervous system. The response of the ferret to increased illumination is abolished if the optic nerves are cut, showing that the propagation of nerve impulses through those nerves to the brain is an essential element of the reaction. Again, the oestrous cycle of the sheep can be shortened by subjecting the uterus to mechanical distension, but this effect is abolished if the distension is applied to a portion of the uterus which has been denervated; here also, then, nerve impulses must be passing centrally from the stimulated receptors. Our argument is that the final link in the chain of communication which leads to the release of gonadotropins from the pars distalis is the connexion between this gland and the hypothalamus, to which these nerve impulses must be transmitted. The importance of this link is shown by the fact that coitus will not evoke ovulation in the rabbit if the connexion between the pituitary gland and the brain has been completely severed, while ovulation can always be induced at any time simply by the injection of gonadotropins.

VI. HORMONES AND REPRODUCTION
(CONTINUED)

WE shall see in a later chapter that the organization of the pituitary gland of mammals, and its relationship with the nervous system, is based upon principles that appear to be operative, although sometimes in a less specialized way, throughout the vertebrates. It is very probable that the same is true of the hormonal interactions which underlie the reproductive cycles of these animals, but we can attempt no more here than to illustrate this very broad generalization with a few examples which may serve to indicate the rich store of information which is available in the literature. In considering them it must be remembered that the gaps in our knowledge are enormous and that far too many of our conclusions are based upon data drawn from a very few species. It has been estimated, for example, that such understanding as we possess of the reproductive processes of teleosts is the result of the study of some fifty of the available 20,000 species included in that group.

1. Sexual periodicity in birds

Gonadotropins are secreted by the pituitary of birds, but it is uncertain whether they are identical with those of mammals or whether, in fact, two separate hormones are present, although there is evidence that the effects of mammalian FSH differ from those of ICSH. Treatment of a hypophysectomized capon with the former results in considerable enlargement of the testes but does not affect the comb, the development of which is known to be dependent upon male hormone; ICSH treatment, however, results in enlargement of both testes and comb. Experiments upon other birds have also provided evidence that the two gonadotropins differ in their effects, but much remains to be learned regarding the details of pituitary functioning in these animals.

Androgens are secreted by the testes, and oestrogens, progesterone (with, perhaps, related compounds for which progestins is a convenient term), and androgens by the ovaries. The oestrogens are secreted by the follicles but the progestins are thought to be produced by the interstitial tissue, so that the remains of the follicles which are left after ovulation cannot be physiologically compared with mammalian corpora lutea. The influence of these gonadal hormones upon the sexual characters of birds is well enough established, although the relationship is not always the same as in mammals. For example, the sexual dimorphism in the plumage of the English sparrow is determined by the direct action of the genes, without the intervention of hormones at all, while the situation in certain finches is curiously varied. In *Steganura* the blackening of the feathers and beak in the breeding male is under the direct control of the pituitary (gonadotropic) secretion, while in *Euplectes* the feather colour is determined in the same way but the beak colour by the secretion of the testes. The domestic fowl provides other familiar examples of these inter-relationships. Thus the capon (castrated cock) retains the male type of plumage, but implantation of an ovary will result in the development of feathers of female type. In this respect, then, the male characterization is essentially the neutral one while the female characterization is hormone-dependent, and we shall see later that the same principle emerges from embryological studies. It is not, however, applicable to all characters, even in this one species, for the exaggerated comb and wattles of the cock undergo atrophy in the capon and can only be brought to full development by the action of male hormone (Fig. 36).

Particularly interesting differences between birds and mammals are seen in the different ways in which their hormonal equipment is deployed in accordance with their different modes of reproduction. The most striking contrast (leaving the Monotremata out of consideration) lies in the serial production by birds of large and yolky eggs which are physio-logically expensive to produce and which require the addition of an elaborate set of egg membranes. In connexion with this we find that oestrogens, in addition to promoting the development of the Müllerian duct system, also bring about the increased absorption of food material and the mobilization of food reserves which are needed to facilitate the manufacture of yolk by the liver, and it is these biochemical effects which presumably underlie the use of stilboestrol by the poultry industry (p. 105). Other examples of the adaptive organization of this system are the control of yolk deposition in the ovum by the gonadotropins, the part played by progesterone in evoking ovulation by stimulating, apparently through a hypothalamic neural mechanism, the release of gonadotropins from the pituitary, and the combined action of oestrogen and progesterone (and, probably, androgen) in promoting the secretion of albumen by the oviduct.

The seasonal onset of reproductive behaviour in birds, often accom-panied by remarkable migrations to areas suitable for the rearing of the young, are matters of common knowledge, and current interpretations of this agree in ascribing the regulation of it to an interplay of exogenous and endogenous factors, although there are differences of opinion as to the relative importance that should be attached to these. The significance of photoperiod in this connexion was first clearly demonstrated in the classical studies of Rowan who, from 1925 onwards, showed that the gonads of the migratory Canadian bunting, *Junco hyemalis*, which normally comes into breeding condition in the spring, could be made to grow and mature during the winter if the animal were subjected to periods of increasing illumination. These results have been found to be applicable to other species, so that the role of exogenous factors in the sexual periodicity of birds must be regarded as well established, although they are now being subjected to an increasingly subtle analysis.

After their seasonal breeding, the gonads of most birds in the temperate zone undergo regression. During this phase the animals lose almost completely any trace of sexual behaviour, and those which live in pairs during the reproductive season will usually form flocks. Under experimental treatment they will not respond to photostimulation, and for this reason the phase is called the refractory period. A. J. Marshall has emphasized that in the male bird there is at this time a more or less complete exhaustion of the interstitial tissue of the testis, and that this is immediately followed by a regenerative phase, during which the Sertoli cells and germ cells give rise to a mass of lipoid material which reacts positively to tests for cholesterol (cf. p. 136 and Plate VI *E* and *F*). Thereafter, the interstitial tissue regenerates and the lipids disappear from the seminiferous tubules.

The regeneration phase is followed automatically by the acceleration phase, during which gonadal hormones come to be secreted once again and there is a return to sexual activity, manifested, for example, in the selection of territory and in the use of song to assert territorial rights. By the end of this phase the testis is fully mature, with abundant sperm, but it is characteristic of birds that the female lags behind in sexual maturation and that ovulation is not rigorously determined by the onset of an oestrus-like phase. Instead, special stimulation is required, peculiar to each species, before the completion of the final stages of oocyte development can be achieved. The song and display of the male are important factors in this stimulation and provide one of the clearest demonstrations that so-called secondary sexual characters are as essential for successful insemination as the genital ducts, for example, so that no useful distinction can ultimately be made between them and the accessory sexual characters (p. 103).

The presence of these exogenous stimulatory factors results in the establishment of the culmination phase, during which ovulation and insemination occur, preceded by the completion of nest-building. There are therefore three phases in the sequence, regeneration, acceleration, and culmination, and Marshall regards these as constituting a primarily endogenous cycle which is modulated by exogenous stimuli, these latter, by their retarding or accelerating effects, contributing to ensure that reproduction shall take place under circumstances which will lead to the successful rearing of the young. One result of the inception of the acceleration phase during the later months of the year is that many birds, in Britain and elsewhere, show signs of sexual activity during the autumn; this, however, is checked by winter conditions such as low temperatures, and photostimulation early in the new year promotes a renewal of the activity in sufficient time to allow the culmination phase to lead to reproduction in the favourable months of spring and early summer.

Another approach to this analysis is illustrated by the interpretation of Wolfson, who prefers to place greater emphasis upon the importance of exogenous factors. He argues that although a bird may be refractory to increased photoperiod during the autumn, it is nevertheless responsible at that time to exogenous stimulation, and is, in fact, reacting to the long, dark periods of the short day-lengths. This reaction characterizes, in his view, a preparatory period which is an essential feature of the cycle because it is this which enables the bird to respond later on to longer photoperiods and thereby to enter into full sexual activity. Part of the evidence for Wolfson's argument is derived from experiments in which juncos were exposed to artificially controlled and alternating periods of short days (9 hours light, 15 hours dark) and long days (20 hours light, 4 hours dark). By this procedure the reproductive cycle could be accelerated, birds which were initially in the active state being brought back into it again on four subsequent occasions during 369 days. As a result of much experimentation along these lines Wolfson concludes that the preparatory phase is completed under natural conditions in late November and December and is succeeded by the progressive phase; this follows automatically upon the preparatory one, but the speed at which it proceeds, and hence the time at which the birds reach full sexual activity, is regulated by the amount of illumination which the animals now receive. Thus the attaining of the pre-migratory physiological state which is normally reached in spring can be accelerated by exposing them to longer photoperiods or delayed by exposing them to shorter ones.

We need not suppose that photoperiod is the only modulating agent in birds, for there are circumstances in which dependence upon it might well prove fatal, as, for example, in the arid environment occupied by the red-billed weaver-finch, *Quelea quelea*. This bird, as Marshall and his fellow-workers have shown, is adapted to its habitat in a remarkable way. The duration of the regeneration phase (in his terminology), with its period of enforced sexual inactivity, is here reduced to a minimum so that the animals can take immediate advantage of the effects of the rainfall upon which they absolutely depend both for the provision of nesting material and for the obtaining of insect food for the young. Once favourable conditions are available the nest-building and courtship activity are rapidly completed, with the result that individuals are able to ovulate within eleven days of the fall of rain.

We can consider only one other example from the many fascinating

ones which could be used to illustrate the principle of the interaction of
endogenous and exogenous factors in birds. The mutton-bird, or short-
tailed shearwater (*Puffinus tenuirostris*), leaves South Australia in flocks
during autumn (April) to undertake a circum-Pacific migration, through

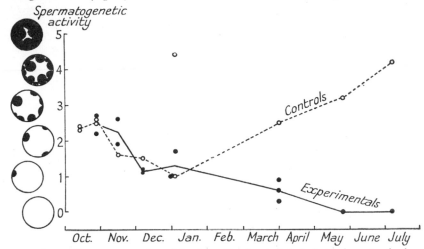

Fig. 41. Spermatogenetic activity from October to July in hypophysectomized
Rana esculenta ('Experimentals') and in unoperated animals ('Controls') living
under laboratory conditions. The circles to the left indicate six stages of spermatogenetic activity, from O (testis tubule with only a few primary spermatogonia)
to 5 (testis tubule almost filled with nests of spermatogenetic cells).
(From Sluiter, van Oordt, & Mighorst, 1950. *Quart. J. Micr. Sci.* **91**, 131.)

Japan and western North America, which brings them back with remarkable regularity to breed at their starting point during a period of
twelve days in November. Captive birds maintained under abnormal
conditions of lighting, food, and temperature have been found to come into
breeding condition at much the same time as that at which they would have
done had they been able to complete a normal migration, which suggests
that an endogenous rhythm exists and can operate without being stimulated by exogenous factors. Nevertheless, the condition of the reproductive
system is not wholly normal in these experimental animals, and there is
a marked retardation of spermatogenesis, which again suggests that such
endogenous rhythms must be modulated by external stimulating factors.

2. Sexual periodicity in the lower vertebrates

The fact that pituitary gonadotropins are essential for reproduction in
Amphibia has been amply demonstrated. Thus hypophysectomy of male
Rana esculenta in autumn leads to degeneration of the primary sperma-
tocytes, so that in the following summer only primary spermatogonia are
present in the testis tubules, although normally spermatogenesis is proceeding actively at that time (Fig. 41). Administration of extracts of frog

pituitaries will restore spermatogenesis in hypophysectomized animals, and will similarly restore the size of the ovaries in amphibians which normally suffer ovarian degeneration after hypophysectomy (Fig. 42). Another illustration is the fact that ovulation can be induced in *Xenopus laevis* at any time of the year by the introduction of pituitaries from the

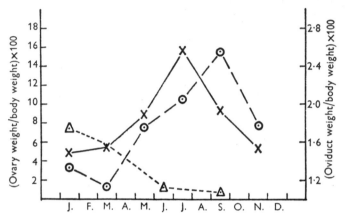

Fig. 42. Seasonal variation in weight of the ovaries and oviducts of *Xenopus laevis* and the effect of hypophysectomy. X——X ovaries and O————O oviducts of free-living animals (Gitlin, 1939); △ - - - - △ ovaries from animals hypophysectomized in February (Shapiro & Shapiro, 1934.)
(From Smith, 1955. *Mem. Soc. Endocrin.* **4**, 41.)

same species or by the administration of extracts of the pituitaries of cattle, while the induction of ovulation in this and other species by treatment with human urine constitutes a well-established diagnosis of pregnancy.

As an illustration of the interplay of endogenous and exogenous factors in these animals we may consider briefly the reproductive cycle of the male frog, which has been extensively studied by many workers. Gallien has divided the cycle in *Rana temporaria* into three phases, the first being the reproductive phase which typically occurs during the first two weeks of March; this phase, immediately following hibernation, comprises ovulation, spawning, and fertilization. It is succeeded by a phase of gonadal activity, extending from April to October, during which time spermatogenesis and oogenesis take place and lead to the establishment of mature testes and ovaries. The third phase, hibernation, is necessarily one of sexual inactivity, but the animals are throughout in a condition that enables them to respond immediately to the onset of spring, and thus to reproduce sufficiently early to permit the tadpoles to grow and metamorphose under favourable circumstances. Interstitial tissue giving positive responses to tests for steroids is well defined in amphibian testes, and it may be accepted that it secretes androgens which promote the development of such sexual characters as the thumb pad in frogs and the crest of the male newt, for these atrophy after castration. Moreover, this tissue shows a well-defined seasonal cycle, being at a maximum development at spawning time and at a minimum one during the late summer.

The restriction of spermatogenesis in *Rana temporaria* to the late spring and summer is an example of the discontinuous cycle which seems to be characteristic of the Anura of temperate zones, and van Oordt has argued that in this species it is determined by a combination of exogenous and endogenous factors. In many anurans, however, sperm can be formed throughout the year (continuous cycle), and the fact that *R. esculenta ridibunda* has a continuous cycle in Mediterranean regions but a discontinuous one in temperate regions suggests that the difference is at least in part an adaptation to the environment. Van Oordt's argument is that the onset of spermatogenesis in *R. temporaria* is determined by an exogenous stimulus, the environmental temperature, but that its termination at the onset of hibernation is brought about by an endogenous rhythm, for it has been shown that the raising of the temperature during the first part of the hibernation period does not increase the activity of the testis. On the other hand, spermatogenesis can be induced at any time in *R. esculenta* by raising the temperature so that in this species the exogenous factor is considered to predominate throughout; its cycle is therefore potentially continuous, even in those populations in which it is actually discontinuous, whereas the discontinuous cycle of *R. temporaria* is innate and, as far as is known, cannot become continuous. The importance of the endogenous rhythm in the latter species was, in fact, noted by Witschi in his pioneer studies of its geographical races in Europe. In one of these, the 'early race', reproduction occurs in March and spermatogenesis from May until September, while in the other, the 'late race', reproduction is delayed until May, with spermatogenesis extending from April to August. These differences are clearly adaptations to the conditions of the Western lowlands and to those of the Alpine and Northern regions in which the 'early' and 'late races' respectively live, but they seem to be largely innate, for they are not modified when, for example, the 'late race' is transferred to lowland conditions.

Finally, we can draw some examples from teleost fish. It is generally supposed that the development of the sexual characters of these animals is determined by the secretion of gonadal hormones, and there is probably justification for this view since, for example, testosterone has been identified in the blood of spawned Pacific salmon, and oestrogens in the blood of spawning Atlantic salmon. Moreover, experiments involving gonadectomy or treatment with steroid sex hormones in certain species have given results in accordance with this view, although castration is difficult to carry out in fish without high mortality, and, as in all animals with a limited reproductive season, the results will be influenced by the time at which the experiments are performed. However, it is known that in *Gasterosteus*, amongst others, there is a relationship between the breeding dress of the male and the presence of testes, while the treatment of both sexes of Poeciliidae and Cyprinodontidae (such as *Lebistes* and *Xiphophorus*) with male hormone, either by injection or by immersion of the fish in a solution of methyl testosterone, will promote the transformation of the anal fin into the characteristic male gonopodium. It is hardly necessary to emphasize that such experiments require the closest control of all conditions, including particularly the strength of the hormone dosage which, as regards the influence of methyl testosterone upon the growth of certain fin rays in *Gambusia affinis*, is said to be optimal at 1 mg in 5,000,000 ml.

Although the exact site of production of the ovarian hormone is a matter of doubt in non-mammalian vertebrates it is usually possible to identify Leydig cells in the male, but teleosts have often seemed to be an exception to this, for although they are readily seen in *Gasterosteus*, it is difficult to find them in many species and they have sometimes been assumed to be lacking. It is now known, however, that in certain forms such as the pike and char they are actually present but not in the interstitial position typical of vertebrates. Instead, they are believed to be represented by cells containing lipids and cholesterol which are situated in the walls of the testis lobules (Plate VI E) and which are derived from fibroblasts. It is of particular interest that the testis of the pike undergoes a seasonal cycle very similar to that of birds, including the breaking down of the lobules into cholesterol-rich material after spawning (Plate VI F) and the disappearance of the lobule boundary cells, a new generation of these beginning to become lipoidal in September. Such a resemblance between two such widely separated groups of vertebrates must be of some encouragement to those who feel that ultimately it should be possible to demonstrate common principles operating in the establishment of vertebrate reproductive cycles. A similar transformation of unshed germinal material into cholesterol-positive lipids has also been found in reptiles, but does not occur in the mole, despite the existence in this animal of a well-defined lipid cycle in the Leydig cells (Plate IV). It may be, then, as Lofts suggests, that this particular phenomenon has been lost from the mammalian cycle but retained in the other vertebrate groups.

The production of gonadotropins by the pituitary gland seems to be well established for fish and probably occurs also in the cyclostomes. Hypophysectomy of the river-lamprey, *Lampetra fluviatilis*, prevents the pre-spawning growth of the eggs while amongst the effects which have been

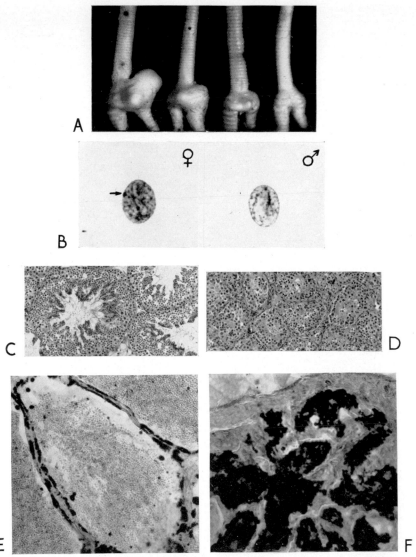

Plate VI. *A*. The effect of different degrees of castration upon the development of
the syrinx in the duck embryo. From left to right: *a*, completely castrated embryo of
unknown genetic sex; syrinx of pure male type. *b*, partially castrated female embryo
with two small remnants of ovaries; intermediate type. *c*, partially castrated female
embryo with left ovary larger; the syrinx still shows the male characteristic of a swollen
tubercle. *d*, ovarian tissue larger; syrinx of normal female type. (× 5.) (From Wolff &
Wolff, 1951. *J. exp. Zool.* **116**, 59–97.)

B. *Left*, nucleus with sex chromatin (arrow) in an oral mucosal smear from a
chromosomal female. *Right*, nucleus without sex chromatin in an oral mucosal smear
from a chromosomal male. (× 1,165.) (From Grumbach & Barr, 1958. *Rec. Prog.
Horm. Res.* **14**, 260–334.)

C. Part of the testis of a lizard, *Agama*, showing seminiferous tubules with normal
spermatogenesis.

D. Part of the testis of a lizard of the same species which had been hypophysectomized for 30 days. As a result of the absence of gonadotropic secretion the tubules
are atretic and spermatogenesis is absent. (× 90.)

(From Wright & Chester Jones, 1957. *J. Endocrin.*, **15**, 83–89).

E. Testis of the pike (*Esox lucius*) in March, just prior to spawning; the lobules are
full of sperm and the boundary cells of the lobule walls are charged with cholesterol-
positive lipids (Formaldehyde-calcium; Sudan black and haemalum). (× 350.)

F. Testis of the pike in May, immediately after spawning; dense cholesterol-
positive lipid is now found in the lumina of the lobules. (× 335.)

(From Lofts & Marshall, 1957. *Quart. J. micr. Sci.* **98**, 79–88.)

reported in elasmobranch fish are a breakdown in the early stages of spermatogenesis and atretic degeneration in the ovaries. It has been noted that in hypophysectomized teleosts the oocytes can begin their growth phase but undergo degeneration at the start of vitellogenesis; there appears, then, to be in these animals, as in mammals, a critical stage beyond which the ovarian function is dependent upon the presence of pituitary gonadotropin secretion. Whether the latter comprises one or more hormones is at present uncertain, as it is for all of the lower vertebrates, since the necessary chemical studies are lacking, nor can we be sure that the gonadal steroids react upon the pars distalis as they are known to do in mammals.

The reproductive cycles of fish are known to be closely linked with annual seasonal changes in their environment, and there is much evidence to suggest that their mode of regulation is similar in principle to that found in higher forms, as we might expect from the nature of the hormonal equipment which we have just outlined. Thus the breeding behaviour of the viviparous South American fish, *Jenynsia lineata*, closely resembles that of the sheep, in that when it is moved from the southern to the northern hemisphere it readily adapts its reproductive cycle to the shift in the seasons (p. 127). Turner has shown that these animals are influenced both by temperature and photoperiod, and he found that by suitable experimental manipulation of these factors it was possible to induce the same fish to breed twice in a year, once under conditions of Argentina day-length (from October to February) and again under conditions of North American day-length (during May, June, and July).

It is impossible to do more than glance briefly here at one or two other examples of reproductive cycles in fish. The minnow, *Phoxinus phoxinus*, breeds in Windermere from May to July, the length of this period resulting from the fact that different individuals mature at different times. Immediately following this there is an initiation of gametogenesis in both sexes and this process continues throughout the autumn but virtually ceases during the winter. With the arrival of spring there is then a rapid completion of maturation in both sexes, with considerable enlargement of the gonads. Bullough showed from this experimental analysis that spermatogenesis and oocyte growth could be accelerated by subjecting the fish during the winter months to an artificially increased photoperiod of seventeen hours, provided that the temperature was maintained above a certain threshold value (Fig. 43). He thus concluded that light and temperature were exogenous factors controlling the reproductive cycle in this species. On the other hand, if the fish were kept in continuous darkness during the early months of the year they still showed gonadal development during the summer, although with some delay, and from this he drew the conclusion that there was an internal reproductive rhythm which could operate

independently of these external factors but which was normally modulated by them. The situation would, however, be worth re-examining in
the light of Wolfson's interpretation of the sexual cycle in birds, with a

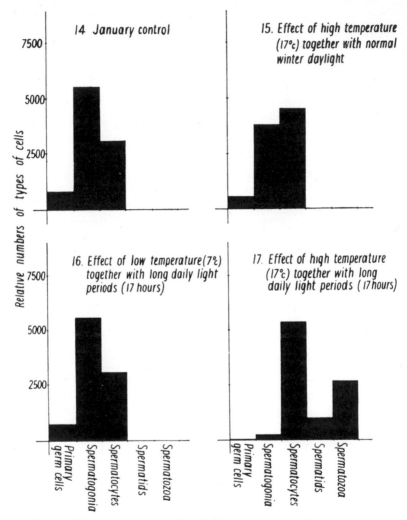

Fig. 43. Histograms showing the relative numbers of cell types in the testes
of minnows subjected to various experimental conditions.
(From Bullough, 1940. *Proc. Zool. Soc. Lond. A* **109,** 79–102.)

view to seeing whether the behaviour of these fish in the early months
of the year has been influenced in any way by exogenous stimuli encountered, for example, during the previous autumn.

A cycle similar to that of *Phoxinus*, but one that illustrates the differences in detail which are to be expected between different species, has been reported for the three-spined stickleback, *Gasterosteus aculeatus*. Here again reproduction occurs in April and May, and maturation of the gonads sets in during the summer, but in this species the development of the germ cells can continue during the winter, although its rate is influenced by the temperature of the water. Moreover, Craig-Bennett concluded from his study of this species that light was not an important factor, and that the final stages of maturation were evoked by the rise in temperature of the water during the early months of the year.

Much experimental investigation will be needed to establish satisfactorily the precise part played by the endocrine system in these phenomena. Our experience with birds suggests that as information accumulates the analysis will become increasingly complex, but we may feel reasonably confident that a fundamental uniformity of principle will eventually be found to be operating throughout the vertebrates. It would be surprising if this were not so, for the capacity to bring internal reproductive rhythms into relationship with a fluctuating environment must have been of prime importance at all stages of vertebrate history. Not only is it essential for the maintenance of the species, but it provides for that extension of the range of distribution which appears to be an important element in the promotion of evolutionary diversification and progress.

3. Hormones and behaviour

Our analysis of reproductive cycles has implied a far-reaching influence of hormones upon behaviour, an influence that is particularly well seen in the female mammal, where the mating responses of oestrus contrast sharply with the maternal activity which develops at the end of pregnancy, and where there is usually a close correlation between high secretory activity of the gonads and the attaining of a complete pattern of mating behaviour. In males this correlation may appear less obvious, but this is merely because both sexual and secretory activity tend to be continuous in those species that are polyoestrous all the year round; in those that have only a limited breeding period the activity of the male does, in fact, coincide with the recrudescence of the interstitial tissue as, for example, in the deer. Because of this correlation, it is not surprising to find that the mating behaviour of the female cat is completely eliminated by the removal of both ovaries, and this in itself is a striking illustration of the dependence of that behaviour upon the ovarian hormone. Another illustration is provided by the treatment of immature female mammals with gonadotropins, for the result of this may be to evoke secretory activity in the ovaries, and this will then bring about precocious sexual activity. Under such circumstances female rats may show the typical behaviour of oestrus when they are only twenty-two days old, and when they are so small that adult males cannot copulate with them. It would appear, then, that the neuromuscular basis of sexual behaviour is organized well in advance of the attainment of sexual maturity, but that the activation of the physiological mechanisms awaits the presence of a sufficiently high level of circulating sex hormone.

The means by which such activation is achieved are difficult to analyse because of the inherent complexity of the situation, but a number of possibilities have been formulated by Beach. It may be that hormones influence behaviour indirectly by their influence upon the growth and metabolism of the whole organism, or upon the maturation of specific structures which are required for effecting a particular response. On the other hand, they may exert a more direct influence by some form of action upon the nervous system, by promoting its development, for example, or by sensitizing peripheral receptor mechanisms, or by facilitating its integrative functions in some way, and Beach has developed on this basis the concept of the sexual arousal mechanism. According to this, sexual behaviour is activated by a variety of sensory stimuli, and it is a function of the gonadal hormones to lower the threshold of this arousal mechanism by exerting a sensitizing action upon the nervous system. To such possibilities we must add that sexual behaviour may be affected by other hormones than those which are regarded as sex hormones in the strict use of that term. The situation here is closely analogous to the control of growth and metabolism which we considered earlier, and which we found to be influenced not only by pituitary growth hormone and insulin but by other hormones with interrelated actions. The thyroid hormones, for example, may be expected to have some effect upon reproduction in mammals simply by virtue of their profound influence on metabolism (Chapter VIII).

An illustration of a direct action of an oestrogen upon the nervous system has been recorded by Michael, who finds that the implantation of stilboestrol or oestradiol into the brain of ovariectomized cats will restore sexual behaviour to an extent amounting sometimes to nymphomania. The effect is strictly localized, and having regard to what we have learned regarding hypothalamic functions it is not surprising to find that the implants must be made into the posterior hypothalamus and upper tegumentum. A particularly interesting feature of this response is that the genital tracts of the excited animals remain in a completely anoestrous condition, so that the hormones must be assumed to be acting directly upon the nervous system without exerting any more generalized effect upon other parts of the body.

The castration of male cats, however, illustrates the complexities of these problems, for the effects of this operation, as estimated from the subsequent sexual behaviour of the operated animals, prove to be curiously

variable. Some will continue to mount females almost indefinitely, and
will achieve successful intromission for several years, others will continue
mounting for a year or more but quickly lose the capacity for intromission,

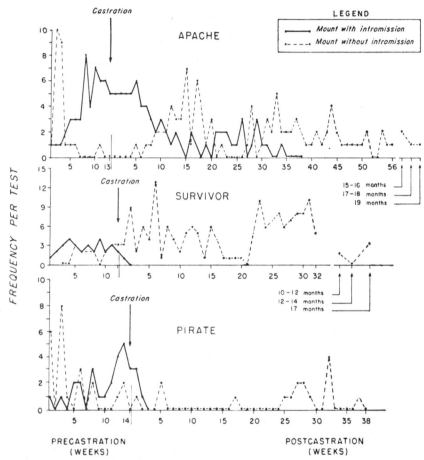

Fig. 44. Comparisons of intromissions and mounts of three male cats, Apache,
Survivor, and Pirate, typifying the three modes of decline of sexual behaviour
after castration.
(From Rosenblatt & Aronson, 1958. *Behaviour* **12**, 285–338.)

while others quickly lose the capacity for both of these components of
successful mating (Fig. 44). It has sometimes been suggested that under
such circumstances the adrenocortical secretions (Chapter x) may be
substituting for the sex steroids, but satisfactory evidence for this seems
to be lacking, and Aronson prefers to ascribe the variable persistence of
sexual behaviour to the diverse effects of the hormones. It may be, for

example, that in their absence there is a decline in the capacity of particular muscles, or in the sensitivity of some of the receptor mechanisms.

An important factor in all aspects of the behaviour of mammals is the importance assumed in its regulation by the higher centres, and especially by the cerebral cortex. As a result, although various reflex elements of sexual behaviour can be elicited by experimental stimulation of the spinal cord, the higher centres seem to be needed for the achievement of the complete integration of an effective behaviour pattern; both hypothalamus and cortex, in fact, have their parts to play, and it would appear that while a totally decorticate male cat loses all sexual responses, a decorticate female is capable of fertile mating provided that her hypothalamus is intact.

Arising from this, it has sometimes been suggested that there is an evolutionary trend in mammals which leads to a more or less complete domination of the sex hormones by the cerebral cortex in man. It is highly doubtful, however, whether there is any evidence for such a trend, and it is certain that the situation in the human is sufficiently remarkable to justify its inclusion amongst the unique features of our species. The essential peculiarity lies in the fact that structurally the human being appears to be capable of sexual behaviour from perhaps five or six years of age, but that the full release of this behaviour through the mediation of the sex hormones is delayed during a prolonged juvenile phase, this being one special aspect of the extended period of development and maturation which is an important characteristic of man. This period of sexual latency, aptly referred to by Waddington as an odd example of 'brinkmanship', creates psychological tensions which are thought possibly to be the origin of the Oedipus complex, and it is by no means surprising to find that when the sexual functions have fully matured they are subservient to cortical control rather than to gonadal hormones. It is perhaps partly because of this that both sexes may continue to show a high level of sexual capacity after removal of the gonads, although, as we have seen, this phenomenon is not peculiar to the human species, even though it may there be exceptional in its degree of development. Indeed, it is arguable that the most important influence of hormones upon sex behaviour in the mammals is to be found in their effect in securing the appropriate degree of structural development and the initial integration of the behaviour patterns. Even in the lower mammals there is some evidence that animals which have been gonadectomized prior to puberty may subsequently show fewer signs of effective sexual behaviour than those which have been gonadectomized after they have had some adult sexual experience.

The considerations which we have outlined seem to be applicable in broad terms throughout the vertebrates, although relevant information is sometimes very limited and, in the case of cyclostomes and elasmobranchs, virtually non-existent. Aronson finds in vertebrates a general tendency for gonadectomy to depress the sexual behaviour pattern more completely and rapidly in females than in males, and for the operated animals to show considerable variation in the extent to which the individual elements of the pattern are affected. As he points out, this may be due to species differences, and also to the difficulty of ensuring in some groups the complete removal of the gonads, but when allowance has been made for these factors it still appears that some elements of the behaviour pattern are affected more than others, and that some males may retain parts of the pattern for a long time after castration. Thus males of *Xiphophorus* may continue to show thrusting and swinging movements of the gonopodium and sidling movements alongside the female for up to nine months after the operation. It may be, then, that reflex responses to sexual situations can still be evoked in gonadectomized animals by the stimuli provided by other members of the group, but even so it would be unwise to assume that the gonadal hormones are the only endocrine factors likely to be involved in the regulation of sexual behaviour in fish.

Two examples must serve to illustrate this point. The salmon (*Salmo salar*), in addition to its upstream spawning migration, also carries out a downstream migration at the smolt stage; the smolt is sexually immature, from which it follows that migratory movements in this animal are certainly not dependent upon gonadal hormones, and, therefore, that the factors which promote migratory movements in the immature animal may well be operative also at sexual maturity. Again, populations of the cod, *Gadus callarias*, which feed during the summer on the Bear Island-Spitzbergen Banks, undertake in the autumn, at the onset of sexual maturation, a migration of hundreds of miles to their spawning grounds off the north Norwegian coast. It would seem natural to ascribe this to some stimulatory effect exerted by the sex hormones were it not for the fact that immature fish undergo a similar migration, known as the 'dummy run', which takes them in the same direction and sometimes over very much the same distance. The most obvious endocrine factor that the immature and mature animals have in common is a high level of activity of the thyroid gland, which suggests that the thyroid hormones rather than the gonadal ones may be the significant endogenous factor.

Such considerations lead us to look for some direct evidence that hormones can influence the behaviour of fish, perhaps by regulating their activity or their sensitivity to stimulation, or by influencing the nervous system or by exerting some more general influence upon metabolism. There is, in fact, some evidence that individuals can be so influenced, for Hoar found that goldfish which were immersed in solutions of testosterone or stilboestrol were more active than untreated animals, and he found also that immersion in thyroxine had similar effects. Such results (Fig. 45) are a reminder that it is an unwise abstraction to seek in the sex hormones alone a complete explanation of sexual behaviour. The endocrine glands constitute an interacting and integrated system, each element of which may have its particular contribution to make to the execution of a complex

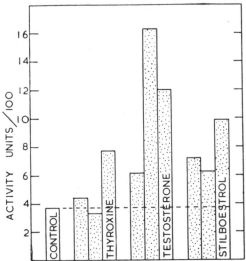

Fig. 45. Influence of hormones on the activity of goldfish. The total number of lines crossed in circular channels during three 10-minute periods (p.m., noon, and p.m.) were recorded with three fish in each of two channels. The three bars in the experimental group from left to right show values for 5, 10, and 15 days hormone treatment. (From Hoar et al., 1955. Can. J. Zool. 33, 428–39.)

response, and we shall see evidence later that thyroxine may, by its influence on osmotic relationships, regulate the pre-spawning movements of sticklebacks, and that the secretions of the adrenocortical tissue may be involved in the promotion of a high level of activity in fish.

4. Hormones and viviparity

Our analysis of the reproductive cycle of the female mammal has shown that its endocrine control is of a dual character, comprising as it does a follicular phase, which we may think of as concerned with the production of the ova and the ensuring of internal fertilization, and the luteal phase, concerned with the safeguarding of the embryo. We should naturally expect the former to be the more primitive, and the evidence for a functional relationship between the pituitary gland and ovary in fish is sufficiently well established to suggest that it is, in fact, one of the primary elements of the endocrine organization of vertebrates. As regards the luteal phase, it is well known that viviparity has been repeatedly evolved within the group in every major class from fish to mammals, with the exception of birds, and we might as a result expect to be able to learn something of the evolutionary history of its endocrinological mechanisms. Unfortunately, however, our information relative to this aspect lags far behind the many detailed accounts of the morphological and histological relationships between the parent and the developing young.

After ovulation has occurred in non-mammalian vertebrates the empty follicles commonly give rise to structures to which the term 'corpora lutea' is often given, but it must be said at once that no endocrine function has yet been convincingly attributed to them. They are best developed in elasmobranchs and reptiles, in which groups they arise as a result of hypertrophy of the follicle cells and an ingrowth of connective tissue and blood vessels. Their formation appears, therefore, to be an expression of positive growth and differentiation, and in this respect the situation in these two groups differs from that found in the cyclostomes, teleosts, amphibians, and birds, for in these the 'corpora lutea' can be said to be regressing from the time of ovulation onwards. In fact, it has been suggested that these structures are initially no more than a device for tidying up the discharged follicle and, where necessary, for the ingestion of moribund ova. What is certain is that they are not confined to viviparous forms, and that their presence is not essential for prolonged gestation in those that are viviparous, whether elasmobranch or reptilian. It is said, for example, that ovariectomy during the later stages of pregnancy does not interfere with normal gestation in the ovoviviparous garter-snake *Thamnophis sirtalis* and water-snake *Natrix sipedon*, and it is known, too, that 'corpora lutea' can form in these animals and in the dogfish *Mustelus canis* in the absence of the pituitary, so that they are not dependent upon any luteinizing action of its secretions. On the other hand, ovariectomy is said to interrupt gestation in some snakes if carried out during the early stages of pregnancy, and this has led to a suggestion that maintenance may, after all, depend upon the 'corpora lutea' but that in the later stages a secretion from some secretory tissue analogous to the mammalian placenta (p. 147) may be substituting for them.

While, then, we cannot entirely discount the possibility of the 'corpora lutea' in lower forms having some endocrine function, it is only in the mammals that this principle has been clearly demonstrated and, in view of the way in which mammalian structural features gradually became established in the extinct synapsid reptiles, we may reasonably assume that this new function was evolving at the same time. Brambell has pointed out that this may have resulted from gestation coming to depend upon a metabolic product of the degenerating follicle, while other factors, as Hisaw has suggested, may have been the absorption of steroidal products by the follicle cells, combined with the production of progesterone from the cholesterol present in yolk. This would have been accompanied or followed by the development of the response of the corpora lutea to the luteinizing action of pituitary gonadotropins, and it is particularly interesting in this connexion to recall the evidence that prolactin may be an ancient feature of the vertebrate endocrine system, with functions antedating the establishment of its luteotropic ones.

The modification of the reproductive cycle in adaptation to the demands of viviparity is seen in a well-defined yet simple form in the marsupials, for here ovulation is followed by a luteal phase of about the same length as the very short period of gestation. In the opossum (*Didelphis virginiana*), for example, which is seasonally polyoestrous, a cycle extends over about twenty-eight days and gestation over about twelve and a half days, so that ovulation could theoretically occur at the end of gestation without disturbing the regularity of the oestrous cycle. In fact, however, the occurrence of ovulation is further delayed after the young have been transferred to the pouch as a result of the stimulation of the teats; oestrous cycles are thus postponed for the duration of suckling.

A comparison of the marsupials with the placentals makes it clear that the important endocrinological advance shown by the latter is the development of means for lengthening the period of gestation by prolonging the luteal phase of the reproductive cycle, and we find that this has been achieved in two ways. One of these is based on continued reliance upon the corpora lutea for the production of progesterone, an additional source of luteinizing or luteotropic hormone being developed in order to maintain their activity. The other involves the development of an additional source of the progesterone so that the corpora lutea are no longer required to be present throughout gestation. Unfortunately, too little is known of the endocrinology of the various placental groups for it to be possible to organize the facts into any evolutionary series, and in any case it may well be that there has been much independent and parallel evolution within this field. We shall therefore merely consider one or two examples in which the facts have been clearly determined.

The rat is one of a number of mammals (the opossum, rabbit, goat, and cow are others) in which the ovary must be present for at least the greater part of pregnancy in order to ensure the maintenance of gestation; resorption or abortion will occur if the ovaries are removed, particularly if the operation is carried out during the first half of pregnancy. The pars distalis is also essential for the establishment of pregnancy and its presence is needed up to the eleventh day, but from then onwards it can be removed without interrupting gestation. It is supposed that by that time another source of prolactin must have become available for the maintenance of the corpora lutea (p. 113). There is good evidence that the placenta is the additional source of this hormone, for pregnancy can be maintained in rats that have been hypophysectomized on the sixth day of gestation provided that placental tissue is implanted into them. It has been shown, too, that if extracts of rat placentae are administered to hypophysectomized rats they will continue to be able to develop uterine deciduomata. Both results must mean that the extracts contain a tropic hormone capable of maintaining the activity of the corpora lutea in the absence of the prolactin (luteotropin) of the pituitary.

We find, therefore, in the rat an illustration of the first of the two methods suggested above for the prolongation of the activity of the corpus luteum, but it cannot be assumed that an exactly similar method will be found in other groups, nor is it clear that the luteotropic action of prolactin is at all widespread. The mouse does, in fact, seem to be very much the same as the rat in this regard, but in the hypophysectomized rabbit it has been possible to maintain luteal function by treatment with oestrogens as well as with gonadotropins, a result which has led to the suggestion that in this animal the latter hormones act only indirectly on the corpora lutea by promoting the secretion of oestrogen by the ovary. Such differences are, of course, to be expected if, as suggested above, some degree of independent evolution has occurred in the various groups.

Another illustration of this is the fact, first demonstrated by Aschheim and Zondek in 1927, that pregnancy in the human female is characterized by the appearance in the urine of a gonadotropin which reaches its maximum concentration between the sixtieth and eightieth days of pregnancy. Similar hormones have been found also in the rhesus monkey and the chimpanzee, although with marked differences in the amounts excreted and the lengths of time during which they are pregnant. The properties of these three hormones are closely similar, and are essentially luteinizing, for while they will not stimulate follicular growth in hypophysectomized rats they will luteinize follicles that are already present. In the intact animal, however, they react synergistically with the pituitary gonadotropins, and in the immature mouse will produce both follicle stimulation and luteinization, a reaction which is the basis of the Aschheim-Zondek pregnancy test. Injected into mature non-pregnant rabbits they will produce ovulation and luteinization, reactions which normally, as we have seen, would not occur unless the animals had copulated, and this is the basis for the Friedman test for pregnancy. Chorionic villi are known to be able to synthesize a hormone of this type in tissue culture, and since under these conditions the villi give rise to cytotrophoblast but not to syncitiotrophoblast it is now accepted that the hormone arises from the former tissue; it is thus known as chorionic gonadotropin, and it will be noted that it is being secreted by the embryo and not by the mother.

Another illustration of independent evolution in the promotion of the activity of the corpora lutea is provided by the appearance in the serum of the pregnant mare of a gonadotropin, known as pregnant mare serum gonadotropin, which reaches a maximum concentration at about the eightieth day of pregnancy. This differs from chorionic gonadotropin both in its origin and in its mode of functioning. As regards the former, it is believed to originate not in the chorion but in the specialized uterine tissue known as the endometrial cups. Functionally, the effect of this hormone on hypophysectomized animals is to bring about follicular growth with considerable increase in ovarian weight, stimulation of the interstitial cells, and an increased output of oestrogen, while ovulation and corpus luteum formation may also occur. It thus differs from the chorionic gonadotropin of primates in its marked capacity for stimulating follicular development, and its particular significance in pregnancy may be associated with the presence in the mare of many accessory corpora lutea.

We have so far considered the endocrinology of pregnancy in terms of the production of progesterone, but in fact it appears that oestrogen is also necessary for the maintenance of gestation, for the administration of both these hormones is needed to achieve this in the ovariectomized pregnant rat or hamster, despite the fact that the ovariectomized mouse and rabbit require only progesterone alone. On the other hand, neither of these hormones is needed by the ovariectomized mare, monkey, and human once a certain state of pregnancy has been reached. These facts, if we follow Amoroso's analysis, suggest that the placenta has gradually become a source of these steroid hormones so that eventually complete independence of the ovaries is achieved. The assumption would be that neither hormone is secreted by the placenta of the rat and hamster, that oestrogen is secreted by it in the mouse and rabbit, and that in the other three mentioned it secretes both oestrogen and progesterone.

The evidence for steroid secretion by the placenta is, in fact, very convincing. In the human there is an increase in oestrogen excretion during pregnancy and an abundance of oestrogen is found in the placenta, while oestradiol, oestriol, and progesterone have been extracted from the placenta of the rhesus monkey. In the horse the oestrogens secreted by the placenta are apparently chiefly equilenin and equilin (Fig. 32), which are only present in the pregnant animal. It is of great interest that this trend towards the independent action of the placenta is accompanied by its independence of the pituitary gland, for the presence of the pars distalis is not necessary for the maintenance of placental secretory activity. Thus pregnancy in the monkey will continue without interruption after hypophysectomy at the thirty-second day, and a woman has been successfully delivered at the end of the thirty-fifth week after having been hypophysectomized nine weeks previously. In the words of one writer, the embryo is registering a very early vote of no-confidence in its parent!

It must be emphasized once again that these data refer to only a very few mammalian species, and that they cannot possibly be regarded as indicative of a phylogenetic series. However, the general principle of the involvement of the placenta in prolonging the life of the corpora lutea and, probably later, coming to substitute for them, seems to be very well founded, and we must hope that future work will see this amplified with more detail and correlated with the earlier manifestations of viviparity in the vertebrate series.

It remains to mention a hormone or hormone complex which was first demonstrated in 1926 by Hisaw in the guinea-pig and to which the name relaxin has been given. This is present in the blood and reproductive tract of many other species, including man and the dog, sheep, whale, and rat, the content being low during early gestation, increasing later, and then rapidly falling again after parturition. Its actions, which are dependent upon the previous sensitizing or 'priming' of the connective tissue by oestrogen, are so varied that it is by no means clear that they can be ascribed to a single substance, and the situation in this respect will remain obscure until the active material has been purified and chemically characterized. In general, however, the functions of relaxin are particularly associated with parturition, the best known one, and the one from which its name is derived, being the relaxation of the symphysis pubis and sacroiliac joints. These effects appear to result from the breaking-down of the cartilage and collagen fibres and depolymerization of the matrix of the connective tissues, responses which give the hormone an obvious potential value in the clinical treatment of collagen diseases. It is believed to be involved also in other functional changes associated with pregnancy and parturition, including, for example, the inhibition of spontaneous contractions in the uterine myometrium and increase in the distensibility of the cervix uteri, but the exact nature of its actions vary a good deal from species to species, as also does the actual amount of the hormone produced. It would seem, therefore, that there, as with the placental gonadotropins, the physiological adaptations of pregnancy have been achieved by routes which have resulted in the establishment of much interspecific variability.

5. Sexual differentiation in Amphibia

We have so far considered the endocrine activity of the gonads only as it is seen in the sexually mature animal, but we cannot hope to understand one particular phase of the life cycle unless we are able to relate it to the whole sequence of events by which it has been determined. The importance of this aspect of the dimension of time (the evolutionary aspect is another one, and no less important) is well shown in the analysis

of the development of sexual organization, a problem which, in the vertebrates, has been studied with particular reference to amphibians, birds,
and mammals.

The principle that sex determination in vertebrates depends initially
upon the operation of a genetic switch mechanism is now very well estab-

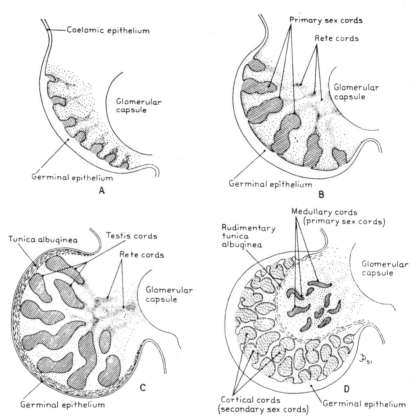

Fig. 46. Diagrams illustrating the developmental history of the medullary
and cortical components of the gonads of mammals. *A*, Genital ridge, with
incipient primary sex cords originating from the germinal epithelium. *B*, Indifferent gonad, in which the medullary component is present as the primary sex
cords, while the cortex is potentially represented by the germinal epithelium.
C, Development of the testis, with disappearance of the germinal epithelium.
D, Development of the ovary, with the production of dominant secondary sex
cords and cortex, and reduction of the primary sex cords.

(From Burns, 1955. 'Urinogenital system', in *Analysis of Development*, ed.
Willier *et al.* Saunders.)

lished. The explanation of this, stated in a generalized form, is that each
individual carries a pair of sex chromosomes. In one sex (digametic sex)
the two members of the pair are unequal, so that two types of germ cell
are produced, one carrying one of the sex chromosomes and the other

carrying its unequal partner. In the other sex the two members of this chromosome pair are identical and the germ cells are all of the same type (homogametic sex). Provided that the digametic sex produces its two types of germ cells in equal numbers this system will result in the production of equal numbers of males and females.

The gonad of vertebrates is sexually undifferentiated when it first appears in the form of the genital ridge. The latter is covered by the germinal epithelium, a derivative of the coelomic epithelium which comes to contain the primordial germ cells at the end of their migration from the site of their origin, usually in some part of the endoderm, and it is from this epithelium that primary sex cords (medullary cords) grow inwards (Fig. 46). Following this sexually indifferent stage the sex of the gonad becomes distinguishable, for in the male the medullary cords, with their contained germ cells, continue their development to form the seminiferous tubules; these eventually become connected with the mesonephric tubules by the growth of rete cords which form the vasa efferentia, the germinal epithelium meanwhile becoming reduced to the thin layer of epithelium overlying the layer of mesenchyme which gives rise to the tunica albuginea. In the female it is these medullary and rete cords which become reduced, and the germinal epithelium proliferates secondary sex cords (cortical cords), the germ cells in these forming oocytes, each of which, as we have seen earlier, becomes surrounded by a group of follicle cells (p. 96).

There is an exception to this situation in the cyclostomes and the teleosts, for no medullary component appears in these groups and the undifferentiated primordium of the gonad is said to correspond to the cortex of other vertebrates. Apart from this, however, the facts outlined above are of general applicability throughout the vertebrates and they are sufficient to indicate the fundamental endocrinological problems of early sexual differentiation: What is the function fulfilled by the genetic mechanism, what part, if any, do the embryonic gonads play in the chemical coordination of sexual development, and what is the nature of the relationship between the medulla and cortex?

It seems, according to Witschi's analysis, that the evolution of the sex chromosomes has proceeded at different rates in the different vertebrate groups, and that the Class Amphibia is one of those in which the rate has been rather slow, so that the genetic differentiation of sex still stands at a somewhat primitive level. Although breeding experiments have made it certain that sex chromosomes exist in this group it is difficult to identify them by morphological criteria, and they have been recognized only in some frogs and in *Triturus*. Moreover, their physiological differentiation shows some signs of limitations; thus a transient hermaphroditism is normal in certain races of *Rana temporaria*, all individuals in these races passing through a female stage, and this has been ascribed to the restricted degree of differentiation between the unequal members of the sex chromosome pair. This differentiation seems to have proceeded along divergent lines within the group, the digametic sex in frogs being the male while in toads and urodeles it is the female.

The gonads of the hermaphrodite frogs mentioned above may undergo a transition from ovary to testis during the period of sexual maturity, so that sperm and ova develop within the same organ; the animal concerned can thus both fertilize eggs from a normal female and at the same time provide eggs for fertilization by a normal male. Under such circumstances it has been shown that a hermaphrodite may be actually a genetic female, and that both its ova and its sperm are homogametic, as is shown by the fact that the offspring which result when its sperm fertilize the eggs of a normal female are all female; if those eggs had been fertilized by sperm from a normal male, the latter would have been digametic and equal numbers of each sex would have resulted. It thus follows that the fate of a germ cell, at least in these animals, is determined not by its genetic constitution but by the position that it takes up in the developing gonad; germ cells that enter the cortex become female, those that enter the medulla become male, and in embryological terminology these two regions are said to act respectively as female and male inductors. It would further seem that the essential function of the sex chromosomes, where these are fully differentiated, is to determine which of these two regions shall have the dominating influence, the cortex exerting overriding control in the genetic female and suppressing the development of the medulla, while the reverse occurs in the genetic male. The early differentiation of the amphibian gonad is thus visualized as involving a local interaction between the cortex and medulla, and this has been interpreted as depending upon the secretion by these regions of hypothetical chemical inductors to which have been given the names of corticin and medullarin respectively. The action of the developing gonads, may, however, extend beyond their boundaries, as can be illustrated by two types of experiments.

Firstly, it is possible to graft two early amphibian embryos together so that they will survive united as parabiotic twins (Fig. 47), a procedure that was initially prompted by Lillie's analysis of the free-martin (p. 156). If urodeles such as *Ambystoma* are used for this, and if one partner is a genetic male and the other a female, it is found that the presence of testes in the former results in the inhibition of the development of the ovaries in the latter, the female partner being either partially or completely sterilized (Fig. 47). The supposition is that the male gonad is secreting a chemical inhibitor, which is being distributed from one animal to the other, presumably by the blood stream, for the effect is shown even if the connexion between the two is by a very narrow bridge such as a pair of gill arches.

If frogs are used a similar result is obtained, but instead of both ovaries being completely inhibited the effect falls off with distance from the testes. the regions of the ovaries closest to the latter being the most affected. It would seem that here the secretion is diffusing through the tissues instead of entering the blood stream (Fig. 47). An obvious third possibility would be for the substance not to pass out of the gonad at all, and this is, in fact, found in toads, in which the ovaries of a female are unaffected by the parabiotic union of the animal with a male. The detailed results of such

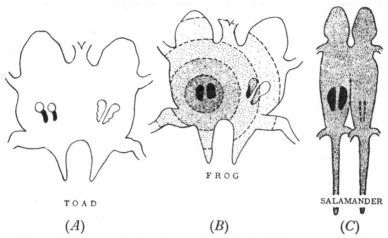

FROG

TOAD

SALAMANDER

(A)   (B)   (C)

Fig. 47. Differences in the degree of spread of male inductor substances in parabiotic amphibians. Male gonad black, female white. A, Toad, in which the substance diffuses through only a very small distance and the ovaries of the female develop normally. B, Frog, in which it diffuses further and produces some inhibition of ovarian development, but with its effectiveness diminishing with distance. C, Salamander, in which inhibition is complete, apparently because the substance is distributed through the blood stream.
(From Witschi, 1956. *Development of Vertebrates.* Saunders.)

experiments will vary greatly with the precise circumstances. For example, should the female *Ambystoma* be of a larger and more rapidly developing race than the male, the ovaries may come to inhibit the testes, or again the inhibition of the gonad of one sex may be followed in the affected animal by some degree of differentiation of the gonad of the other sex. In general, however, the results suggest that the cortical-medullary interaction may be based upon the capacity of the cortical and medullary inductor substances to suppress respectively the further differentiation of the medulla and cortex, although Witschi believes that the inhibiting action is due to substances which are actually different from corticin and medullarin.

The influence of the tissues of the developing gonad is not confined to inhibition, as is shown by the results of experiments involving castration of larval urodeles. Males of this group differ from females in the possession of elaborate cloacal glands. These fail to differentiate after castration, but they will do so if testis tissue is grafted into the castrate. Similar results are found with the Wolffian and Müllerian ducts; these will remain in an indifferent condition in both sexes after castration, but the grafting of either testis or ovary will evoke the differentiation of the duct appropriate to the sex of the graft, the Müllerian duct, for example, differentiating in response to an ovarian graft while remaining rudimentary if a testis is introduced.

6. Sexual differentiation in birds and mammals

The above results, allowing for some divergencies of interpretation, show that the developing gonad of amphibians secretes chemical regulating agents, which may diffuse within the gonad itself or outside it, or may pass into the blood stream. They may, under conditions of parabiosis, act upon the gonad of the other sex, while under normal conditions they determine the direction of differentiation of the ducts, these remaining in a neutral or undifferentiated condition in the absence of this chemical stimulus. Experiments upon birds have shown that in this group the gonads exert effects that are similar in principle, although the end-results differ in an important way.

Earlier attempts to carry out grafting of gonads in chick embryos were unsuccessful, but Wolff succeeded with intracoelomic transplants, and was able to show that the ovary, both the normal left one and the rudimentary right one, will feminize the testes of a recipient male. These become ovotestes, but the effect is a graded one, those parts of the testes being most affected which are nearest to the implants, so that the substance concerned is probably not entering the circulation. This result resembles that obtained with parabiotic grafts of frogs, but the reciprocal experiment shows an important difference; here it is found that although a testis grafted into the coelom of an embryonic female will bring about regression of the Müllerian duct it has no effect at all upon the ovaries. Exactly the same results are obtained from the *in vitro* culture of embryonic gonads when these are placed in direct parabiotic association; the testis never affects the ovary, but the latter feminizes the testis, and this occurs even when the gonads have been taken from chicks at the fifth to sixth day of incubation, at a time, that is, when sexual differentiation is only just beginning.

The influence of the ovary thus appears to predominate over that of the testis in the developing bird, and this is well shown in the reaction of the secondary sexual characters of the duck. In the male of this animal a well-developed syrinx and a penis appear early in development but remain rudimentary in the female. Now it is possible to castrate the very young embryo by irradiating the germinal ridges with X-rays, and under these circumstances the syrinx develops into the enlarged male type both in the castrated female and male. Should a small portion of ovary remain in the former the syrinx develops into a type intermediate between the normal male and the normal female form (Plate VI *A*). Exactly the same response is given by the genital tubercle; after complete castration this goes on to develop into the male type of penis, while the persistence of a small amount of ovarian tissue will determine the development of an intermediate type.

It thus appears that these two organs have an innate capacity for developing into the male type, which is therefore also the neutral type, while the

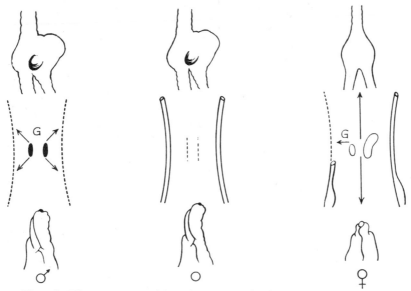

Fig. 48. Diagram summarizing the embryonic development of three sex characters of the duck in the male (left), castrate (middle), and female (right). The upper row shows the syrinx, the middle row the Müllerian ducts, and the lower row the genital tubercle. Arrows indicate an inhibitory action of the secretions of the gonads (*G*) during sexual differentiation. Cf. Plate VI *A*.
(From Wolff & Wolff, 1959. *J. exp. Zool.* **116**, 59-97.)

development of the female type can only take place under the influence of an ovarian secretion (Fig. 48). This has been confirmed by culturing the organs *in vitro*. Provided that they are removed before the sexual differentiation of the gonad has been established they will develop into the male form irrespective of the sex of the embryo from which they were removed, but if they are removed from a female embryo after the gonad has established its sexual differentiation they will develop in the manner appropriate to that sex, the genital tubercle undergoing regression. The delicacy of these relationships is shown by the fact that the Müllerian duct differs in its reactions from the syrinx and the penis, for it persists in castrated embryos and continues its development *in vitro* if it is alone. In its neutral form it therefore conforms fairly closely with the female type, while it regresses if it is associated with a testis.

The starting point for much of the experimental analysis outlined above was Lillie's classical study of the free-martin in cattle, which provided in 1916 the first demonstration of the probable importance of gonadal secretion in embryonic differentiation. The fundamental assumption in his interpretation is that the testes of the male embryo secrete a male-determining substance into the blood stream at a very early stage of development, an assumption which is in line with the fact that cells resembling Leydig cells are identifiable in the testis of mammalian embryos almost as soon as histological sex differentiation becomes apparent.

Now during the development of twin calves the foetal membranes may unite in such a way that anastomoses form between the chorio-allantoic vessels of the two embryos. If these are of opposite sexes the male-determining substance will circulate also in the female, and will cause it to develop testes in place of ovaries, with concomitant suppression of the Müllerian duct system and development of the epididymis and Wolffian ducts. This intersexual individual, with essentially male internal organs but with external genitalia only partially masculinized, is the free-martin, the result of what is in effect a natural experiment in parabiosis.

Support for this interpretation can be found in the results of castration, which has been successfully carried out in embryos of the rabbit, mouse, and rat. This operation, if it is performed before morphological differentiation of the genital duct system, results in general in a failure of the male type of differentiation but not of the female, so that the individual, irrespective of its genetic sex, closely resembles a female, with persistence of Müllerian duct derivatives and with external genitalia of the female type. Here again, then, it seems probable that the embryonic testis is controlling sex differentiaion by secreting a male-determining substance into the blood stream.

Confirmatory evidence of the existence of this hormone is given by an experiment in which an adult male rat was castrated, with consequential reduction of its seminal vesicles. It was found possible to restore completely the differentiation of the epithelium of the latter by transplanting on to the vesicle an embryonic testis removed from a rat at the beginning of its sexual differentiation. Thus the latter appears to be capable of secreting a substance similar to the adult hormone as far as its effects upon this particular epithelium are concerned, and it is especially instructive to find this substance acting through direct contact in a manner essentially similar to that of the inductor substances of embryos. Such a situation justifies our belief (p. 4) that similarities of principle will be found to underly different expressions of chemical regulation.

Another approach to these problems has been devised by Price, who has made use of the culture of explants of the genital tract of rat foetuses (Fig. 49). In this way, using cock plasma and chick embryo extract as the

culture medium, she has found that while the complete male reproductive tract, including the gonads, will continue its development after
being explanted at $17\frac{1}{2}$ days, the removal of both testes from the explant
will result in regression of the Wolffian duct and in failure of the seminal
vesicles to appear. It is concluded from these and other experiments

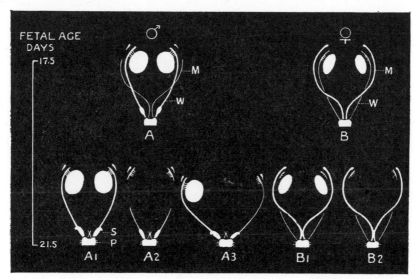

Fig. 49. Diagrams of the effects of explantation experiments upon the reproductive tracts of male and female rat foetuses. M, Müllerian ducts; W, Wolffian
ducts; P, prostate; S, seminal vesicle.

A, Male tract at $17\frac{1}{2}$ days, the age of explanting. A_1, Development has continued for 4 days after explanting; note the appearance of seminal vesicles and
prostatic buds and the retrogression of the Müllerian ducts. A_2, Removal of
both testes results in retrogression of the Wolffian ducts and failure of development of the seminal vesicles and some of the prostatic buds, indicating that
these are all dependent on a secretion of the testes. A_3, With one testis remaining
and the other duct widely separated, the latter undergoes some regression
indicating a limited degree of diffusion of the secretion. B, Female tract at
$17\frac{1}{2}$ days. B_1, Development has continued for 4 days after explanting, with
retrogression of Wolffian ducts and the formation of the utero-vaginal canal
(the stock of rats used had spontaneously developing female prostrates). B_2,
Removal of both ovaries does not affect the development, indicating that female
differentiation of the ducts and accessory glands is not hormone-dependent.

(From Watterson (ed.), 1959. Endocrines in Development. University of
Chicago.)

(Fig. 49) that the embryonic testes are secreting a substance which
diffuses into the culture medium and promotes sexual differentiation of
the explant, and this is confirmed by the fact that one testis by itself can
ensure normal development. Explants of female systems, however, are
not influenced by removal of the ovaries, for in such material the Müllerian
ducts persist and the Wolffian duct regresses, exactly as in the female
system that retains its gonads.

If we can generalize from the results of these very difficult experiments, and it is certainly encouraging to find that the results obtained with rabbits and mice are in substantial agreement, it follows that there is a fundamental distinction between birds and mammals. In the former (Fig. 48) it is the male type which is the neutral one, and the female type

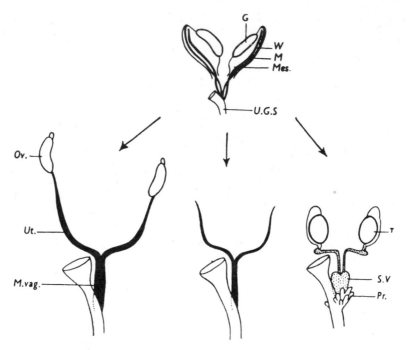

Fig. 50. Diagram summarizing the development of the sex duct in the rabbit embryo. From the undifferentiated condition (*upper part*) may arise either the female structure (*lower left*), male structure (*lower right*) or gonadless feminine structure in castrated embryos of either sex (*lower middle*). G, gonad; M, Müllerian duct; *Mes.*, mesonephros; M. vag., Müllerian vagina; Ov., ovary; Pt., prostate; S.V., seminal vesicle; T, testis; U.G.S., urinogenital sinus; Ut, uterine horn. W, Wolffian duct (stippled).
(From Jost, 1960. *Mem. Soc. Endocrin.* **7**, 49–62.)

which is hormone-dependent, with the ovarian secretion therefore playing the principal part in sexual differentiation, while in the mammals (Fig. 50) the situation is the exact opposite. We may speculate whether this difference is related in some way to the fact that the male is the digametic sex in mammals and the female the digametic sex in birds. It is possible, too, that the mammalian arrangement may be related to the existence of the intra-uterine phase of development and the consequent need to ensure that the factors determining the sexual differentiation of the male embryo are sufficiently well established to override any possible feminizing influence of the female environment in which the early stages of its development have to be passed.

Consideration of the facts thus established for amphibians, birds, and mammals leaves us in no doubt regarding the activity of the embryonic and foetal gonads in influencing the course of the development of the sexual characters, but the nature of the chemical substances produced by them, as also that of the primary sex inductors, and the relationship of these to the gonadal hormones of the adults, remain somewhat uncertain. The availability of steroid hormones has made possible extensive studies of their action when they are introduced into embryos, but the results have been less clear-cut than could have been wished. Androgens and oestrogens may reverse the sex of the differentiating gonads of amphibians if the treated individuals are of the homogametic sex. So-called 'paradoxic effects', however, are also obtained, as, for example, the masculinization

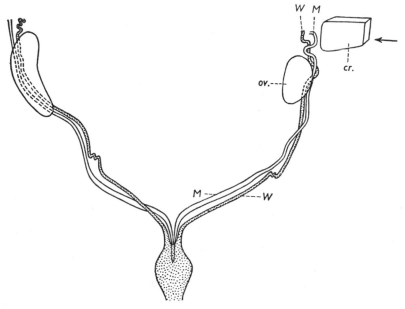

Fig. 51. *A*. Graphic reconstruction (slightly schematized) of the genital tract of a female rabbit foetus 28 days old which received on day 20 a single crystal (*cr*) of testosterone proprionate close to the ovary (*ov*). Note that the Wolffian duct (*W*) has persisted, but that there is no regression of the Müllerian duct (*M*). (From Jost, 1955. *Mem. Soc. Endocrin.* **4**, 237–48.)

of the gonads of female (homogametic) frogs by oestrogen treatment, but these, according to Gallien, are pathogenic in nature. These steroids seem to produce little effect upon the differentiation of the mammalian gonad, although in birds the introduction of oestrogens into the egg of male embryos causes a virtually complete feminization of the gonads. Oestrogens are said also to feminize the development of the syrinx and penis in the duck embryo, but androgens have little effect on these in the female, being apparently unable to override the influence of the ovary. As for mammals, it is known that testosterone will promote normal development

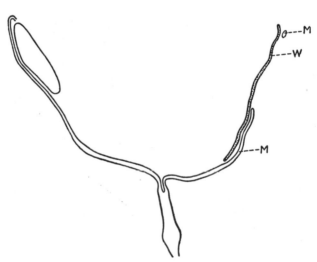

Fig. 51. *B.* Graphic reconstruction (slightly schematized) of the genital tract of a female rabbit foetus 28 days old, upon which was grafted on day 20 a 20-day old testis (*t*), inserted on the left ovary (*ov*); this ovary has been displaced upwards. The upper part of the Müllerian duct (*M*) is suppressed, except for a small cyst; the masculinizing effect on the Wolffian duct (*W*) is less pronounced than in Fig. *A*, a section persisting on the grafted side only. (From Jost, 1955. *Mem. Soc. Endocrin.* **4,** 237–48.)

of explants of male duct systems from which both of the embryonic testes have been removed, but even here there still remains some doubt whether or not the hormone of the embryo is identical with that of the adult. One difficulty is that while the grafting of testicular tissue on to the ovary of a rabbit foetus will cause regression of the Müllerian duct, it does not seem possible to produce this effect with testosterone (Fig. 51 *A* and *B*).

Such considerations have led some investigators to regard the secretions

of the developing gonads as being distinct from the sex hormones produced in the adult, but against this extreme view it must be remembered
that the sex steroids can undoubtedly counteract many of the effects of
castration in the embryo, and that the gonads of embryos can be used to
counteract effects of castration in the adult. What is quite clear is that
secretion by the developing gonad does have a profound effect upon
sexual differentiation, and there is much to be said for adopting the
cautiously conservative view of one writer, that while there is no justification for assuming that these secretions are precisely identical with any
particular known steroid there is also no justification for assigning them
to an entirely different category.

7. Intersexuality and sex reversal

It will now be apparent that the cortical-medullary interactions offer
a field in which disturbance of the finely balanced relationships of the
gonadal inductor substances could lead to a far-reaching distortion of
subsequent sexual development. The possibilities are too wide-ranging
for any comprehensive discussion to be attempted here, but one or two
examples will illustrate the possibilities in so far as they affect human
beings.

The analyses of these has been greatly facilitated by the discovery that it
is possible to determine the genetic sex of individuals by a relatively
simple histological procedure which depends upon the fact that the
heterochromatin of the sex chromosomes persists as a recognizable inclusion in the intermitotic nucleus (Plate VI B). It can be distinguished, in
skin preparations or in mucosal smears, as a small mass, about 1μ in
diameter, lying close against the nuclear membrane, and its value is shown
by the fact that in one set of samples it was found in 50–90 per cent. of
the nuclei of female tissues, with an average incidence of 72 per cent. as
compared with only 0–20 per cent. of the nuclei of male tissues, with an
average incidence of only 6 per cent.

One type of sexual abnormality, known as male pseudohermaphroditism,
is found in genetic males in which the gonads develop as testes but are
associated with a mixture of male and female sexual characters. They may
range from individuals with quite a normal female appearance but with
abdominal testes to individuals who are almost completely masculinized.
It seems to be agreed that this condition is genetic in origin, being transmitted by a dominant gene, and that the effect of this gene is exerted upon
the mother, who passes into her male foetus a substance that antagonizes
its medullary inductor. As a result of this the subsequent development
becomes a compromise between these two agents, the variable sexual

854108   M

constitution of the sexual characters reflecting the level of compromise achieved.

An example quoted by Greenblatt is of a young 'woman' who at the age of sixteen had failed to menstruate and who was showing some degree of maleness in the sexual characters. She possessed abdominal testes, with numerous Leydig cells but no sperm, and after these organs had been removed, and with oestrogen therapy and some surgical treatment of the accessory structures, this patient became 'a strikingly beautiful female, enjoying male companionship . . . feminine in her habits, attitudes and aptitudes'. None the less, her sex chromatin pattern showed that she was unquestionably a genetic male.

Probably the nearest approach to complete sex reversal in man is found in certain cases of Klinefelter's syndrome, with female nuclear sex. Here the characteristic features include a female type of breast growth (a consequence of the chromosome constitution) and the possession of small testes, the latter showing functional Leydig cells but a variable degree of hyalinization of the seminiferous tubules. In those individuals it is assumed that there has been a complete failure of the cortex of the embryonic gonad. Under these circumstances the medulla would be able to exert its properties as a male inductor, and because of this it becomes possible for any surviving germ cells to complete their development in a male environment. This accounts for the very remarkable fact that mature sperm have been demonstrated in the gonads of certain individuals afflicted in this way, which means, of course, that germ cells which are genetically female in type are developing as spermatogonia, just as in the hermaphrodite frogs discussed earlier (p. 152). It is in this sense that such cases present an almost perfect example of sex reversal.

So-called 'true' hermaphroditism is a condition in which both ovarian and testicular tissue are present in the same individual, although this term should strictly be reserved for naturally functional hermaphrodites such as oligochaete worms. The ideal or classical case is one in which there is a testis on one side and an ovary on the other, but there are other possibilities, including the presence of ovotestes, and the accessory structures can also vary in their sexual combination. It is said that about sixty cases of 'true' hermaphroditism have been reported, and that they have shown a preponderance of female nuclear sex. In such individuals it is supposed that the cortical-medullary relationships have been unbalanced during the development of one or other of the ovaries, with the result that the medullary component has been able to persist and differentiate into testicular tissue.

One such case, in which there was a functional ovary on one side of the body and a non-functional testis (with Leydig cells but no sperm) on the other, illustrates very well the close correlation between clinical findings in man and the results of experimental investigations on the rabbit, for the genital duct on each side corresponded in its sex to the adjacent gonad. We have seen that this is substantially what is found when a testis is grafted on to an ovary in a rabbit foetus (Fig. 51 *B*); in such an experiment the Wolffian duct persists and the Müllerian duct regresses as a result of the action of the secretion of the testis, but the effect is a local one and there is a diminishing gradient of response from the region nearest to the graft.

Such agreement between observation and experiment is impressive, for it makes possible a rational interpretation and, where possible, a treatment of such cases (see also p. 251) which is calculated to bring a greater satisfaction to the afflicted individuals than the divinity which was attributed to Hermaphroditos by the ancient Greeks.

VII. THE ENDOCRINE GLANDS
OF THE PHARYNX

1. The parathyroid glands and ultimobranchial bodies

THE stomach and intestine are not the only regions of the vertebrate alimentary tract that have contributed to the endocrine system. The pharynx has also played an important role, in part, perhaps, because of the inherent tendency to proliferation which underlies the formation of the branchial pouches and lungs, and in part because of the changes in function which have marked the evolutionary history of this region.

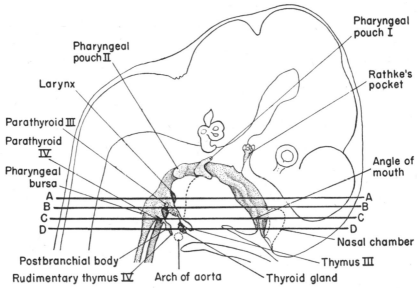

Fig. 52. Pharynx of 15 mm pig embryo, schematically represented in relation to the outline of other cephalic structures. The heavy horizontal lines indicate the levels of the correspondingly lettered sections in Fig. 53.
(From Patten, 1948. *Embryology of the Pig*. Blakiston.)

The thymus gland, present in fish as well as in tetrapods, is doubtless an expression of the proliferative tendencies, but it is still uncertain whether or not this organ possesses any endocrine function. No such doubt, however, attaches to the parathyroid glands (epithelial bodies), which develop from the ventral region of certain of the visceral pouches, and, appearing first in the amphibians, seem to be a product of the reduction of the gills which results from the assumption of terrestrial life. In mammals (Figs. 52, 53), as in amphibians, they take their origin from the third and

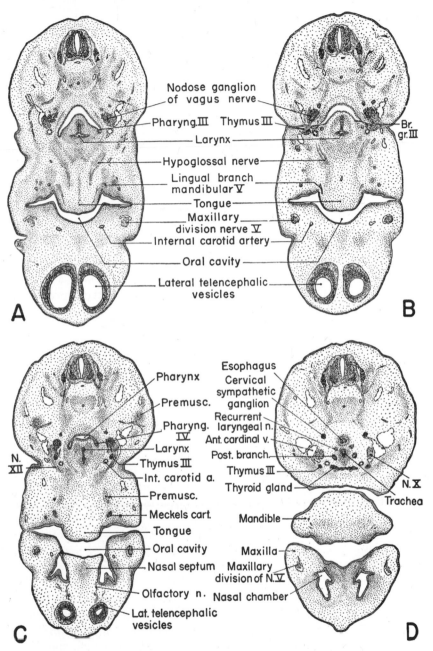

Fig. 53. Transverse sections through the pharyngeal region of a 15 mm pig embryo at the levels indicated in Fig. 52. *Br. gr. III*, third branchial groove; *Pharyng. III & IV*, third and fourth pharyngeal pouches; *Premusc.*, premuscular concentration of mesenchyme; *N. XII*, hypoglossal nerve.

(From Patten, 1948. *Embryology of the Pig*. Blakiston.)

fourth pair of pouches, but there is some variation in this respect in other groups. In lizards, for example, they arise from the third pair, the fourth and fifth making contributions which later atrophy, but such variations are unimportant, for the homology of these organs throughout the tetrapods clearly resides in the capacity of the relevant morphogenetic field rather than in the relationships of the particular pharyngeal segment in which that capacity comes to expression.

The parathyroid glands of mammals are often four in number, in correspondence with the four visceral pouches from which they are derived, but there is a good deal of variation in this also, both between individuals and species. They take their name from their close association with the thyroid gland, the single pair of the rat, for example, being embedded in its surface, and it is this which was the cause of the fatal results which followed early operations for total thyroidectomy both in humans and in dogs. Histologically, however, they remain sharply differentiated from thyroid tissue, being composed of closely packed cells with no follicular organization. These cells are unusual in lacking any clearly defined granules such as are commonly associated with the production of a secretion, although some changes in their appearance have been observed and correlated with fluctuations in activity.

In 1908 and 1909 MacCallum and Voegtlin showed that the convulsions which followed the removal of the parathyroids from dogs were caused by a fall in blood calcium, and that the condition could be relieved by the injection of calcium salts. It was thus apparent that the glands must have a special association with calcium metabolism, but it was not until 1925 that their endocrine nature became well defined as a result of the work of Collip. He succeeded in preparing an extract of the glands which raised the level of the blood calcium in parathyroidectomized animals and thereby abolished the convulsions, which appear to be a consequence of increased neuromuscular irritability accompanying the initial fall in that level. The hormone (parathormone, as it is often called) has now been purified and is known to be a protein with a molecule containing 83 amino-acid residues and with a molecular weight of 9,500.

The secretory activity of the mammalian parathyroid is not controlled by the pituitary gland, but is directly regulated by the concentration of calcium in the blood, the primary function of parathormone being to maintain, in association with an adequate supply of vitamin D, an appropriate blood calcium level. A fall in this level evokes an increased output of hormone, which then promotes the absorption of calcium by the intestinal epithelium, an increased reabsorption of it by the kidney tubules, and an increased release of it from bone. It will be observed that in this way the blood calcium level is restored by the integration of several different responses, which draw in part upon internal resources and in part upon external supplies. In consequence, as Rasmussen points out, the animal is able to achieve both a wider range and a finer degree of control than would be possible if only one source were used, and we may compare this subtlety of organization with the analogous uses of inter-locking mechanisms which we find in the autonomic nervous system and in the regulation of carbohydrate metabolism.

The absence of parathyroid glands from fish raises the question whether this can be associated with any metabolic peculiarity of these animals. It certainly is a striking fact that the evolutionary history of all the main groups of fish, and also of the Agnatha, has involved a very marked and consistent tendency towards the reduction of ossification, and it is interest-ing to speculate whether the appearance of the parathyroids in tetrapods is in any way indicative of a need for regulating and stabilizing calcium metabolism in correlation with the increased importance of the skeleton in terrestrial animals. As against this, however, two points should be remembered. Firstly, we shall see below that the establishment of thyroidal function preceeded the establishment of the typical form of the thyroid gland, and we cannot, therefore, assume that parathyroidal function is lacking in fish merely because discrete glands cannot be identified. Secondly, and arising out of this, the ultimobranchial bodies may be of some significance in this connexion.

These (Fig. 54) are follicular structures which develop as a pair of outpushings from the hinder end of the pharynx, immediately behind the last pair of gill pouches; in fact, in the mammal embryo they seem almost to be a part of the latter, but the presence of an arterial arch between the two clearly shows that they are a separate element of the branchiomeric system. In terms of descriptive embryology they might be interpreted as vestigial gill pouches, but it is probably better to regard them as an expression of the activity of the peripheral part of the branchial morpho-genetic field. On this interpretation they would be expected to have some-thing of the competence of the other branchial derivatives, and they do, in fact, tend to become closely associated with the thyroid in mammals and, under some circumstances, to give rise to thyroid-like tissue. Sehe, in a study of these bodies in certain fish and amphibians, found no evidence of thyroidal activity in them, and doubted whether they had any endocrine function at all. Rasquin and Rosenbloom, however, noted that they became considerably enlarged in individuals of the teleost *Astyanax mexicanus* which had been maintained for a long time in dark-ness and which were showing, amongst other features, some defective calcification of the skeleton; they therefore suggested that these bodies might be associated with calcium metabolism and might be functionally comparable with parathyroid tissue, an interesting proposal that merits further exploration.

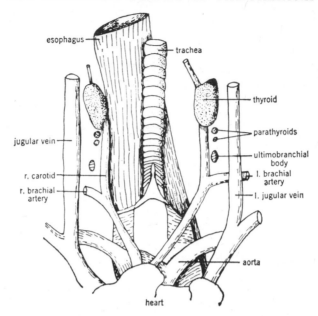

Fig. 54. Relationship of the thyroid, parathyroid, and ultimobranchial bodies to the blood vessels in the region of the heart in the domestic fowl.
(From Adams & Eddy, 1949. *Comparative Anatomy*. Wiley.)

2. The pseudobranch

A characteristic feature of the pharynx of teleosts is the closure of the spiracle and an interesting by-product of this is the persistence of its pseudobranch as a glandular organ. This structure is composed of acidophilic secretory cells, which are supplied through a capillary system with arterial blood from the next succeeding branchial arch; from these capillaries the ophthalmic artery takes blood forward to another capillary organ, the choroid gland of the eye. It has long been suspected that the pseudobranch might have some endocrine functions, and this view has been strengthened by the discovery that its removal leads in several species to a darkening of the operated animal and to a degeneration of the choroid gland. A suggested interpretation of this, put forward by Parry and Holliday, is that the pseudobranch is concerned with the production, or activation, of a hormone which produces concentration of the pigment of the melanocytes (see Chapter XI), and that the choroid gland regulates the release of this hormone into the general circulation. It is supposed that if the capillaries of that gland were fully dilated there would be a maximum flow of blood through the pseudobranch and that the animal would, in consequence, be pale, while with contraction of the capillaries the flow would be reduced and the animal would be dark. We shall see later that the means by which colour change is controlled in teleosts is by no means fully understood, and that there is certainly room for the incorporation of such promising new hypotheses as this.

3. Structure of the thyroid gland

The best known and most thoroughly studied endocrine derivative of the pharynx is the thyroid gland. This was first described anatomically in 1656 by a London physician, Thomas Wharton, who also gave to it its accepted name, deriving this from the Greek (*thureos*, a shield, and *eidos*, form). It lies in man and other mammals on either side of the larynx, with a median isthmus connecting the two main lateral portions, and, noting this and also its follicles with their contained colloid, Wharton concluded that it served in human beings to smooth the contours of the neck, a supposition which conveniently accounted for it being larger in females, whose necks were thereby made more even and more beautiful.

It develops as a median downgrowth from the floor of the pharynx, a mode of origin which, as we shall see, reflects its derivation from the endostyle of the protochordates. Remnants of its connexion with the pharynx may sometimes persist as accessory thyroids in man, but normally in all vertebrates it separates off as a quite independent organ which is usually compact and median, but sometimes paired, as in amphibians (Fig. 55) and birds (Fig. 54). Its appearance in teleost fish is unusual in that, with rare exceptions, it forms a loosely organized gland which extends along the ventral aorta (Fig. 56) and often into the branchial arches; this is thought to result from the tendency of thyroid cells in these animals to migrate during development, a tendency which in extreme cases results in the establishment of thyroid tissue in unusual parts of the body (heterotopic), more particularly in the kidneys. Such a situation, and the possibility of its occurrence in other animals, needs to be borne in mind in assessing the results of experimental studies on thyroid function.

The histological structure of the gland is very characteristic (Fig. 70, p. 201), for its secretory product is stored in hollow follicles, the walls of which are formed by the secretory epithelium. This varies in its appearance according to the condition of the cells, which may range from a very flattened and almost squamous shape to a cubical or even columnar form. It is generally held that this variation reflects the activity of the gland, the cells being at their most flattened when the activity is least, and this is probably true, although the relationship may not be an entirely simple one. The gland is richly vascularized, networks of capillaries closely surrounding the follicles and carrying with them a delicate investment of connective tissue cells and fibres. The vessels are accompanied by non-medullated nerve fibres, which take their origin from the cervical sympathetic ganglia, but they appear to be entirely vasomotor in their function and it is agreed that the secretory cells are themselves without any motor innervation. As with the gonads, then, we shall have to examine in due course how the activity of this gland is regulated.

The material which fills the follicles, and which is also visible as small droplets within the cells, stains brilliantly with acidic dyes such as eosin

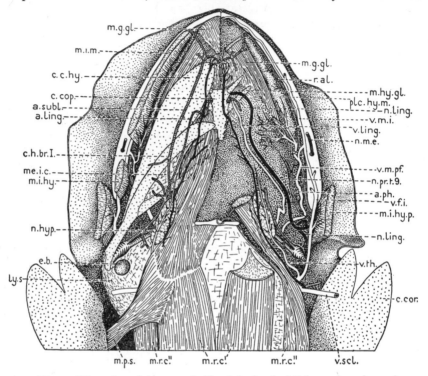

Fig. 55. Dissection of the ventral side of the head of *Salamandra salamandra*. *a. subl.*, sublingual artery; *e.b.*, parathyroid gland; *n. hyp.*, hypoglossal nerve, under which is seen the thyroid gland; *n. ling.*, lingual nerve; *v. scl.*, subclavian vein.

(From Francis, 1934. *The Anatomy of the Salamander.* Oxford: Clarendon Press.)

or phloxine, while with the Azan procedure it may be coloured either by the azocarmine and orange G or by the aniline blue; the difference is said to depend upon the viscosity of the material, although there is some doubt as to whether this is of any very definite significance. There is also some doubt as to the significance of the numerous vacuoles which are seen around the edge of the colloid mass when the gland has been fixed with one of the standard reagents. These have been thought to arise from the breaking-down of the colloid and to be an index of the amount of secretion which is being discharged into the blood, but if the gland is prepared by freeze-drying they are not usually visible at all, and it has therefore been argued that they are merely an artifact of fixation. It is probably reasonable, however, to regard their existence as reflecting in at least some degree the condition of the colloid, even though they may not be present in that form in the unfixed material.

An important histochemical property of the colloid is its strong positive reaction to the periodic acid/Schiff (PAS) procedure (see p. 284), which indicates the presence of carbohydrate. Its composition is now well known,

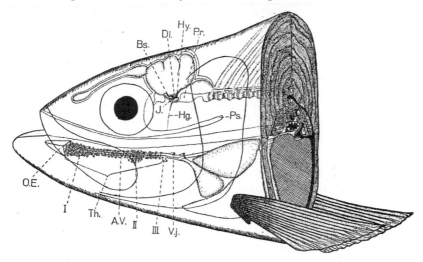

Fig. 56. The head of the herring. *A.V.*, ventral aorta; *Bs.*, basisphenoid; *Di.*, diencephalon; *Hg.*, closed vestige of the hypophyseal duct; *Hy.*, pituitary gland; *Ps.*, parasphenoid; *O.E.*, os entoglossum; *Pr.*, prootic; *J.*, infundibulum; *Th.*, thyroid; *V.j.*, jugular vein; *I, II, III*, afferent branchial arteries. (From Buchmann, 1940. *Zool. Jahrb. Abt. Anat.* **66,** 191–262.)

since it can be extracted from the gland with cold saline and purified by subsequent treatment of the extract with ammonium sulphate, and chemical analysis shows that its main component is thyroglobulin, a protein containing, according to one analysis, 2·3 to 2·4 per cent. hexosamine and 4·2 per cent. galactose, mannose, and glucose. These carbohydrate moieties are undoubtedly firmly bound, and it is agreed that thyroglobulin is a glycoprotein (p. 113).

Additional information relating to the organization of the secretory epithelium has been obtained by electron microscopy, which has revealed that the apical cell membrane is folded into many minute villus-like processes. The significance of these is not clear, but they may well be related in some way to the dual mode of action of the cells, which are concerned both with the secretion of thyroglobulin into the lumen and also with the subsequent reabsorption of the thyroid hormones prior to their transmission into the blood stream. In all cells concerned with protein synthesis great functional importance attaches to the ergastoplasm (endoplasmic reticulum). This region is shown by the electron microscope to consist of parallel membranes, which enclose areas filled with more or less structureless protoplasm and which bear on their outer surfaces numerous fine granules, these being regarded as the site of ribonucleic acid. In the thyroid epithelial cell the endoplasmic reticulum is dilated into ergastoplasmic sacs, and a dense material, thought to be the colloid, is said to appear within these while the granules on the outer surface disappear. It has been suggested, therefore, that the ergastoplasm is responsible for the formation of the colloid secretion, but against this it has also been claimed that the Golgi region (see also p. 75) is primarily concerned with this and that the ergastoplasm functions during the passage of hormonal material inwards towards the blood vessels.

4. The clinical approach to the problems of thyroid function

As with some of the other endocrine glands, it is the study of disturbances of function in human beings which has provided the foundation of our understanding of the thyroid. By far the commonest of these disturbances, and they are by no means restricted to man, are the 'non-toxic' or endemic goitres which occur in all parts of the world, but especially in those regions (not necessarily mountainous) where the iodine of the soil has been reduced by flooding or by glacial action. As a result of this iodine shortage, and for a reason which we shall examine later, the thyroid enlarges to form a simple or diffuse goitre, and the prevalence of this response may be judged from the fact that in 1944 the goitre Subcommittee of the Medical Research Council estimated that in England and Wales, amongst young people of ages ranging from five to twenty years, there were perhaps as many as 500,000 cases showing some degree of thyroid enlargement. Nodules may sometimes appear in enlarged thyroids, apparently as a result of alternating phases of hyperplasia and involution, and this gives rise to adenomatous or nodular goitre, but both this and the diffuse form are fundamentally different from the 'toxic' goitres, which are characterized by an increased output of thyroid secretion.

The ashes of marine sponges are said to have been used by the Chinese as long ago as 1500 B.C. for the treatment of goitre and, although some doubt has been cast upon the correctness of this statement, the remedy, with the use of sea-water as a variant, has been widely recommended by European medical writers in the past and must presumably have been based upon some degree of success. The explanation of this did not become apparent until the nineteenth century, the first step towards it being the isolation of iodine from the seaweed *Fucus vesiculosus* by the French chemist Courtois in 1811, and the identification of this as a new element by Gay-Lussac. Fyfe's demonstration in 1819 that iodine was present in sponges (a discovery from which he himself drew the conclusion that these organisms must be plants) suggested that this element might account for their value in the treatment of goitre, and it was particularly the Swiss physician Coindet who drew public attention to this possibility. By the middle of the century Chatin, in France, had strengthened the argument by bringing forward evidence that endemic goitre was associated with the use of water of low iodine content, but his conclusion was rejected by the French Academy of Sciences. This setback seems to have resulted partly from certain weaknesses in the medical procedures which were then being brought into use but even more from the fact that, as Harington has pointed out, 'the notion that a disease could be caused, not by an actively noxious agent, but by the mere deficiency of an element which in any case was never present except in minute quantities, was one for which medical and scientific opinion was quite unprepared.' In other words, the successful exploitation of new ideas in science needs a proper climate of opinion, and this was not available either for Coindet or for Chatin.

During the early years of the present century, however, the relation-ship between goitre and iodine shortage became increasingly clearly established, and it is of particular interest to the comparative endocrin-ologist to find that one of the most significant contributions was Marine's study of goitre in the American brook-trout, *Salvelinus fontinalis*. This condition, which was marked by a conspicuous swelling or reddening of the pharyngeal floor, had arisen in fish which were being reared in a hatchery, and he was able to show that it resulted from a deficiency of iodine in the food, and that it could be alleviated by the addition of whole sea-fish to the diet.

Meanwhile, clinical observations had been leading to the recognition that a disorder of the thyroid underlay the condition long known as cretinism, in which a variety of characteristics, including stunted growth and feeble-mindedness, are associated, as we now know, with thyroid deficiency of various types. Such deficiencies become apparent at the beginning of life, but in 1873 Gull presented to the Clinical Society of London an account of 'A Cretinoid State supervening in Adult Life in Women', and shortly afterwards two more cases of this adult type were described by Ord who, in 1877, named the condition myxoedema. This is characterized by thickening of the subcutaneous tissue, sensitivity to cold, lethargy, and progressive loss of the mental faculties, features which had suggested to Gull the comparison with cretinism, and Ord made the very important observation that in one of his patients the thyroid had become atrophied. In itself this suggested a direct relationship between the condition and a lack of thyroid tissue, and a striking confirmation of this came from the experiences of Swiss surgeons who, as a result of the discrediting of iodine medication, had been treating goitre by removal of the thyroid gland. They found that in some patients from whom the whole of the gland had been removed there later supervened a condition which they realized was identical with the myxoedema described by Gull and Ord, a good demonstration, incidentally, of the importance of a clear definition of the syndrome associated with a specific clinical condition.

These circumstances led after fourteen years to the use of thyroid extract by Murray for the treatment of myxoedema, the patient being a woman who in 1891, at the age of 46, showed an advanced stage of this condition. There resulted a rapid and dramatic return to health which was maintained for twenty-eight years, initially by the use of injections of thyroid extracts and subsequently by oral administration of these. The patient finally died at the age of 74, having during the course of her treatment made use of the thyroids of over 870 sheep. She provides a famous and classical example of the employment of replacement therapy, and the work of Gull, Ord, and Murray must be reckoned as providing one of the major steps in the development of endocrinology.

5. The thyroid hormones

The comparatively leisurely rate of scientific advance in these fields at that time is illustrated by the fact that it was not until 1895–6 that Baumann demonstrated that iodine was actually present in the thyroid, and in organic combination, and that another twenty years was to elapse before Kendall, working at the Mayo Clinic, succeeded in isolating an iodine-containing hormone from the gland on Christmas Day, 1914. He named it thyroxin (thyroxine in conventional English usage) and obtained 33 g of it from about three tons of pig thyroid. This achievement made clear the nature of the association of the element with the gland, and at the same time paved the way for the elucidation of the structure of thyroxine by Harington and Barger in England, and its synthesis by these same workers in 1927. As a result of their work it was established that it is an iodinated amino acid, tetraiodothyronine (T4; Fig. 57), formed in the thyroid gland by the iodination of tyrosine in a way which we shall consider below. The L-isomer, which can be obtained by synthesis from L-tyrosine, is the natural form of the hormone, and is three times as active as the D-isomer.

For many years it was supposed that the sole hormonal product of the gland was thyroxine, but the whole field of thyroid biochemistry has now been transformed by the use of the radioactive isotope of iodine, I^{131} (radio-iodine), and by the introduction of paper chromatography, for these techniques make possible the separation of the iodinated products of the gland in micro-quantities. A typical procedure is to inject a dose of radio-iodide into a rat and to kill the animal one or two days later. The thyroid is removed and hydrolysed (e.g. with buffered trypsin solution),

the iodinated amino acids extracted with butanol, and the extract chroma-
tographed together with non-radioactive amino acids termed carriers.
The positions of the radioactive drops on the chromatograms are visualized by exposure on X-ray film, and those of the carrier drops by a
suitable colour reaction (using, for example, diazotized sulphanilic acid,
or the ceric sulphate/arsenious acid reaction in which the iodine catalyses
the decolorization of the yellow solution). A comparison of the treated

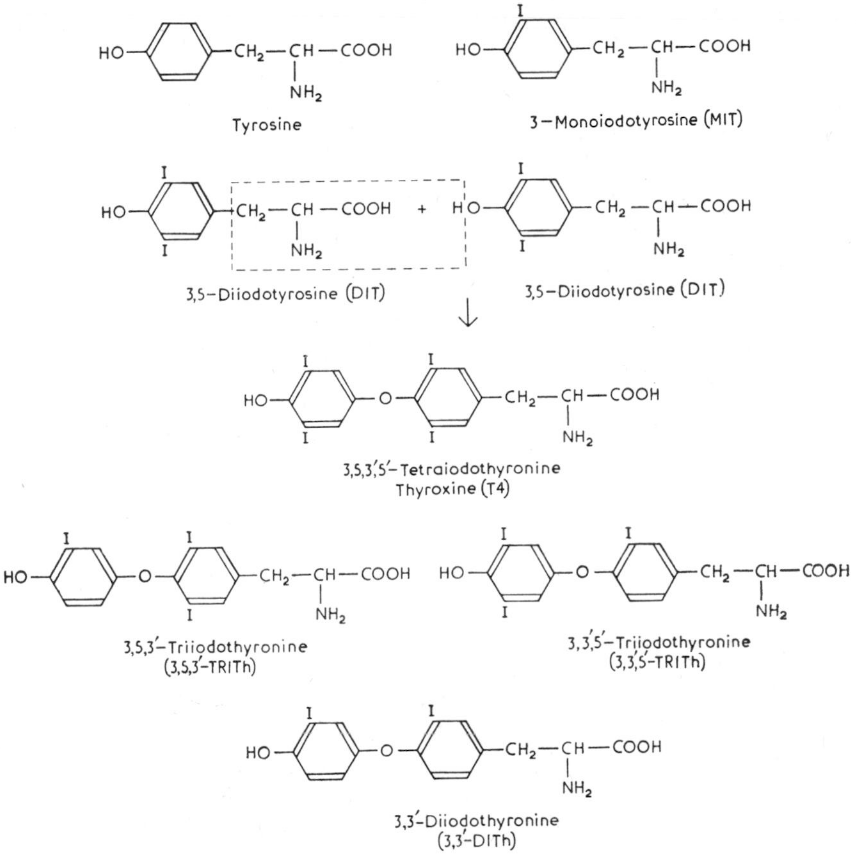

Fig. 57. Tyrosine and its iodination products.

paper with the film then makes it possible to identify which amino acids
are present in the radioactive spots, and the activity of these can be
measured with a Geiger counter.

These technical advances led in 1951 to the discovery by Gross and
Leblond of an unknown iodine-containing compound in hydrolysates of
the thyroid of the rat. Gross and Pitt-Rivers showed that this substance
was also present in the blood of human patients who had been treated

with radio-iodide, and after comparisons with various thyroxine derivatives they were able to establish that it was 3, 5, 3'-triiodothyronine
(T_3; Fig. 57; Plate VII). Its importance is shown not only by its wide
distribution (it has been found, for example, in the thyroid of man, the
fowl, the anuran tadpole, and certain fish), but even more by its high
biological activity, in some respects greater than that of thyroxine. It is
now accepted that it must be grouped with the latter as a true hormone, and
its discovery, like that of aldosterone (p. 240), is a useful reminder that we
must not expect the biosynthetic activity of endocrine glands to be confined to those substances which are most readily detectable by our laboratory procedures.

6. Thyroidal biosynthesis

Iodine is normally ingested by animals as iodide and is absorbed into
the blood stream in that form. The first step in the biosynthesis of these
hormones is the trapping of this iodide by the thyroid gland, which has
a remarkable capacity for doing this, being able to maintain a concentration gradient between itself and the serum of about 25 to 1. The action
of this so-called iodide pump can be followed by administering radio-
active iodine as iodide and measuring its uptake by the gland (p. 186),
but it is important that it should be given in very minute quantities
called tracer doses, for the administration of larger amounts will disturb the normal iodide balance and will actually depress the rate of
uptake.

Some capacity for concentrating iodide is not in itself peculiar to the
thyroid gland, for the iodide content of the notochord of the lamprey is
100 to 300 times higher than that of the plasma, and the ovaries of
lampreys, trout, and frogs are other examples of organs that accumulate
large amounts. Such iodine remains largely, if not entirely, inorganic, and
the unique properties of the thyroid depend upon the association of the
iodide pump with a highly specialized biochemical mechanism which
binds iodine to organic molecules and thus leads to the production of the
hormones. It is agreed that this is initiated by the rapid oxidation of the
iodide to iodine within the secretory cells, although the precise mechanism
by which this is accomplished is uncertain, and that thereafter the iodine
is combined with tyrosine. This, it is thought, leads first to the formation
of 3-monoiodotyrosine (MIT; Fig. 57), which is present in the gland in
only small amounts, and was not even known to exist in it until 1948,
when it was identified chromatographically in extracts of the thyroid of
the rat. It has been synthesized, but has not yet been isolated from the
gland in a crystalline form.

The next stage is the formation of 3,5-diiodotyrosine (DIT, Fig. 57),
a substance which was first isolated in 1895 from the gorgonid *Eunicella*

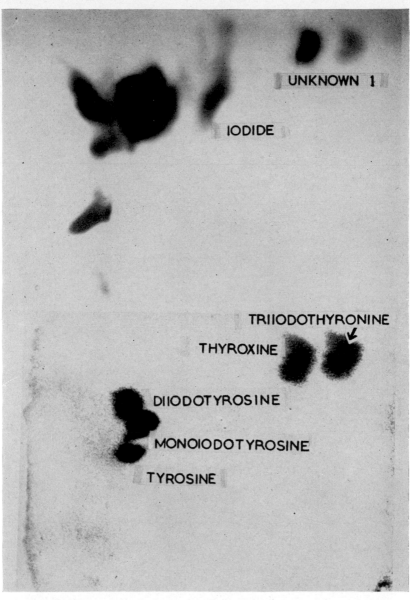

Plate VII. Identification of tri-iodothyronine as a constituent of the thyroid gland. *Above*. Autoradiogram of the paper chromatogram of the butanol extract from a tryptic hydrolysate of the thyroid glands of rats which had been given radio-active sodium iodide. The black spots indicate the positions of the radio-active components in the extract. *Below*. Photograph of the paper chromatogram showing the positions of known carrier substances added with the radio-active material. The carriers were visualized by spraying with diazotized sulphanilic acid and the correspondence between the radio-active spot *unknown* and triiodothyronine is evident. Origin is at the lower left-hand corner; the solvents were butanol-acetic acid vertically, and butanol-dioxan-ammonia horizontally. (From Gross & Pitt-Rivers, 1953. *Biochem. J.* **53**, 645–52.)

verrucosa (p. 180) and which was at that time called iodogorgonic acid. It was isolated from the thyroid by Harington and Randall in 1929 and it was then thought that it and thyroxine were the only iodinated amino acids present, a natural enough conclusion, for it represents a large proportion of the total organically bound iodine in the gland. Neither of these iodinated tyrosines are biologically active, their presence in the gland being a consequence of the stepwise biosynthetic process.

The pathway of thyroidal biosynthesis originally proposed by Harington postulated the formation of thyroxine by the coupling of two molecules of diiodotyrosine with loss of an alanine side-chain (Fig. 57), and this has been generally accepted, although, as we have seen, the subsequent identification of monoiodotyrosine in the gland naturally suggests that this substance is likely to be the first stage in the binding process. That this is indeed so is clearly shown by an analysis of the proportions of the several iodinated amino acids present in hydrolysates of thyroids at known intervals after the injection of radio-iodide. The results of such an analysis of the dogfish gland are given in Fig. 58, from which it is apparent that monoiodotyrosine appears first, that diiodotyrosine appears later and increases at its expense, and that thyroxine is then formed at the expense of diiodotyrosine; similar evidence has been obtained from mammalian material. 3, 5, 3'-triiodothyronine could theoretically be synthesized either by the coupling of one molecule of monoiodotyrosine with one of diiodotyrosine, or by a deiodination of thyroxine, but it is probable that the former is the path followed in the gland. It should be added that two other thyronines are said to be present in the glands of the rat and pig. These are 3,3',5'-triiodothyronine and 3,3'-diiodothyronine, the latter having also been detected in the rat's blood. These are only present in very small amounts, however, and since their biological activity appears to be doubtful there is at present no justification for regarding them as hormones.

When these biosynthetic reactions have been completed the hormones are firmly bound in the thyroglobulin molecule, and there is good reason for thinking that the tyrosine is thus bound during the whole of the iodination process. This does not mean that the iodide is confined to the colloid in the lumen of the follicle; in fact, autoradiographic studies have given some indication that the initial stages of binding occur in the cells, prior to the secretion of the colloid into the lumen, but the evidence on these points is not conclusive and demands, of course, a very critical and refined cytological analysis. What is certain, however, is that the hormones must be released from the thyroglobulin before they can be liberated into the blood, and this is effected by a thyroid protease which hydrolyses the thyroglobulin. This enzyme has been found in the gland of the dogfish (*Scyliorhinus canicula*) as well as in mammals, so that the mechanism is probably universal in vertebrates. It results in the liberation of all the iodinated amino acids, but it is a remarkable demonstration of the refinement of adaptation which has developed in these processes that only the thyronines are actually found in the blood and that monoiodotyrosine and diiodotyrosine do not normally leave the gland. This is because the

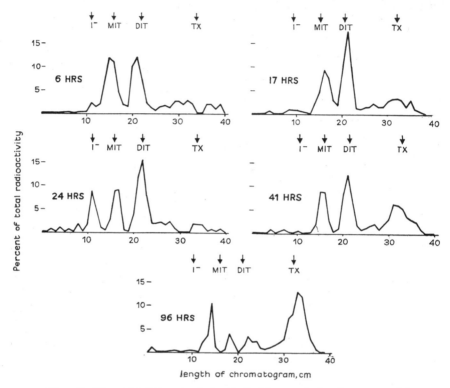

Fig. 58. Thyroidal biosynthesis in *Scyliorhinus canicula*, demonstrated by filter-paper chromatography of tryptic hydrolysates of thyroid tissue removed at the stated intervals of time after intra-peritoneal injection of radio-iodide. The figures show the distribution of radioactivity along the length of the chromatogram, the arrows indicating the position of known chemical compounds which were run in parallel with the thyroidal hydrolysates. I, iodide; MIT, monoiodotyrosine; DIT, diiodotyrosine; Tx, thyroxine. Note that at 17 and 24 hr DIT has increased at the expense of MIT, and that at 41 and 96 hr the thyroxine fraction has increased at the expense of the iodinated tyrosines. (From Gorbman *et al.*, 1952. *Endocrin.* **51**, 311–321.)

latter contains an enzyme that deiodinates the tyrosines with the release of iodine, this being presumably taken up again into the biosynthetic cycle. The action of this deiodinase, which can be demonstrated *in vitro*, seems to be restricted to the free tyrosines and it is without effect upon them when they are bound in the thyroglobulin molecule.

Although for many years there was doubt as to the true nature of the circulating thyroid hormone it has now been made clear by chromatographic studies that thryoxine is certainly present in the blood and that it usually represents the major secretory product, with small amounts of triiodothyronine accompanying it. It is also well established that these circulating hormones are bound to plasma proteins, as a result of which they cannot be separated by dialysis but come down with the protein on treatment of the plasma with protein precipitants. The hormones so precipitated, however, can readily be extracted with butanol and can thus be estimated. In this way it is possible to determine the concentration of what is called the protein-bound iodine, and this will reflect the dynamic balance between the rate of output of secretion from the gland and the rate of its use and metabolism by the body. It is important to realize that this binding of the hormones in the blood has nothing whatever to do with their binding to thyroglobulin in the gland. The latter is directly involved in the mechanism of biosynthesis; the former presumably provides a convenient means of transport, and may also be expected to set some limit on the rates at which the hormones can react with the cells. It has, in fact, been suggested that the greater biological potency of triiodothyronine results from its looser binding to the plasma protein.

The rate of metabolism of thyroidal iodine varies a good deal from species to species, even within the mammals, and this can be expressed by reference to the progressive fall in the amount of an injected dose of radioiodine which is retained in the thyroid, the time taken for this amount to fall to 50 per cent. of the maximum uptake being called the biological half-life of thyroidal iodine for that species. Some values for thyroxine are given in Fig. 59, and it will be noticed that they are smaller for the smaller animals; in other words, this hormone is used more rapidly in smaller mammals, and we can reasonably ascribe this to the part played by it in the maintenance of metabolic rate (p. 191). Owing to their relatively small surface area the smaller mammals must have a relatively higher heat production, weight for weight, in order to maintain their body temperature, and this evidently requires a more rapid use of thyroid secretion, although other factors will also influence this, violent exercise, for example, increasing the demand for thyroid hormones in rats. The liver of mammals plays an important part in the metabolism of these hormones, for thyroxine accumulates in it in large amounts and it carries out a considerable amount of de-iodination, but the final path of disposal varies; in the rat, for example, much iodine is discharged in the faeces still bound in the thyroxine molecule, whereas in man the excretion is mostly through the kidney as inorganic iodine.

7. Some evolutionary aspects of thyroidal biosynthesis

Our knowledge of the sequence of events involved in thyroidal biosynthesis is sufficient to justify some appraisal of its possible evolutionary background, and perhaps the first point to make in this connexion is that the iodination of tyrosine seems to be a very widespread reaction. Even the treatment of casein with iodine under laboratory conditions will result in the production of iodinated tyrosine compounds, including thyroxine, and this process attracted much attention during the 1939–45 War in view of the possibility which it suggested of manufacturing a cattle food which might stimulate the yield of milk and butter-fat. It is particularly the use of radioactive iodide, however, combined with chromatography

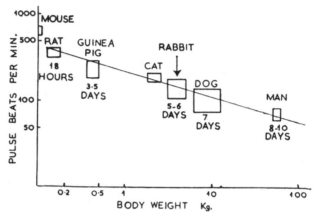

Fig. 59. The relationship between the rate of peripheral utilization of thyroxine, body weight, and metabolic rate (expressed in terms of pulse rate) on body weight in certain mammals. The values of 18 hr, 3·5 days, etc., are the average figures for the biological half-lives of thyroxine in the different species. (From Pitt-Rivers & Tata, 1959. *The Thyroid Hormones*. Pergamon.)

and auto-radiography, which has advanced our understanding of the occurrence of iodine binding in the lower animals. Auto-radiographic procedures involve the treatment of an animal with radioactive iodide, either by immersion or injection, sections being then exposed against a photographic film; subsequent development of the film reveals images indicating the sites of accumulation of the radioactive material, which can then often be analysed by paper chromatography. Using the chromatographic method, together with direct measurements of radioactivity, it has been shown that sponges, antipatharians, and the gorgonid *Eunicella verrucosa* can concentrate iodide with the formation of monoiodotyrosine and diiodotyrosine, these products being incorporated by the soft tissues into the skeletal material which they secrete. Similar results have been obtained with molluscs (Fig. 60), but earlier reports that thyroxine is synthesized in these animals and in the cockroach have been questioned, although both this substance and triiodothyronine are thought to be present in trace amounts in *Eunicella*.

It seems that the iodination process in these invertebrates must be fundamentally similar to that occurring in the thyroid gland, and must involve the reaction of iodine with tyrosine in a protein molecule, although it is not clear whether it is mediated by enzymes or whether it is a result of slow chemical combination. The proteins concerned are thought to be the skeletal scleroproteins, a type of substance for which there is no very clear-cut definition, although in general the term is applied to materials

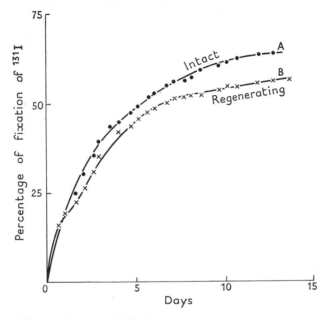

Fig. 60. Fixation of I^{131} from the surrounding sea water by groups of nine mussels (*Mytilus galloprovincialis*), measured by direct counts of radioactivity. *A*, intact animals; *B*, animals with byssus regeneration; prior section of the byssus has no significant effect upon the rate of uptake. Abscissae: time in days. Ordinates: % I^{131} fixed.

(From Roche *et al.* (1960). *C.R. Soc. Biol.* Paris. **154**, 2201.)

that are resistant to the action of proteolytic enzymes. They vary in their composition, and it has been noted that in the gorgonids the degree of iodination which they show is proportional to their tyrosine content. The extent to which thyroxine is formed is thought to be dependent upon their molecular structure and, in particular, upon the facility which this offers for the polymerization of the iodinated tyrosine residues. Since scleroproteins are relatively inert and insoluble, it has been thought that such thyroxine and triiodothyronine to which they give rise could not readily be made available to the animal concerned, and that they should be regarded as chance by-products of the constitution of their skeletal material, and of no biological value. However this may be, it seems likely that iodinated amino acids were becoming available before either the vertebrates or their thyroid gland had appeared, and it is therefore of interest to inquire how this circumstance may have influenced the evolution of that organ.

Vertebrate animals are associated in the Phylum Chordata with certain marine forms, collectively known as the Protochordata, which, while lacking a vertebral column, yet have sufficient features in common with vertebrates to justify the belief that they represent a stage of evolution ancestral to the latter. Filter-feeding is a characteristic feature of these protochordates, and in connexion with this the Tunicata and amphioxus possess a spacious pharynx, along the floor of which runs a mucus-secreting groove, the endostyle. It is generally accepted that this organ is homologous with the endostyle of the ammocoete larva of the lamprey, and since this organ gives rise to the thyroid gland at metamorphosis, it follows that during the early evolution of the vertebrates an externally secreting alimentary organ has become transformed into an endocrine gland. Thus it becomes of importance to determine at what stage of that evolution the mechanism of thyroidal biosynthesis was first established.

The endostyles of amphioxus and of the tunicates function in essentially identical ways and closely resemble each other in structure, the only real point of difference in their organization, and it is a minor one, being that there are two pairs of glandular tracts in the former and three pairs in the latter. The resemblance in the ammocoete, however, is less close, for at this stage of evolution the feeding process has come to depend upon muscular rather than ciliary movement, and the endostyle itself has been transformed from an open groove into a sac with only a very narrow opening into the pharynx. There is still, however, a striking histological resemblance between this endostyle (Fig. 61) and that of the protochordates, for all have glandular tracts formed of elongated cells which, in transverse section, are arranged in an unusual fan-shaped pattern, their secretion being discharged through a narrow plug-like structure formed by the closely approximated tips of the cells.

At the metamorphosis of the ammocoete these tracts disappear and play no part in building the thyroid. This arises by a transformation of certain areas of the columnar or squamous epithelium lining the endostylar cavity, an epithelium which for descriptive purposes can be differentiated into several regions, each characterized by a distinctive type of cell (Fig. 61). The type 4 region has been thought to make a major contribution to the thyroid of the adult, but it is now well established that all parts of the endostylar epithelium, with the significant exception of the glandular tracts (type 1), are capable of effecting the organic binding

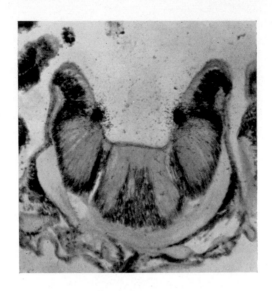

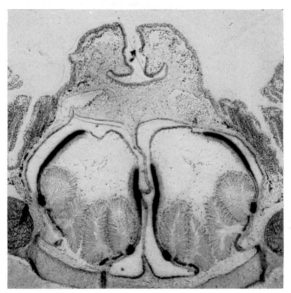

Plate VIII. *Above*. Autoradiogram of a transverse section through the endostyle of an amphioxus which had been immersed in sea-water containing radio-active iodide. Protein-bound I^{131} is visible as two black areas. Original. (× 260.) *Below*. Autoradiogram of a transverse section through the anterior region of the endostyle of an ammocoete larva which had received an intra-peritoneal injection of radio-active iodide. Note the absence of protein-bound I^{131} from the glandular tracts (cf. Fig. 61, p. 183). (× 63.)

(From Clements-Merlini, 1960. *J. Morph.* **103,** 337–56.)

of iodine in the larva, types 3, 2c, and parts of the type 5 region being the most active in this respect (Plate VIII). Moreover, the use of paper chromatography has established that this binding is associated with thyroidal biosynthesis, for extracts of the endostyle have been found to

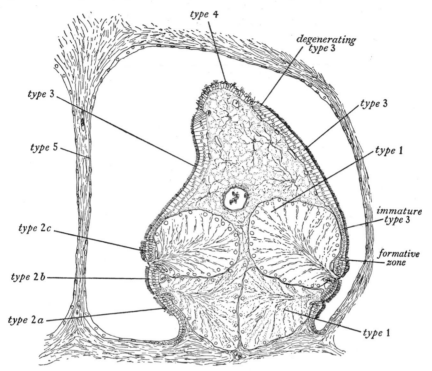

Fig. 61. Transverse section of the right half of the endostyle of an ammo-coete larva anterior to its opening into the pharynx. The different types of epithelium are indicated, the glandular tracts (two pairs) constituting type 1. Compare with Plate VIII.
(From Barrington & Franchi, 1956. *Quart. J. micr. Sci.* **97**, 393–409.)

contain monoiodotyrosine, diiodotyrosine, thyroxine, and triiodothyro-nine.

A very similar situation exists in amphioxus and the ascidians (such as *Ciona*), for in these also it has been shown that iodine-binding occurs in the endostyle (Fig. 62; Plate VIII). Here again the glandular tracts make little if any contribution, the main and perhaps the only site of the binding being a localized area of epithelium lying immediately above the tracts in a position which, allowing for the greater simplicity of the endostylar structure in these animals, is comparable with the site of iodination in the ammocoete. Although the significance of this situation is not yet fully understood, it is known that monoiodotyrosine, diiodotyrosine, triiodothyronine, and thyroxine are present in extracts of the whole body of amphioxus. It is also believed that some at least of these are present in ascidians, and the accumulation of such evidence is providing increasing support for the view that the essential features of thyroidal biosynthesis were already established at the pre-vertebrate stage of chordate evolution.

It has been suggested that the association of iodine-binding with a sharply delimited and presumably specialized region of the endostyle in protochordates implies that it is a biochemically purposive process rather than a product of chance iodination, and this carries the further implica-

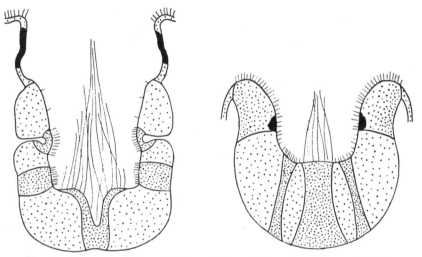

Fig. 62. Diagrams of the endostyles of *Ciona* (left) and amphioxus (right) to show the relationships of the iodination centres to the other regions of the organs. In both animals these centres (black) lie near the lip of the endostyle and immediately above the glandular tracts (light stippling), three pairs in *Ciona* and two pairs in amphioxus. Compare with Plate VIII.
(From Barrington, 1959. *Comparative Endocrinology*, ed. Gorbman. Wiley.)

tion that iodination may already be fulfilling some essential function in these animals. A relevant consideration here is that the organic binding of iodine takes place also in the layer of protein that forms a protective covering to the tunic of ascidians, a situation essentially similar to that in the various invertebrates to which we have already referred. This has led to the speculation that iodine-binding in this group might have begun as a by-product of the structure of the tunic, that the products might then have been drawn into use, either by transport through the blood vessels of the tunic or perhaps by the ingestion and assimilation of iodinated material which was fragmented from the surface, and that this might have led to the evolution of a more specialized iodination mechanism in the endostyle.

The relationship of vertebrates to ascidians is obscure, although the view that they are derived from the ascidian larva by neoteny has much to commend it. What seems certain, however, is that thyroidal biosynthesis evolved under marine conditions, in circumstances in which iodine was relatively plentiful. The site of origin of the earliest vertebrates is a matter of some controversy, but, as we have seen (p. 92), they probably appeared first in the sea, although they early moved into fresh water. Here iodine would have been much scarcer, and this scarcity may be reflected in the transformation of the endostyle into an endocrine organ with unique arrangements for storing its secretion. We can see, too, that the evolution of the thyroid from a digestive gland in this way accounts for the fact that its hormones can still be administered orally and absorbed through the digestive epithelium.

8. The measurement of thyroid activity

All the evidence suggests that the course of thyroidal biosynthesis is qualitatively similar throughout the vertebrates from the ammocoete larva upwards, but there are great variations in the speed and in the maximal values of I^{131} uptake. For example, uptake is very low in lampreys, and has been said not to exceed 0·53 per cent. of an injected dose at 13–15°C, while in teleosts it ranges from 10 per cent. in *Fundulus majalis* at 22°C to less than 1 per cent. in *Cyprinus carpio*. Low uptake values, however, do not necessarily indicate an inactive gland; thus in the lamprey the actual turnover of iodine is very rapid, the maximal uptake level being reached in 6 hours, by which time labelled hormone is identifiable in the blood. Great importance therefore attaches in comparative studies to the measurement of the activity of the thyroid gland, which may be thought of as the rate at which it is releasing its hormones into the circulation. For this purpose several types of procedure are available, and each of these has its value provided that it is carefully related to the known course of biosynthesis in the gland and that due attention is given to its limitations and to the particular sources of error that may be associated with it.

(a) Histological methods

A much favoured method has been the measurement of the heights of the secretory cells, it being assumed that increased height is indicative of greater secretory activity. This assumption has some justification inasmuch as greater cell height is certainly associated with the greater activity which results from stimulation of the gland by thyrotropin (p. 202), but the method needs to be handled with care, for there is much variation amongst the cells and it is necessary to avoid any subjective element in selecting those which are to be measured. Another and more fundamental difficulty is our ignorance of the precise mode of functioning of the thyroid cells, which means that we cannot feel certain that cell height is always related in a simple way to cell activity, while the method is relatively insensitive, so that minor, but possibly important, fluctuations in activity are likely to pass unnoticed. These difficulties are said to be to some extent reduced in a variant of this method, in which account is taken of the amount of colloid present by expressing the activity of the gland as a percentage ratio of epithelial area to colloid area.

(b) Measurement of protein-bound iodine content

It is possible to carry out direct chemical estimations of the protein-bound iodine content of the gland, as has been done by Matty for the parrot-fish, *Scarus guacamaia*, in which animal he has revealed a pronounced sex difference, the gland being larger in the female and containing more protein-bound iodine per unit of body weight. The content also increases in both sexes with the age of the fish, but unfortunately the significance of these data is difficult to judge since, as Matty points out, it is impossible to decide whether an increased content is indicative of diminished demand and increased storage, or of increased demand and increased production.

Some authors have attached importance to estimations of the protein-bound iodine content of the plasma as an index of thyroidal activity, for clinical studies are said to show a good correlation between the two, a high plasma content being associated with a hyperthyroid state and *vice versa*. This correlation remains to be established in the lower vertebrates, however, and in *Scarus* the plasma values, while highly variable, were found to be unrelated to the protein-bound iodine content of the gland, showing, for example, no change with increasing age.

(c) Measurement of the radio-iodine turnover of the gland

The activity of the thyroid will, in general, be reflected in its iodine turnover, and a number of procedures have been used for measuring this, the introduction of radio-iodine making it possible to work with very small quantities of material. Such methods are probably the most useful and reliable of all.

One approach is to inject a standard dose of radio-iodide into a series of animals and then to measure the radioactivity of aliquots of their thyroids by sacrificing individuals at predetermined intervals. This may involve the use of a large number of specimens, and an alternative possibility is to make a series of readings on single individuals by external application of a Geiger counter to the thyroid region (Fig. 63). With such *in vivo* counting it is necessary to pay attention to various sources of error such as the correct and consistent placing of the counter (technically known as the geometry of the apparatus), variations in the exact location of the gland, and (in teleosts, for example) the distribution of heterotopic thyroid tissue. It must be remembered, too, that in the first few hours

after an injection a considerable proportion of the dose will still be in the
body fluids, and this will introduce a further source of error. Thus in the
rabbit (Fig. 64) more than 30 per cent. of the total count in the thyroid
region may be due to this source at four hours, although this will have
fallen to less than 5 per cent. after twenty-four hours, at which time the

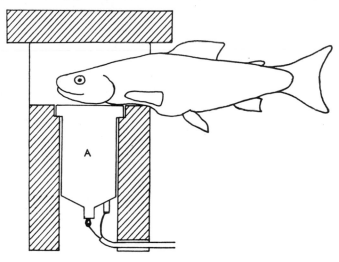

Fig. 63. Diagram to show the procedure for *in vivo* counting
of the thyroidal radioactivity of a teleost fish. The animal is anaesthetized with urethane and placed with its thyroid area over a lead-
shielded end-window type Geiger-Muller tube (*A*).
(From Swift, 1955. *J. exp. Biol.* **32**, 751–64.)

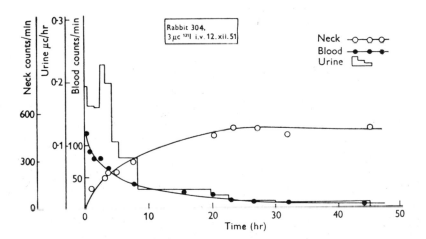

Fig. 64. The distribution of I^{131} in the thyroid region, blood, and urine of
a rabbit following the intravenous injection of 3 μc of I^{131} at o hours.
(From Brown-Grant *et al.*, 1954. *J. Physiol.* **126**, 1–28.)

radio-iodine content of this animal's thyroid may be expected to have reached a maximum. This is also the case in the trout, where there is a high background count from the body during the first few days after an injection into the body cavity. This count drops rapidly, however, falling

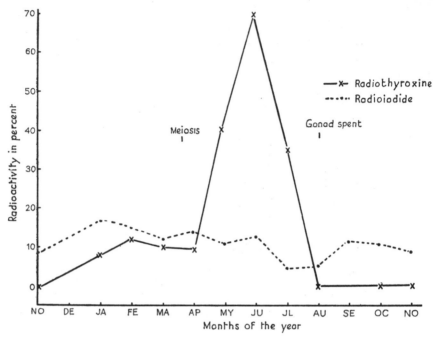

Fig. 65. Radio-iodide uptake and radio-thyroxine production in *Fundulus heteroclitus* during eleven months of the year.
(From Berg *et al.*, 1959. *Comparative Endocrinology*, ed. Gorbman. Wiley.)

by some 50 per cent. during the first two and a half days, so that it is particularly during this early phase that it is important to make corrections for background count when measuring thyroidal activity.

Data obtained in these ways need to be interpreted with caution. As we have remarked, the rate of uptake of iodide is not necessarily a measure of the rate at which the products of biosynthesis are released; this is well seen in a study of *Fundulus heteroclitus* (Fig. 65), in which animal the production of radio-thyroxine was found to reach a sharp peak in June which was not reflected at all in the radio-iodide uptake measurements. Another difficulty is that the level of radio-iodine in the gland at any one time is a resultant of uptake and of secretion, so that in effect two different phases of thyroidal metabolism are being measured at the same moment. Further, the amount of iodide trapped by the thyroid will depend upon the amount brought to it in the body fluids, and this will be influenced by factors determining the rates of metabolic and excretory processes, so that it is not surprising to find that in practice such uptake measurements show a good deal of variation both from animal to animal and even in the same animal at different times. This latter difficulty can, however, be dealt with by relating the radio-iodide uptake during a given period of time to the mean concentration of iodide in blood samples taken during the

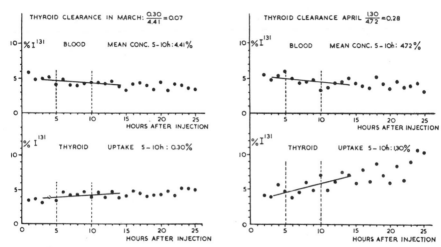

Fig. 66. Uptake of radio-iodine by the thyroid gland, and levels of I^{131} in the blood of coho parr caught in March and at the beginning of April shortly before the onset of migration. Thyroid clearance was determined between 5 and 10 hours after injection of the tracer dose.
(From Baggerman, 1960. *J. Fish. Res. Bd. Canada.* **17**, 295–322.)

same period, this giving a measure of what is called the thyroidal iodine clearance. In the parr of the coho salmon (*Oncorhynchus kisutch*) the curves for thyroid uptake and for disappearance of isotope from the blood follow straight lines during the period extending from 5 to 10 hours after injection, and the thyroidal iodine clearance can be readily calculated from them. The data illustrated (Fig. 66) show that the clearance is higher in April than in March and it is assumed that the gland is more active in the former month, although this cannot be proved from such data.

Another approach to the problem, and one which has been used with success in both mammals and fish, is to determine the rate at which iodine is released from the gland, the procedure being to inject a dose of radio-iodide and then to start regular *in vivo* counts after a suitable interval. Ideally, this would be selected so that the curve of uptake would have reached its peak while the radio-iodine content of the body fluids would have fallen to a negligible value. We have seen that in the rabbit this interval is reached within twenty-four hours, and it has been shown that from this point onwards the radio-iodine content of the thyroid falls exponentially, so that semi-logarithmic plotting of the counts against time gives a straight line (Fig. 71). The slope of this line, or its regression coefficient, can then be taken as a very reliable index of thyroid secretory activity, for the loss of radio-iodine from the gland is a consequence of the loss of labelled hormone.

VIII. THE ENDOCRINE GLANDS OF THE PHARYNX (CONTINUED)

1. Some metabolic effects of thyroid hormones

THE establishment of the hormonal status of the thyronines, together with the analysis of their functions in mammals, has been profoundly influenced by the fundamental demonstration by Magnus-Levy in 1895 that the oxygen consumption was depressed in human beings suffering from myxoedema and elevated in those suffering from Grave's disease, the latter condition being associated with an excessive output of thyroid secretion. This relationship is characteristic of mammals in general, in that the hypothyroid condition is marked by a low basal metabolic rate and the hyperthyroid one by a high rate, and it is often referred to as illustrating a calorigenic action of the thyroid hormones. A consequence of it is that injections of thyroid hormones into human patients or laboratory mammals will produce a marked elevation of the metabolic rate, reflected in a rise in oxygen consumption (Fig. 67) amounting to as much as 60 per cent. in rats and mice, a fall in liver glycogen and a rise in blood sugar being associated with this (p. 62).

It is a peculiar characteristic of these hormones, however, and one which has promoted much speculation, that after an injection there is a marked interval, ranging from several hours to as much as two days (Fig. 67), before this metabolic effect is first manifested. It has been thought that this might be a consequence of the hormones having to undergo some transformation into a more active derivative before they are able to react with their target organs, and at one time, when it became apparent that the latent period of triiodothyronine was much shorter than that of thyroxine, there was speculation as to the possibility of the former being the final active state of the thyroid secretion, with thyroxine having to undergo de-iodinization before it was able to function. There is, in fact, no reason to suppose this to be correct, and the cause of the latent period remains obscure. An important consequence of it is, however, that whereas adrenaline, which also stimulates oxygen consumption (p. 221), will produce its effect not only on the intact body but also on excised tissues, thyroxine will not usually do this. As a result, the effect of thyroid hormones upon the oxygen consumption of tissues can only be demonstrated if these are removed from animals that have previously been treated with the hormones; tissues from such animals will have an oxygen consumption higher than that of identical tissues from untreated control animals, but no response will be obtained if the hormones are added to tissues after they have been removed from untreated animals.

Related to this calorigenic effect is the involvement of the thyroid gland in the regulation of body temperature in mammals. Myxoedematous patients often complain of feeling cold, and it is known that thyroidectomy lowers the resistance of experimental mammals to low temperatures; rats, for example, show a smaller degree of increase in basal metabolic rate under these conditions than do unoperated control animals. Another

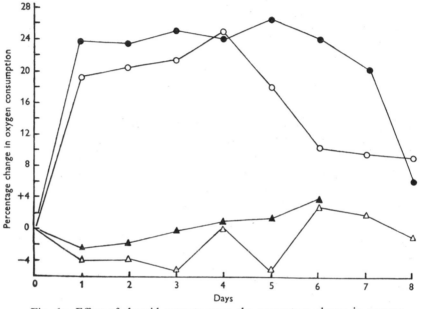

Fig. 67. Effect of thyroid extracts upon the percentage charge in oxygen consumption of rats. △, normal controls; ▲, injected with 2·0 ml 0·9 per cent. NaCl; ●, injected with 100 mg mammalian thyroid powder; O, injected with 95 mg dogfish (*Scyliorhinus canicula*) powder.
(From Matty, 1954. *J. mar. biol. Ass. U.K.* **33**, 689–97.)

aspect of this is seen in Fig. 71, which shows the increase in the rate of output of the thyroid gland provoked by removal of a rabbit from its constant temperature room to a lower temperature. The thyroid, however is only one of the factors involved in chemical thermo-regulation; the sympathetico-chromaffin system (p. 227) also has an important part to play, for exposure of mammals to low temperature brings about an increased output of catechol hormones, this resulting in vaso-constriction, cardiac acceleration, a rise in blood-sugar level, and an increase in the metabolic rate. It has, in fact, been argued that thyroid hormones are not so much concerned with a direct action on metabolism during adaptation to cold as with a potentiation or reinforcement of the action of the secretion of the adrenal medulla, and we shall see that a somewhat similar view has been advanced with regard to the importance of the thyroid gland in supporting the responses of lower vertebrates to crises in their life-histories.

Important though the so-called calorigenic action is in mammals, it is well not to be over-impressed by it in considering the function of the thyroid hormones in the lower vertebrates, but rather to remember that the homoiothermous forms are highly specialized in their thermo-regulatory mechanisms and in the high basal metabolic rate that goes with them. The prominence of this aspect of thyroid function may well be a correlated specialization, and this could be one reason why it has been found difficult to establish any influence of the thyroid upon oxygen consumption in fish. Negative results have been obtained in studies of the elasmobranch *Scyliorhinus canicula*, and the teleost *Scarus guacamaia*; thyroidectomy has been carried out on both of these with no detectable effect upon oxygen uptake, despite the fact that extracts of the elasmobranch thyroid will increase the oxygen consumption of rats (Fig. 67). There are, however, a number of difficulties in such experiments, amongst which may be mentioned the low metabolic rate of fish, their great individual variability, particularly under the confined conditions of laboratory studies, and the possibility of the existence of thyroid tissue in abnormal sites (p. 169). Moreover, a study of the effects of administering thyroid powder to the guppy, *Lebistes reticulatus*, has given evidence of a 15 per cent. increase in oxygen consumption in the treated fish as compared with the controls, and it would therefore be unwise to allow the more numerous negative results to close the door upon further investigations of this problem. It should be noted, too, that removal of the thyroid gland from the newt *Taricha* (*Triturus*) *torosa* has been found to result in a lowering of its oxygen consumption, while implantation of extra thyroid glands into otherwise intact animals produced an increase.

In any case, it may be that the thyroid hormones do influence the oxygen consumption of fish, but only when internal or external factors are making increased metabolic demands upon the animals. Such a possibility is certainly suggested by the fact that increased oxygen consumption at the smolt transformation of the salmon (p. 198) is accompanied by increased thyroidal activity, indicated both in the histological appearance of the gland and in the increased speed of turnover of radioactive iodine. At the opposite extreme Leloup has shown that there is a marked fall in thyroidal activity in the African lung-fish, *Protopterus*, during its summer aestivation. At this time the I^{131} uptake is of the order of 1–2 per cent., whereas in active animals at the same temperature and under fasting conditions this value rises to as high a level as 86 per cent., the significance of this from the present point of view being that oxygen

854108   o

consumption is also lowered during aestivation. Even more suggestive, however, is Hickman's demonstration that the thyroidal activity in the starry flounder, *Platichthys stellatus*, as measured by thyroidal clearance, is much greater when the animal is in salt water than when it is in fresh (Table 3). The significant feature here is that the standard metabolic

TABLE 3

Activity of thyroid gland of the starry flounder, Platichthys stellatus, *expressed as thyroid clearance of radio-iodine from the blood at stated intervals after the injection of a standard tracer dose of I^{131} into the body cavity. The clearance rates are expressed as the volume of blood (as percentage of body weight) cleared of radio-iodine by the thyroid per hour. Note that thyroids of salt-water animals are more active than those of fresh-water ones.* (From Hickman, 1959. *Can. J. Zool.* **37**, 997–1060).

Hours after injection	Mean blood concentration of I^{131} (% of dose per gm of blood × body weight/100)	Thyroid uptake (% of dose accumulated by whole gland)	Clearance
	Fresh-water flounder		
3–4	1·500	0·02	0·0133
4–5	1·485	0·02	0·0135
5–6	1·470	0·02	0·0136
	Salt-water flounder		
2–3	1·6	0·27	0·169
3–4	1·38	0·28	0·202
4–5	1·32	0·29	0·22

rate, as indicated by the oxygen consumption, is also greater in salt water, so that we have a direct correlation between this and the activity of the thyroid gland under circumstances in which metabolic demands are presumably being determined by the osmo-regulatory mechanism. This could mean that the thyroid hormones were merely supporting the latter indirectly, perhaps by facilitating some generalized aspect of cell metabolism, but the possibility that they have some direct relationship with osmo-regulation is certainly not excluded.

An example suggestive of this is provided by the three-spined stickleback, *Gasterosteus aculeatus*, which may winter in the sea and undergo a pre-spawning migration into fresh water during the early months of the year, with a reverse post-spawning migration occurring later in the year and lasting until November. According to Baggerman these migrations are associated with changes in salinity preference, which are determined not by the gonads but by the thyroid gland; removal of the gonads does not eliminate the seasonal change in preference, although it may delay its onset, but immersion of the animals in thyroxine can evoke a fresh-water preference within a few days in fish that were initially showing a preference for salt water. It is typical of the difficulties encountered in attempting to generalize from such data that in *Gasterosteus* thyroxine treatment is associated with the development of a fresh-water preference whereas in the flounder, as we have just seen, it is the salt-water phase that is marked by increased thyroid activity. The situation is, in any case, complicated by the fact that the adrenocorticosteroids (p. 236) are certainly involved in water and salt-electrolyte metabolism in the higher vertebrates, and are probably similarly involved in fish, so that it would be a mistake to suppose that the thyroid hormones are likely to be acting in isolation.

Amongst other effects of the thyroid in mammals may be mentioned its influence upon growth and upon the metabolism of protein, fat, and carbohydrates (p. 62). It seems to be well established that thyroid hormones exert a katabolic effect upon protein metabolism, but there is also evidence that they may have an anabolic one, particularly when they are administered to hypothyroid children or to thyroidectomized animals. The supposed influence of these hormones upon growth is often referred to as their maturation effect, although it should be borne in mind that growth of the body as a whole, particularly under experimental conditions, need not necessarily proceed at the same rate as the differentiation and maturation of its constituent parts. One expression of these effects is probably seen in the responses of the skin of vertebrates, for thyroxine has been reported to cause thickening of the epidermis in animals as widely separated as chick embryos and young individuals of *Salmo salar*. Thyroid activity in *Lacerta agilis* is said to fluctuate in accordance with the moulting cycle, and removal of the gland has been found to eliminate moulting in this animal and to prolong the intermoult period in the gecko, *Hemidactylus brookei*. Curiously enough, however, thyroidectomy increases the rate of moulting in snakes, while thyroid treatment of pythons is said to reduce it.

Protein metabolism is, of course, directly bound up with growth, if we accept that this must involve the production of new tissue, and it seems clear that thyroid medication will restore a considerable degree of this in congenital dwarf cretins. It is well known, too, that thyroidectomy will result in impaired growth in mammals and birds, although the interpretation of this is complicated by the metabolic consequences of the withdrawal of thyroid hormones. Moreover, the growth-promoting action of the latter cannot be dissociated from the action of the pituitary growth hormone itself, and it may well be that the activities of these hormones are closely interrelated. It has been suggested, for example, that the thyroid secretion may interact synergistically with growth hormone, or that it may exert some priming or supporting effect which facilitates the action of the latter.

No doubt the balance between the anabolic and katabolic effects of thyroid treatment must be affected by the size of the administered dose, so that some of the results obtained may in any case be of pharmacological rather than physiological significance, and this is probably a major factor in the contradictory results reported from fish. Some investigators of this group have made use of the fact that the injection of radio-iodide in suitably high dosages will be followed by its accumulation in the gland to an extent that will destroy the secretory tissue, while other tissues may be expected to remain largely unaffected by the radioactive material. Young individuals of *Salmo salar* have been reported to survive for up to six months after the thyroid gland has been destroyed in this way, and their growth in weight is said to have remained unaffected. On the other hand, the immersion of *Salmo gairdnerii* in thyroxine solutions has been found to result in a substantially increased growth rate, both weight and length being influenced. One of the most clear-cut results in this field is the silvering that occurs in salmonids undergoing thyroxine treatment. This is due to increased guanine deposition, and clearly suggests that the hormone is influencing nitrogen metabolism in some way, but unfortunately, while it is often assumed that guanine is a product of the metabolism of nucleic acids, the precise source of this material remains obscure.

2. The thyroid hormones and vertebrate life-cycles

The best-known example of the effect of the thyroid gland upon growth and differentiation is its influence upon the metamorphosis of amphibians, which, as is very well known, will not take place in animals that have been thyroidectomized. The first indication of this relationship was the observation, announced by Gudernatsch in 1912, that administration of thyroid substance to frog tadpoles would bring about precocious metamorphosis, and Witschi has recalled the profound impression which this now familiar observation made at that time. The reason was that the development of the concept of internal secretion was still in its early days, and it had been assumed that the main effects of endocrine glands were physiological, influencing, for example, blood pressure and metabolism. This new discovery, however, showed that their effects could also be exerted in an integrated manner upon the growth and differentiation of all parts of the animal body. The general course of amphibian metamorphosis is too well documented to need discussion here, but we may note that studies with radio-iodide have shown that both thyroxine and triiodothyronine are present in the thyroid gland of tadpoles. They have shown, too, that in tadpoles of *Xenopus*, during the stage known as prometamorphosis (from the fourth to the sixth week of larval life), there is a considerable uptake and storage of radio-iodine by the gland, and that reduction in the amount of colloid which characterizes the metamorphic climax is accompanied by a decrease in the amount of stored iodine retained in the gland. These and other data confirm the view, previously based only upon consideration of the histological appearance of the gland, that there is an increased release of thyroid hormones at the climax; it will be noted, however, that the gland has also been active in the earlier stages, and it is believed to influence development well in advance of the actual climax.

It is disputed whether metamorphosis is accompanied by any significant change in the oxygen consumption of the entire animal, and because of this, and because of the clear-cut nature of the metamorphic response, some writers have drawn a sharp distinction between what we have earlier referred to as the calorigenic and the maturation effects. With our present ignorance as to the mode of action of the hormones, however, there is no real basis for this. What one may reasonably suppose is that where hormones are identical in chemical constitution throughout the vertebrates, as they seem to be in this case, adaptive responses of tissues will be built up by the establishment of coded instructions in the reacting cells, and not the least interesting aspect of metamorphosis is that it provides very clear examples of such differentiation.

Thus it is well known that anurans and urodeles differ in their responses to hormonal action, and a good illustration is given by the corneal reflex, a reaction in which the bulb of the eye is withdrawn, with raising of the nictitating membrane, when the cornea is touched. This reflex is dependent for its full development in frogs upon the presence of an adequate concentration of thyroid hormones, whereas in urodele larvae it will appear in animals in which the development of the thyroid has been arrested by adenohypophysectomy (p. 202). The neural centre for this reflex is situated in the medulla, and Kollross has clearly shown the direct action of thyroxine upon it in anurans. The addition of this substance to the water in which frog tadpoles are being reared results in the development of the reflex being accelerated rather less than that of the body as a whole. If, however, the hormone is applied locally to the medulla, by the implantation of an agar pellet that has been soaked in thyroxine, the opposite result is obtained, the development of the reflex being accelerated in relation to the metamorphosis of the body as a consequence of the high concentration of hormone to which the centre is now subjected.

Another striking example of such differential responses is provided by the fate of Mauthner's cells, giant cells lying one on either side of the hind-brain, for they regress at metamorphosis while the neighbouring cells undergo further development. It has been shown that the implantation of thyroid tissue into this region, with the consequent exposure of the neural tissue to the direct action of thyroid hormones, rapidly evokes enlargement and increased mitotic activity in the adjacent cells of the hind-brain with the exception of this particular cell, which reacts in exactly the opposite manner by undergoing regression.

Other examples of the adaptive relationships which exist between cells and hormones are revealed in the characteristics of those urodeles which show a tendency to revert to a more completely aquatic life. This situation involves a retention of larval characteristics in the adult, the familiar condition of neoteny, and it is known to result in part from the tissues having become insensitive to thyroid hormones, as is shown by the inability of *Necturus*, for example, to give any significant sign of metamorphosis in response to thyroid treatment. This is not the only factor, however, for radio-iodide studies by Gorbman have shown that the thyroid of this animal is also very inactive; he found that the uptake of iodide is remarkably low, amounting to only 1·5 per cent. of an injected dose, and that no thyroxine was produced during the eight days following injection.

Part of the great interest of the metamorphic role of the thyroid hormones in the Amphibia lies in the possibility that they may be similarly drawn upon in comparable crises in the life-histories of other vertebrates. Thus metamorphosis occurs also in certain teleost fish, a well-known example being the transformation of the freshwater parr into the migratory smolt during the life-history of the salmon. This involves, in addition to the silvering produced by the deposition of guanine (p. 196), a number of physiological changes which seem, in general, to be correlated with the requirements of the marine life which the smolt will undertake. It develops an increased resistance to saline conditions, for example, and the fact that this is accompanied by an increase in metabolic rate and by clear signs of hyperactivity of the thyroid, as shown by its histological appearance, has been thought to imply an involvement of the thyroid hormones in the metamorphosis, although the nature of their action awaits further analysis. The thyroid is said to show similar signs of hyperactivity during the relatively slight metamorphosis of the herring and during the much more drastic metamorphosis of the flounder, of the leptocephalus larva into the glass eel, and of the yellow eel into the silver eel, while thyroid treatment of the larva of the mud-skipper, *Periophthalmus*, is said to induce premature assumption of the semi-terrestrial life of the adult. It may be of significance here that this last fish has been found to have a particularly active thyroid, as measured by radio-iodide uptake.

Despite this evidence for the involvement of the thyroid hormones in the metamorphic changes of teleost fish, it would be unwise to look for too close a parallel with the situation in Amphibia. Where a problem is solved independently in two different groups, as it must have been in these, we should expect to find that the two solutions are different in detail, even though they may make use of similar principles, for natural selection will operate upon those physiological mechanisms which happen to be already characteristic of the groups concerned. This is well illustrated in the metamorphosis of the ammocoete larva of the lamprey, for it has so far proved impossible to influence this by thyroid treatment. Such a result is not surprising, for the Cyclostomata are widely separated from both teleosts and amphibians, and the thyroid is represented in the larva by the endostyle (p. 182), which itself undergoes reorganization at metamorphosis. Adrenocortical tissue is present, however, and Sterba believes that this may be a causative agent in the onset of metamorphosis, for it increases

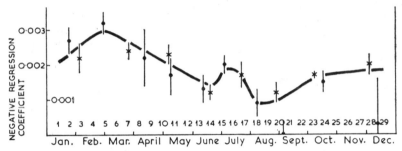

Fig. 68. Seasonal variation in the rate of loss of radio-iodine from the thyroid gland of yearling brown trout (*Salmo trutta*). Data from Swift (*J. exp. Biol.* **36.**) (From Swift, 1960. *Symp. Zool. Soc. Lond.* **2**, 17–27.)

greatly in amount in the late larva, and it is claimed that injections of corticotropin (p. 250) will induce a certain degree of precocious change.

Other suggestions as to the function of the thyroid in these lower vertebrates have been drawn from the results of studies of the activity of the gland, based upon one or other of the methods already mentioned. These have given strong indications of seasonal fluctuations, examples being shown in Figs. 68 and 69, and it has been suggested that they may be correlated with the reproductive cycle, a high level of thyroid activity in the minnow (*Phoxinus*), for example, occurring during the period preceding spawning. Associations of this sort are not necessarily good evidence for causal relationships, however, and the example of the cod (*Gadus callarias*) illustrates the need for caution. Populations of this fish feeding near Spitzbergen migrate in late September to spawning grounds off the north Norwegian coast, and their thyroids show signs of hyperactivity at this time (Fig. 69). This might easily be held to imply a correlation between the thyroid gland and reproduction, were it not that immature fish make a similar run and also possess hyperactive thyroids, a fact which suggests that the gland may be involved in some way in the migratory movements (p. 143).

However, there are undeniably grounds for assuming some participation of the gland in the reproductive cycle, for, to mention only a few examples,

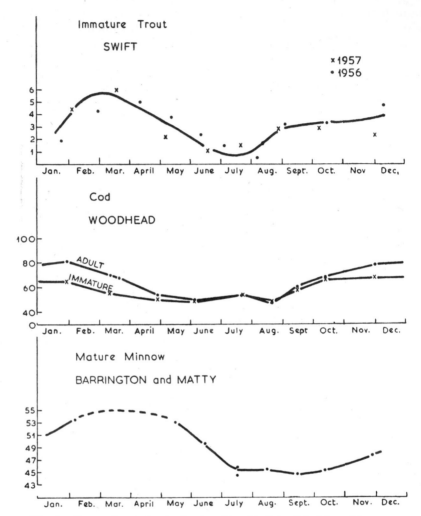

Fig. 69. Seasonal variation in the thyroid epithelial cell heights of immature (yearling) brown trout (*Salmo trutta*), mature and immature cod (*Gadus callarias*), and mature minnows (*Phoxinus phoxinus*). Data from Swift (*J. exp. Biol.* **36**), Woodhead (*J. mar. biol. Assoc. U.K.* **38**), and Barrington & Matty (*Proc. Zool. Soc. Lond.* **124**).
(From Swift, 1960. *Symp. Zool. Soc. Lond.* **2**, 17–27.)

there is histological evidence of thyroid hyperactivity in spawning herring (Fig. 70) and in the females of viviparous dogfish during gestation, and direct experimental evidence of maximal output of thyroxine during the period of reproduction in *Fundulus*, while there are also reports of sex differences, such as those found in the protein-bound iodine content of

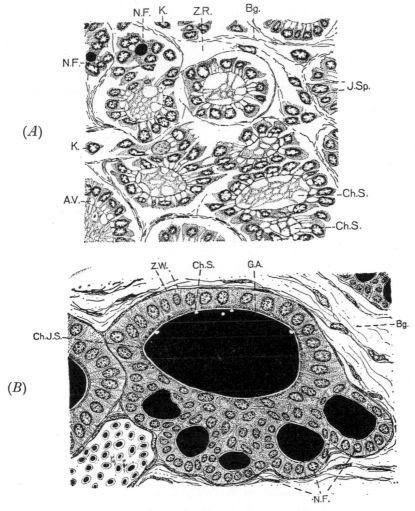

Fig. 70. Sections of the thyroids of herring from *A*, an individual shortly after metamorphosis, with much stored colloid, and *B*, a post-spawning individual, with reduced and vacuolated colloid, and with new follicles and colloid forming. *Bg.*, connective tissue; *Ch. J.S.*, secretion droplets; *Ch. S.*, chromophobe secretion or vacuoles; *J. Sp.*, inter-cellular spaces; *K.*, nucleus; *N.F.*, young follicle; *Z.W.*, cell wall.
(From Buchmann, 1940. *Zool. Jahrb. Abt. Anat.* **66**, 191–262.)

the thyroid of *Scarus*. Some association between the thyroid and sexual reproduction has, in fact, long been suspected, and it is curious to find that not much more than fifty years ago Gaskell was using this supposed association to support his theory of the derivation of vertebrates from eurypterids, his suggestion being that it justified a belief in the homology of the thyroid with the uterus of scorpions!

There is no doubt but that much of the uncertainty in our interpretation of the functions of the thyroid hormones is derived from the fact that we are dealing with the expression of hormonal actions which are being exerted at a much deeper level, and that the key to these must be sought within the field of cell physiology, as we have already noted in more than one context. We understand too little of this at the moment, but an example of the type of thinking which is likely to prove helpful is provided by the work of Cooper, Lehninger, and Tapley, which ascribes the effects of thyroid hormones to their action upon the permeability of mitochondria. The latter are now well known to be the site in which the energy released by oxidation processes is incorporated into adenosine triphosphate (ATP) and it has been suggested that this process is influenced by the thyroid hormones, the hyperthyroid condition involving an impairment of the phosphorylation of ATP. There is also evidence, however, that these hormones stimulate the activity of the microsomes, which suggests that they may influence the organized enzyme systems of the cell in some more generalized way than this. Whatever the truth of the matter may eventually prove to be, such hypotheses surely illustrate the type of paths along which solutions must be sought as to the mode of action of the thyroid hormones or, indeed, of any hormone.

3. Thyrotropin

The thyroid gland resembles the endocrine tissue of the gonads not only in its lack of a secreto-motor nerve supply, but also in the system of control by which its secretory activity is regulated. It is now accepted that one factor in this system is its reciprocal feedback relationship with the pars distalis, a relationship to which the term thyro-pituitary axis is often applied, and which is essentially similar in principle to that existing between the gonads and the pituitary gland.

Evidence indicative of this relationship was available in the last century, although it was not possible at that time to present a satisfactory interpretation of it. For example, it was recognized that the human pituitary might become greatly enlarged, to a weight as much as four times the normal, in goitrous cretins and in thyroidectomized individuals. The first comprehensive experimental demonstration came, however, from 1914 onwards with a recognition that the 'anterior lobe' of the pituitary, as well as the thyroid gland itself, was a significant factor in the regulation of amphibian metamorphosis. It was shown in that year by Adler, and later confirmed by others, that the removal of the 'anterior lobe' from frog tadpoles would retard the growth of the thyroid and that no colloid would be deposited in it; as a result, metamorphosis would not occur. It was later found that if the 'anterior lobe' was implanted into a hypophysectomized tadpole, or if saline or acetic acid extracts were injected into its body cavity, the animal would metamorphose, and for a time it seemed to some investigators that this indicated that the pituitary was itself exerting a direct control over metamorphosis. It was soon apparent, however, that this could not be so, for it was then shown that a thyroidectomized tadpole, which would not, of course, metamorphose, could not be induced to do so even if additional 'anterior lobe' material were implanted into it, despite the fact that the implant maintained itself in what seemed to be good functional condition. The only reasonable explanation was that the thyroid was dependent upon the 'anterior lobe' for the maintenance of its normal functioning, and that the effect of the latter gland upon metamorphosis was an indirect one, exerted through its effect upon the thyroid.

With these considerations as a starting point, it has now been thoroughly established that the maintenance of the activity of the thyroid gland throughout the vertebrates, at least from fish upwards, is dependent upon a hormone secreted by the 'anterior lobe', and that this activity is reduced as a result of hypophysectomy (Fig. 71). Injections of pituitary extracts prepared separately from the pars distalis, pars intermedia, and pars nervosa have shown that only the first of these is active in this respect, so that it must be the source of this secretion as it is of the gonadotropins. By analogy with the latter, the hormone is best termed thyrotropin, but thyrotrophin and TSH (for thyroid-stimulating hormone) are alternatively used names. Like FSH and ICSH, it has been isolated in a highly purified form, which is believed to have a molecular weight of about 26,000–30,000 and to be a glycoprotein, but further purification studies are still in progress.

The simplest demonstration of its existence is secured by injecting into a test animal a suitable adenohypophyseal extract, the result being an enlargement of the follicle cells which can then be measured in terms of cell-height. In this way the thyroid of the guinea-pig, for example, has been found to respond to pituitary extracts of mammals, chick, and amphibians, and that of the goldfish to extracts of fish, amphibians, chick, and mammals. The full effects will depend upon the strength of the injected extracts. With larger doses, or with sufficiently frequent injections, the gland will become hyperplastic (with increased numbers of cells) as well as hypertrophied, and this, together with its increased vascularization, results in a marked increase in volume and weight. The biologically significant result of an increased supply of thyrotropin is, of course, an increase in the output of thyroid hormones into the circulation, the first step being an acceleration in the proteolysis of the colloid and in the release of the

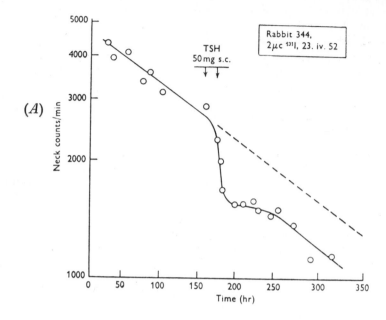

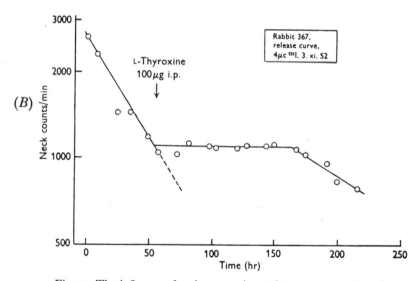

Fig. 71. The influence of various experimental treatments on the release of I^{131} from the thyroid gland of the rabbit. The data are plotted semi-logarithmically, the slope of the line representing the ratio of hormone secreted per unit time to the total amount in the gland (see also p. 190). A, Injection of thyrotropin; B, injection of thyroxine; C, removal to colder environment; D, hypophysectomy.

(From Brown-Grant *et al.*, 1954. *J. Physiol.* **126**, 1–28.)

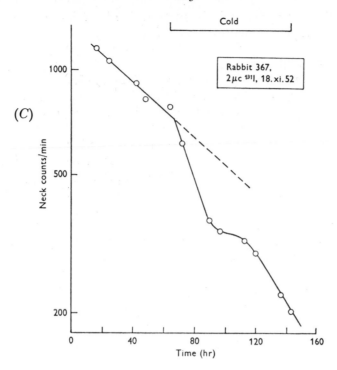

(C)

Cold

Rabbit 367,
2μc ¹³¹I, 18.xi.52

Neck counts/min

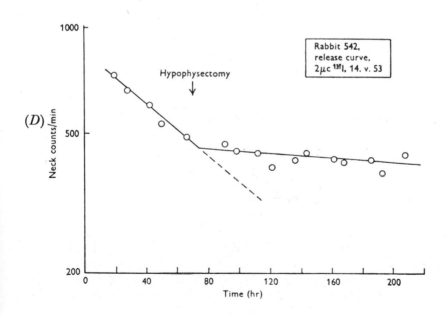

(D)

Rabbit 542,
release curve,
2μc ¹³¹I, 14.v.53

Hypophysectomy

Neck counts/min

Time (hr)

stored secretion (Fig. 71); this is succeeded by an increased rate of synthesis, marked by an increased rate of iodide uptake and cell hypertrophy.

These facts indicate that the goitrous enlargement of the thyroid resulting from iodine deficiency is a consequence of stimulation of the gland by an increased output of thyrotropin, and there is good evidence that this is a reaction to a low level of circulating thyroid hormones. Conversely, a high level of these will depress the output of thyrotropin, and this will result in a reduction of output from the thyroid gland, as can readily be shown by injecting thyroxine into an experimental animal (Fig. 71). Here, then, is another example of a feedback mechanism in operation, and an excellent demonstration of it under experimental conditions is seen in the action of certain so-called anti-thyroid compounds, the administration of which (in the food or drink, or by injection, or, in the case of aquatic animals, by solution in the surrounding medium) causes a blockage of one or other of the steps of thyroidal biosynthesis. As a result, there is a fall in the level of the circulating thyroid hormones; this brings about the usual response of an increased output of thyrotropin, and this leads in its turn to a goitrous enlargement of the thyroid. The administration of these compounds to the rat, for example, results in indications of heightened epithelium and loss of colloid appearing within twenty-four to forty-eight hours of the beginning of the treatment; after two weeks there is extensive hypertrophy and hyperplasia, with almost complete loss of colloid and greatly increased vascularization. With discontinuation of treatment there is a rapid reversion to the normal functioning of the gland, with a re-accumulation of colloid, although it may be some time before a normal size is regained. The reaction, which gives to these compounds the name of goitrogens, is in effect a form of compensatory hypertrophy, but one which brings no benefit to the animal since biosynthesis will continue to be inhibited for as long as the goitrogens are administered. The conclusion that it is mediated by thyrotropin rests not only on its similarity to the response induced by direct administration of that hormone, but also on the fact that it does not occur in hypophysectomized animals. Further, the pars distalis of intact animals treated with goitrogens shows characteristic changes in certain secretory cells which can be directly correlated with the discharge of the hormone (p. 286).

The study of anti-thyroid compounds arose in part out of the investigation of the goitrogenic action of certain food materials. From 1928 onwards it became apparent that the leaves of *Brassica* plants contained a goitrogen which was believed to be an organic cyanide, and it was shown that the effect of this could be overcome by the administration of iodine to the affected animal. Later it was found that certain *Brassica* seeds, including rape, were also goitrogenic, but that their influence, believed to be due to a derivative of thiourea, differed from that of the leaves in that it could not be overcome by iodine treatment. The intensive modern study of the phenomenon dates, however, from 1941, in which year an investigation of the action of sulphaguanidine upon intestinal bacteria brought unexpectedly to light the fact that this substance was goitrogenic, while another group of investigators then showed that thiouracil also possessed this property.

It is now recognized that anti-thyroid compounds fall into two main categories, the action of one of these depending upon the presence of certain monovalent anions, including thiocyanate and perchlorate, which block the iodide-trapping activity of the thyroid and at the same time cause a discharge of stored iodine from the gland. The effect of these can be alleviated by the administration of iodide in amounts sufficient to overcome the blockage, in which respect such substances differ from those of the second group. These inhibit thyroidal activity by blocking a later stage of biosynthesis, most probably, it has been suggested, the enzymic oxidation of iodide to iodine, so that their effect can only be alleviated by the administration of the thyroid hormones which the animal is unable to synthesize for itself. Included in this second group are thiocarbamide derivatives such as thiourea, thiouracil, propylthiouracil, and carbimazole (Fig. 72), and aniline derivatives such as p-aminobenzoic acid, sulphaguanidine, and sulphadiazine. The recognition of symptoms of myxoedema in a patient whose varicose ulcers were being treated with resorcinol led to the further discovery that this substance was also included in this category, together with a number of its derivatives, although its isomers, quinol and catechol, are inactive.

Results of goitrogen action similar to those found in the mammals have been reported for all groups of vertebrates from fish upwards, and the effect is particularly striking in frog tadpoles, since it necessarily affects metamorphosis. This can be indefinitely postponed by the immersion of tadpoles in solutions of thiourea or thiouracil, while for some time the thyroid will show a reduction in colloid, a heightened epithelium, and an increased vascularization. After some months of this treatment, the thyroid is said to revert to a more normal appearance, probably because of a failure in the output of thyrotropin; this does not, of course, in any way facilitate metamorphosis, but merely represents a failure in the reciprocal relationship of pituitary and thyroid. The sulphonamides, incidentally, are without effect on tadpoles, and the thyroids of the chick and of the mature fowl have also been reported to be refractory to these substances.

The effects of goitrogens on fish, administered by immersion of the animals, have been particularly studied in teleosts because they provide a means of carrying out 'chemical thyroidectomy' in a group which, apart from exceptional forms such as *Scarus*, does not lend itself to surgical thyroidectomy owing to the diffuse nature of the gland. Thiourea and its derivatives evoke a goitrous response throughout the scattered follicles, and they will presumably affect also any heterotopic tissue which may be present, but it would be unwise to assume that they constitute a perfect substitute for the surgical approach. It would be easier to judge this if the

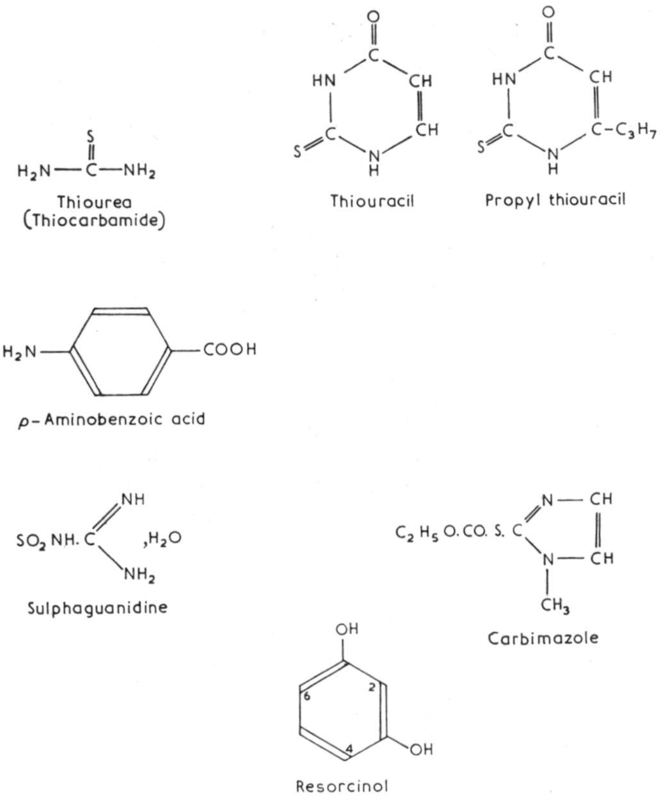

Fig. 72. Goitrogenic substances.

mode of action of these substances was entirely clear, but it is at least known that thiourea and its derivative are anti-oxidants, and it seems likely that prolonged immersion of aquatic vertebrates in solutions of such compounds must have deleterious effects. It would be prudent, therefore, to interpret studies of the metabolism of such animals with caution. Subject to this provision then, it can be said that the results of 'chemical thyroidectomy' of teleosts have given no indication of any fall in metabolic rate resulting from the withdrawal of thyroid hormones, which certainly provides some support for the view that the latter are not stimulators of metabolism in these animals. However, we have seen that the results of thyroxine treatment are not at present concordant, and it is doubtful whether the unsatisfactory aspects of goitrogen treatment enable these substances to contribute much in the way of clarification.

4. Neural regulation of thyrotropin secretion

The role of the pars distalis in the regulation of thyroid secretion is thus very clearly demonstrated, but there is good evidence that the latter is also under the influence of the nervous system. One example of this is illustrated in Fig. 71, which shows how the rate of output of radio-iodine from the rabbit's gland is increased by removal of the animal from its constant temperature room to a lower temperature. The explanation of this appears to be that the release of thyrotropin, like that of the gonado-tropins, is regulated through the hypothalamus.

The earliest evidence for this, closely analogous to that obtained from the gonadotropic studies which we have already discussed, was derived from studies of the effects of localized hypothalamic lesions, which showed that if, in the rat, these were placed mid-ventrally, from the anterior region of the median eminence to the optic chiasma, the animals would not develop goitrous enlargements in response to propylthiouracil treatment. Similar conclusions followed from experiments in which lesions in the same area were applied to rats from which about three-quarters of the thyroid had been surgically removed; such a loss of thyroid tissue would normally result in compensatory hypertrophy of the remaining part owing to the increased output of thyrotropin, but out of one group of thirty-one rats with lesions, twenty failed to show this response. Again, out of a group of twenty-three dogs with hypothalamic lesions, five showed marked reduction of the thyroid to a level similar to what might be expected from hypophysectomy, and in these five the lesions were in or immediately adjacent to the anterior end of the median eminence. In the other dogs the lesions were outside this area, and in them the thyroid activity appeared to be normal.

The role of the hypothalamus has been studied further by Harris, using the same method of electrical stimulation by remote control (p. 117) as was described earlier. The procedure is complicated here by the fact that stimulation of the hypothalamus can also release corticotropin (p. 253), the consequent increased circulation of cortical steroids resulting in a depression of thyroid activity. It is necessary, therefore, to carry out such experiments both with intact animals and with adrenalectomized ones, the latter being maintained with daily doses of cortisone. Harris summarizes the results of this work in the following terms. Stimulation of the anterior part of the median eminence adjacent to the supraoptico-hypophyseal tract results in increased thyroid activity, and the effect is greater after adrenalectomy than it was before. Stimulation in the median eminence posterior to the tract increases thyroid activity after adrenalectomy, but either shows no effect or an inhibitory one in intact animals. Stimulation in other parts of the hypothalamus, or even in the pituitary itself, has no effect either before or after adrenalectomy. The suggestion is that a neural mechanism concerned with the regulation of thyrotropin secretion is situated anteriorly, and that one concerned with corticotropin secretion is situated further back, so that while stimulation of the anterior region would always evoke a response in the thyroid gland, stimulation more posteriorly would evoke a mixed adrenal and thyroid response, and the latter component would not be revealed until after adrenalectomy. On this interpretation the site of thyrotropin control as defined by direct stimulation agrees very well with the site suggested by the use of lesions.

5. The thyro-pituitary feedback mechanism

The above data justify us in accepting that the hypothalamus is involved in the regulation of thyrotropin secretion, and in the light of this it becomes possible to examine what paths of communication are actually involved in the feedback mechanism. The original conception of Aron, as formulated in 1931, was that reduction of circulating thyroid hormones acted directly upon the pars distalis to bring about an increased output of thyrotropin, but this simple concept is no longer wholly adequate. We must conclude from what has been outlined above that under some circumstances the functioning of the thyro-pituitary axis is being mediated by neural pathways involving the hypothalamus. It need not be assumed, however, that this excludes the possibility of a direct action of the thyroid secretion upon the pars distalis, and, indeed, there is good evidence that this may occur. Thus, it is known that the temporary inhibition of radio-iodine release from the thyroid, which we have seen to be produced by the injection of thyroxine into rabbits, can be evoked even in hypophysectomized animals if these have functional implants of pituitary tissue in their eyes, a result which implies that the thyroxine must be acting directly upon the implants. It is known, too, that inhibition of release can also be produced by direct injection of thyroxine into the pars distalis of the rabbit in doses that would be too small to produce any effect if they were injected into the general circulation. It would seem, however, that the thyrotropin-controlling region of the hypothalamus may also be sensitive to direct stimulation by thyroxine, for an inhibition of thyroid secretion in rats can be produced by the injection of as little as 0·05 μg either into that area or into the pars distalis itself; moreover, injections into the hypothalamus of rats that are under treatment with propylthiouracil have been shown to inhibit the goitrous response that would normally be evoked by the latter.

It appears likely, then, that both the hypothalamus and the pars distalis are capable of responding to changes in the concentration of circulating thyroid hormones, so that the feedback can operate through either path. Superimposed on this, however, will be the reflex neural control arising from environmental stimulation and it may be, as Harris has suggested, that this takes functional priority, the feedback relationship serving to ensure the maintenance of an optimal level of circulating thyroid hormones under basal conditions.

Evidence as to the route by which the influence of the hypothalamus is actually transmitted to the pars distalis is not as complete as could be wished, but the situation at present is very much as we found it to be with the control of gonadotropin secretion. Observations on rabbits in which the pituitary stalk has been severed have suggested that thyroid activity, as measured by the release of radio-iodine, is lower in those animals in which no regeneration of the portal vessels occurs, and that their thyroids do not show the inhibitory effect that normally follows emotional stress. There is thus some presumption that the hypothalamus is exerting its control by chemical transmission through the hypophyseal portal vessels, but the problem awaits further study.

IX. THE CHROMAFFIN TISSUE OF THE ADRENAL GLAND

1. General organization of the adrenal gland

A MISUNDERSTANDING of St. Jerome's translation of the Vulgate seems to have led at one time to a belief that the adrenal glands of mammals were known to Moses, but we may accept that the first account of them

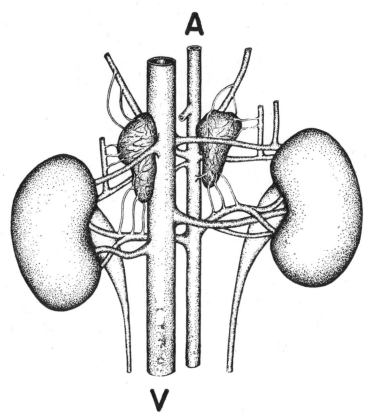

Fig. 73. The adrenal glands and kidney of the dog and their vascular connexions. *A*, dorsal aorta; *V*, vena cava.
(From Hartman & Brownell, 1949. *The Adrenal Gland*. Lea & Febiger.)

was published in 1563 in a review of human anatomy by Bartolomeo Eustachius. Later authors found that they were filled with fluid and, not realizing that this was a product of post-mortem decay, referred to them

as the suprarenal capsules, a term which also expresses their close association with the anterior end of the kidneys, in man, although this relationship is not necessarily present in other mammals (Fig. 73). Cuvier drew

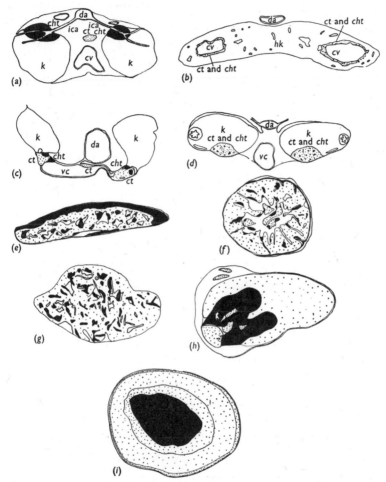

Fig. 74. Diagrams to show the intermingling of chromaffin tissue and
adrenocortical tissue in the vertebrates. *a*, Dogfish (from Young, 1950); *b*, perch
(from Baecker, 1928); *c*, *Ichthyophis* (from Dittus, 1941); *d*, frog; *e*, lizard;
f, Crocodilia; *g*, pigeon; *h*, echidna (from Bourne, 1949); *i*, rat. *cht*, chromaffin
tissue (black); *ct*, cortical tissue (stippled); *cv*, cardinal vein; *da*, dorsal aorta;
hk, head kidney; *ica*, intercostal artery; *k*, kidney; *vc*, vena cava.
(From Chester Jones, 1957. *The Adrenal Cortex*. Cambridge University Press.)

attention in 1805 to the fact that they were fully differentiated into the
inner and outer regions which are now commonly known as the medulla
and cortex, but since this pattern of organization is peculiar to the
mammals, and even in the monotremes is not sharply defined, we shall

follow Chester Jones by referring to them respectively as the chromaffin and adrenocortical tissues.

In birds the adrenal glands are present as distinct organs just anterior to the kidneys, but the two component tissues are here intermingled to a varying degree without forming a sharply defined cortex and medulla (Fig. 74). In reptiles the organs are elongated and are composed of irregular cords of adrenocortical tissue, the chromaffin tissue being present in part

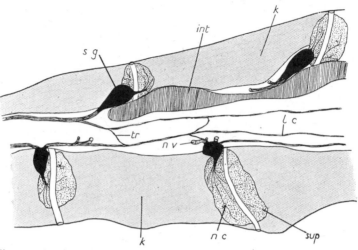

Fig. 75. Semi-diagrammatic representation of a horizontal section of the kidney region of *Scyliorhinus canicula* (female). *int*, adrenocortical tissue; *k*, kidney; *lc*, longitudinal connective; *nv*, nerve to viscera; *nc*, nerve cell amongst chromaffin cells; *sup*, chromaffin body, embedded in kidney and receiving post-ganglionic nerve fibres from the adjacent sympathetic ganglion (cf. p. 227); *sg*, sympathetic ganglin; *tr*, transverse commissure.
(From Young, 1933. *Quart. J. micr. Sci.* **75**, 571–624.)

at the surface and in part as islets amongst the cords or as tongues extending inwards from the surface layer (Plate x). In Amphibia the glands are associated with the mesonephric kidneys, for the most part lying on the surface of these organs or being embedded in them; they are composed of cords of adrenocortical tissue, but the chromaffin tissue is scattered amongst these without the addition of the surface layer found in reptiles.

In elasmobranch fish (Fig. 75) the two components are separated from each other and are not so easily identified as in the higher groups. The chromaffin tissue takes the form of a series of segmental glands which lie immediately above the dorsal wall of the posterior cardinal sinus; some of these can be seen by removing the ventral wall of the latter, but the more posterior ones are embedded in the kidney, and in that region are larger in the male than in the female. They are sometimes called the suprarenal glands, but this term is better avoided since, as we have seen, earlier writers applied it to the whole gland of mammals and the same usage still persists. The adrenocortical tissue of elasmobranchs lies in the kidney region and is often called the interrenal gland or glands (Fig. 76); it may have the form of a compact body, or of an elongated rod with small accessory portions at its anterior end, or it may form a horseshoe-shaped structure.

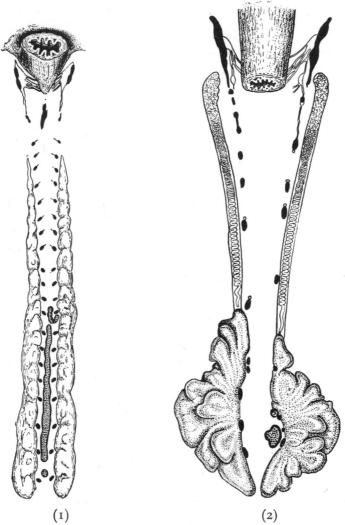

(1)   (2)

Fig. 76. Diagrams of the arrangement of the adrenal homologues in 1, *Mustelus canis* and 2, *Raja diaphanes*.

1. Chromaffin tissue, double row of black bodies; adrenocortical tissue, stippled. The kidneys have been turned outwards to uncover these. The adrenocortical and the more caudal chromaffin bodies are within the kidneys, the more anterior chromaffin bodies are dorsal to them.

2. The chromaffin tissue is black and the adrenocortical tissue stippled.

(From Hartman & Brownell, 1949. *The Adrenal Gland*. Lea & Febiger.)

In teleost fish the separation of the two components is less pronounced than in elasmobranchs, and they may even be intermingled. The adrenocortical tissue forms groups of cells lying in close relationship with the cardinal veins in the region of the pronephros, itself usually a lymphoid organ (the so-called head kidney) in the adult; there is much variation in the amount of the tissue and in its distribution between the two halves of the body, but practically nothing is known of the factors which may determine this. The chromaffin tissue is found as groups of cells in the same region, especially localized around the cardinal veins, but not necessarily intermingled with the cortical tissue. In addition to these structures there are also to be found, lying on or embedded in the mesonephric kidney, small gland-like bodies known as the corpuscles of Stannius, composed of cells with granules which appear to be lipoprotein in nature. These bodies were at one time regarded as adrenocortical tissue, but this view has fallen into disfavour, partly because they differ in their embryological origin, arising as evaginations from the wall of the pronephric duct, and partly because they are not influenced by corticotropin (p. 250). There is some physiological division of labour in the adrenocortical tissue of mammals, however, leading to part of this (the zona glomerulosa) becoming apparently freed of corticotropin control (p. 251), so that it will be well to maintain an open mind regarding the true nature of the corpuscles of Stannius and await the results of further investigations.

This is true also of the general situation in the Cyclostomata. The arrangement of adrenal tissue in this group has not been very critically studied, but it seems probable that both adrenocortical and chromaffin components are represented by scattered groups of cells, distributed through most of the length of the body, and related particularly to the cardinal veins (Fig. 77). If this interpretation is correct, it follows that adrenocortical and chromaffin tissue were established very early in vertebrate evolution, but as two separate tissues which, to judge from the situation in the other groups, have become increasingly closely associated. We shall see below that everything else which we know about them supports this view, and we shall therefore deal with them separately, beginning with the chromaffin tissue.

2. The catechol hormones

It is rightly claimed that one of the outstanding landmarks in the development of endocrinology was the publication in 1896 by Oliver and Schäfer of their classical study of the physiological effects of extracts of the mammalian adrenal gland, a study which began with that element of the accidental which is so often a component of successful research. Dale has told the story of how Dr. George Oliver, a Harrogate physician, discovered while experimenting upon his young son that injections of such extracts affected the radial artery. Proceeding to London to inform Schäfer of this, and finding him engaged upon an experiment which involved recording the blood pressure of a dog, he urged him to inject some of the extract which he had brought with him; this was done, and

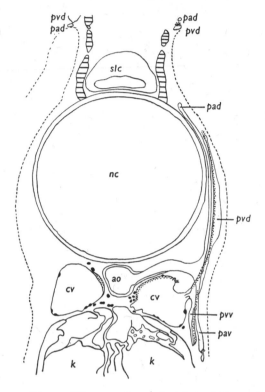

Fig. 77. Diagram of a section through the mid-part of the trunk of *Petromyzon marinus*. *ao*, aorta; *cv*, cardinal veins; *k*, kidney; *nc*, notochord; *pad* and *pvd*, dorsal parietal arteries and veins; *pav* and *pvv*, ventral parietal arteries and veins; *slc*, spinal cord. Small groups of cortical cells, black; chromaffin tissue, stippled.

(From Chester Jones, 1957. *The Adrenal Cortex*. Cambridge.)

Schäfer 'stood amazed to see the mercury mounting in the arterial manometer till the recording float was lifted almost out of the distal limb'.

As a result of their subsequent investigations they concluded that the organs were ductless secreting glands, and an analogy was drawn with the thyroid gland for which, as we have seen, a similar conclusion had by then been developed. Oliver and Schäfer found that the secretion was restricted to the medulla, and that its most striking effects were exerted

upon muscular tissue, its action being to increase muscular tone, to produce some constriction of arterioles, and to increase the blood pressure,
bringing about thereby a marked shrinkage of the kidney and spleen.
A tracing prepared in the course of one of their experiments and illustrating some of these results is seen in Fig. 78.

Developments rapidly followed these discoveries, aided by the fortunate
circumstance that large amounts of the secretion are stored within the
gland and are readily extractable. Its *N*-benzoyl derivative was isolated
by Abel under the name of epinephrine (*epi*, upon; *nephros*, kidney),
and by 1901 Takamine had isolated the active principle itself in pure
form and had called it by the Latin equivalent, adrenalin. This substance,
the first hormone to be isolated in crystalline form, was then synthesized
by Stolz in 1904. It is now known in this country as adrenaline, the
terminal 'e' indicating by convention a basic substance, although the
Greek form is still commonly used in the United States.

Adrenaline (Fig. 79) is an amine with a molecular structure based upon
the catechol grouping, and it exists in two optically active forms owing
to the presence of one asymmetrical carbon atom. In its naturally occurring
form it is laevo-rotatory, this isomer being some twelve to fifteen times as
active as the dextro-rotatory form; the synthetic material is also available
in the L-form, although the initial product is, of course, racemic. It has
been suggested that the rapid progress in the isolation and characterization of the hormone was a discouragement to further exploration of this
particular field, and it is certainly remarkable that although Stolz also
synthesized the non-methylated homologue noradrenaline (Fig. 79), it
was not until 1946 that the physiological importance of this became appreciated, largely through the work of von Euler. It was first shown to be
present in extracts of various mammalian organs, and also in the splenic
and splanchnic nerves and in the nerves of the sympathetic chain. Subsequently it was found to be present with adrenaline in the adrenal gland,
in part, no doubt, because it seems to be a precursor of that substance;
both, however, are discharged into the venous effluent of the gland and
must therefore be regarded as joint hormonal products, just as are
thyroxine and triiodothyronine. Like adrenaline, the naturally occurring
form of noradrenaline is laevo-rotatory and this is twenty-five to thirty
times more active than the D-isomer.

There is reason to believe that a continuous secretion is released spontaneously from the chromaffin tissue in mammals but, unlike so many of
the endocrine glands of vertebrates, this is also under the direct control of
the nervous system through the mediation of sympathetic fibres running
in the splanchnic nerve. Stimulation of this nerve in a mammal, therefore,
evokes an increased output of secretion, as also do a variety of conditions
such as pain, fear, low temperature, muscular activity, and a fall in the

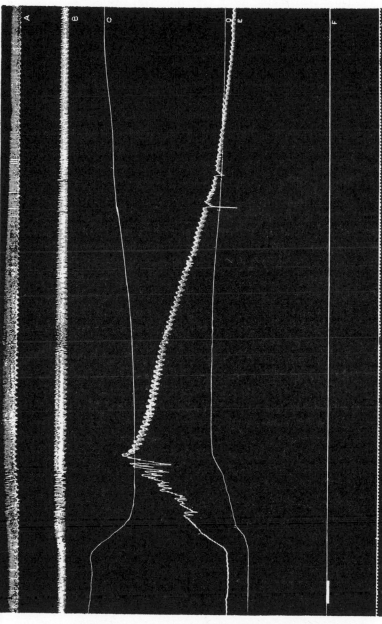

Fig. 78. A tracing from the classical paper of Oliver and Schäfer, illustrating the effect of an intravenous injection of an extract of the adrenal gland of the calf into a dog which had previously received morphine and atropine. Note the rise of blood pressure (vasopressor effect). The spleen decreases in volume as a result of the contraction of the arterioles, while the arm increases in volume because of the concomitant passive expansion of the larger vessels. A, auricle; B, ventricle; C, spleen; D, arm volume; E, blood pressure; F, abscissa and signal; G, time in seconds.

(From Oliver & Schäfer, 1895. *J. Physiol.* **18**, 230–76.)

blood-sugar level. As would be expected from the original observations of Oliver and Schäfer, adrenaline has a very powerful vasopressor action; this seems to result largely from an increase in the volume and frequency of the heart-beat, the effect, in conjunction with vasoconstriction in the skin and vasodilation elsewhere, being to bring about an increased flow of blood to the internal organs. Adrenaline also relaxes the smooth muscle of the bronchi and of the alimentary tract, thus inhibiting the passage of food through the latter, while, as we have seen earlier (p. 57), it has

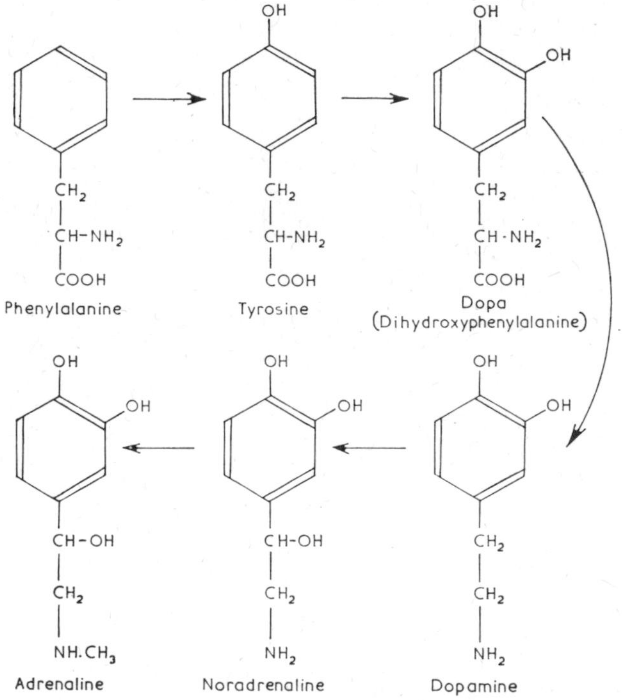

Fig. 79. The catechol hormones and related compounds.

important effects upon carbohydrate metabolism, for it stimulates the conversion of liver glycogen to glucose and thus brings about a consequential rise in blood-sugar level. It evokes, too, some unpleasant subjective symptoms of expectancy and anxiety when injected into man. It is apparent from Table 4 that the effects of noradrenaline do not exactly parallel those of adrenaline; for example, the former is less potent in promoting the discharge of liver glycogen and produces little or no change in cardiac performance, but has a more marked vasoconstrictor effect, although this vascular action tends to be unremarked in humans since it is not accompanied by subjective symptoms. Such differences make possible the quantitative determination of both substances in a single

TABLE 4

Comparison of the effects of L-*adrenaline and* L-*noradrenaline in man.* (From Bell *et al.*, 1956. *Textbook of Physiology and Biochemistry*. Livingstone.)

	Adrenaline	Noradrenaline
Heart rate	increase	decrease
Blood pressure	rise	greater rise
Skin vessels	constriction	less constriction
Muscle vessels	dilatation	constriction
Bronchus	dilatation	less dilatation
Metabolism	increase	slight increase
Blood sugar	increase	slight increase
Eosinophil count	increase	no effect
Oxygen consumption	increase	no effect
Central nervous system	anxiety	no effect

extract by bio-assay procedures; von Euler's method, for example, makes use of the fact that noradrenaline has the stronger effect upon the blood pressure of the cat while adrenaline has the greater relaxing action upon the rectal caecum of the fowl.

The facts that we have so far reviewed make clear the widespread nature of the actions of the catechol amines, but before we can assess their physiological importance it will be necessary to examine the significance of the special relationship of the chromaffin tissue to the nervous system, and this in its turn necessitates consideration of the organization of the tissue itself.

3. Functional organization of chromaffin tissue

The cells of the chromaffin tissue of mammals are arranged in a closely packed network of cords, between which extend capillary vessels, and it is said that they exhibit a constant polarity with respect to the vessels, one end being related to the arterial side of the circulation and the other to the venous. The characteristic feature of these cells is the presence within their cytoplasm of a very large number of fine granules, and it has been known since 1865 that these react with potassium dichromate or chromic acid to give a yellowish or brown colour. This is known as the chromaffin reaction, and it is because of this that the cells themselves are called chromaffin cells. They constitute the diagnostic feature of the chromaffin tissue, throughout the vertebrates, but they occur also in the ventral nerve cord of annelid worms, being regularly distributed in, for example, the segmental ganglia of the leech, *Hirudo medicinalis*.

After the discovery of adrenaline it was natural to ascribe the chromaffin reaction to the reducing properties of that substance, the reaction being regarded as a result of the reduction of the dichromate to a yellowish-brown compound. Later, however, it was shown that an identical effect could be produced by fixing chromaffin tissue in a fluid containing potassium iodate, and it became apparent that the reaction was in fact due to the oxidation of the granule substance by the dichromate or iodate as the case might be. According to Lison's interpretation, not only adrenaline but all substances belonging to the series of aromatic photographic developers will give the chromaffin response in reaction with mild oxidants.

The earlier view implied that any reducing substance might give a chromaffin reaction. The importance of the later interpretation is that it indicates a much greater degree of histochemical specificity in the reaction and this explains why it has been possible, by applying techniques of controlled and differential oxidation, to demonstrate in the chromaffin tissue two kinds of cells, one of which is believed to secrete adrenaline and the other noradrenaline. The fact that the latter substance differed from the former in having a characteristic tendency to form a darker pigment on oxidation had been noted in 1950, and it was subsequently shown by Hillarp and Hökfelt that, in contrast to adrenaline, it was selectively transformed into a dark pigment within a few minutes when medullary slices were oxidized with potassium iodate (Plate x F). Both substances can be demonstrated simultaneously in thin slices of fresh tissue by using a reaction mixture consisting of 5 per cent. potassium dichromate containing sufficient 5 per cent. potassium chromate to make a pH of between 5 and 6; under such circumstances the two cell types appear distributed as irregular patches, those containing adrenaline being darker. Clearly this demonstration could provide an acceptable histological basis for the selective release of adrenaline and noradrenaline (p. 229), a response which would be more difficult to account for in the absence of two distinct types of secretory cell.

The implication of the above interpretation is that the catechol amines are located within the granules of the medullary cells, and there is good experimental confirmation of this. These granules can be isolated by the differential centrifugation of homogenates of medullary tissue, using isotonic sucrose solution as the medium, and they have been found to contain as much as 60 to 70 per cent. of the total catechol amine content of the gland; since there must be some loss and destruction during preparation, their actual content must be higher and it may well be that they contain all of the adrenaline and noradrenaline. The procedure is similar in principle to that used in the isolation of mitochondria, and it has been suggested that the granules may actually be identical with these. The evidence from electron micrographs, however, indicates that the two inclusions are distinct from each other (Plate IX), for the granules appear to consist of droplets of catechol amines which are enclosed within limiting membranes,

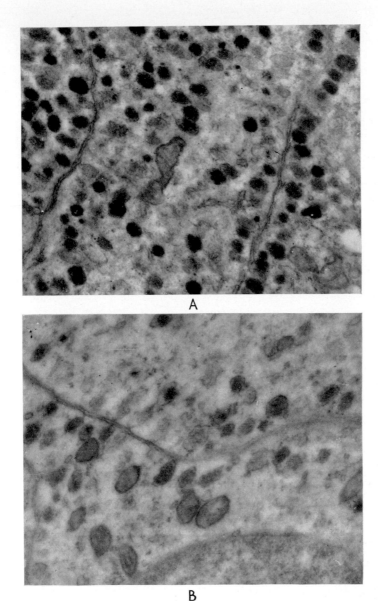

A

B

Plate IX. Electron micrographs of the cytoplasm of chromaffin cells
from the adrenal gland of the rabbit. *A*. Normal animal. A mitochondrion
lies towards the centre of the field. The catechol droplets are numerous,
and some of them are lying close to the cell membranes which are seen at
the sides of the field. *B*. After stimulation of the splanchnic nerve (cf.
Fig. 80). The catechol droplets are fewer, and their contents reduced
and less dense, so that their limiting membranes are correspondingly
clearer, one example being visible at the extreme top edge of the field and
another vertically below it. A cell membrane crosses the middle of the
field; droplets lie close to this, and several empty ones are attached to it.
Part of a nucleus is seen at the bottom of the field; several mitochondria
lie above it and to the left, one example being visible at the bottom edge
of the field. (A, × 30,750; B, × 33,250.)

(From de Robertis & Sabatini, 1960. *Fed. Proc.* **19**, 70–78.)

these remaining behind as empty vesicles after secretory discharge has taken place. Such an association of secretion and membranes has already been noted in our consideration of the hypothalamic centres, and it seems to be a common feature of the organization of neurosecretory cells (see also p. 75, Plate xiv).

The purification and artificial synthesis of the catechol amines have made it possible to establish the probable mechanism of their biosynthesis. The likelihood that the aromatic amino acids, phenylalanine and tyrosine, (Fig. 79) might be the precursors was suggested long ago, and recent work, more particularly with the aid of radioactive isotopes, has shown that this is almost certainly true. Amongst the many relevant findings may be mentioned the fact that after labelling phenylalanine with tritium (in the ring) and C^{14} (in the side-chain) and administering this to rats it is possible to recover from the chromaffin tissue some adrenaline showing the same labelling. C^{14}-labelled adrenaline can also be recovered after administration of labelled tyrosine, and, since phenylalanine is known to be converted into tyrosine in the body, it seems likely that this reaction is involved in the biosynthesis of the adrenaline molecule.

An acceptable interpretation (Fig. 79) of the course of biosynthesis is that the tyrosine is oxidized into dopa (dihydroxyphenylalanine), this being transformed into dopamine by the action of dopa decarboxylase which is known to be present in chromaffin tissue. Thereafter, and probably within the cell granules, some of the dopamine is hydroxylated to noradrenaline and some of this in its turn is methylated, with the formation of adrenaline. Support for this view is given by the demonstration, dependent upon chromatographic techniques, that in the presence of chromaffin tissue C^{14}-labelled dopa can be transformed into C^{14}-labelled noradrenaline.

4. The autonomic nervous system and chemical transmitter substances

We must now consider the fundamentally important relationship that exists between the chromaffin tissue and the autonomic nervous system. It has been known since the work of Magnus in 1904 that the wall of the intestine exhibits rhythmical contractions when it is maintained *in vitro*, although it is still uncertain how far such movements are initiated spontaneously within the muscle cells themselves, and how far they involve activation and regulation by the myenteric nerve plexus. This matter of interpretation need not concern us here, the point of present importance being that the alimentary canal as a whole has considerable intrinsic powers of initiating and regulating its movements in response, for example, to the ingestion and passage of food, powers analogous to its intrinsic capacity for hormonal regulation. Despite this, the movements of the gut are also regulated by the body as a whole through the autonomic nervous system, and we have seen that on the whole, and with exceptions in detail, the parasympathetic and sympathetic divisions of this system exert antagonistic effects upon the gut musculature in mammals. The question thus arises how it is that nerve fibres in one division can bring about excitation of the musculature by discharging impulses at a particular point, while fibres in the other, discharging at the same point, can bring about inhibition, for it is accepted that this cannot be accounted for by any qualitative difference in the fibres or in the impulses which they propagate.

The experimental basis for a solution to this problem was given in 1921 in the classical experiments of Loewi, who made use of the well-known fact that the heart-beat of the frog can be inhibited by stimulation through the vagus nerve. Using a heart which had been washed and filled with Ringer's solution, Loewi showed that after a period of such stimulation the solution took up some chemical substance which had the property of causing inhibition in another heart when it was transferred to it. He referred to this substance as '*Vagusstoff*', but it soon proved possible to identify it as a result of work carried out some years earlier by Dale, who, owing to what he later came to describe as a 'lucky encounter with a peculiar ergot extract', had been led to a study of the properties of a choline ester known as acetylcholine. Dale had been struck by the resemblance between the effects of this substance and the effects of stimulation through certain tracts of the autonomic nervous system, mainly of the parasympathetic division. He had recognized the potential importance of this, but had put the matter on one side because there was not at that time any evidence that a substance resembling acetylcholine actually existed within the body. Seven years afterwards, however, Loewi had found this evidence, for it became apparent that his '*Vagusstoff*' was identical with acetylcholine, and the way was now open for the recognition of the latter as a chemical transmitter operating between parasympathetic fibres and their end organs.

Meanwhile the basis of a similar interpretation of sympathetic innervation had been developing, for in 1905 Elliott had drawn attention to the close similarity between the action of adrenaline and the effects of the sympathetic nervous system, and had even gone so far as to suggest that it 'might be the chemical stimulant liberated on each occasion when the sympathetic impulse arrives at the periphery.' This was the first formulation, however tentative, of the theory of the chemical transmission of the nerve impulse, but the identification of the sympathetic transmitter actually developed more slowly than that of the parasympathetic one, although it seemed clear that it must at least have some very close relationship with adrenaline. W. B. Cannon, however, who especially concerned himself with the problem, doubted its complete identity with the latter and preferred to call it sympathin, a caution that was amply justified by the subsequent discovery of the physiological significance of noradrenaline, for it is now known that this is the main, if not the only, sympathetic transmitter substance.

The present state of our knowledge of these matters may now be summarized in these general terms. The nerve cell and its axon can be regarded as a closed system, excitation of which leads to the conduction of nerve impulses through it. This conduction depends upon excitation of the cell membrane with consequent movements through it of sodium and potassium ions, these movements setting up a flow of electric current (the action current) and promoting similar changes in the immediately adjacent portion of the membrane, so that the activity is self-propagating. These reactions are not peculiar to nerve cells, for muscle cells have similar excitable membranes, and their responses are brought about in essentially the same way, impulses being propagated by action currents with consequent activation of the contractile mechanisms of the cell. There is, however, a point of discontinuity between the nerve ending and the effector cell at the nerve-muscle junction or end-plate, and it is here that the chemical transmitter is released from the nerve ending, to react immediately with the end-plate. The result of this is probably a depolarization of the latter and the setting up of a flow of current with consequential excitation of the muscle cell. The transmitter released in this way at autonomic nerve endings may be either acetylcholine, the fibres concerned being then termed cholinergic, or noradrenaline, such fibres being termed adrenergic, the distribution of these two possibilities agreeing closely, but not quite exactly, with the distinction between, respectively, the parasympathetic and sympathetic divisions. The differences between the properties of adrenaline and noradrenaline, and the fact that it is the latter that is particularly released at adrenergic nerve endings, explains the lack of precise agreement, to which we have already referred, between the effects of the former and those of stimulation through the sympathetic division.

We thus see that the link between the postganglionic nerve cells of the autonomic system and their smooth muscle effector cells depends upon the transmission of a chemical substance secreted by the former, but the principle of chemical transmission of the nerve impulse is not confined to these endings alone. It is now accepted as probable that a similar process occurs where similar endings excite secretory cells, and there is certainly good evidence that acetylcholine acts in this way at the nerve-muscle junctions of striated muscle. The same transmitter is also liberated at the synapses between the pre-ganglionic and post-ganglionic neurones of the autonomic system, and it is at least possible that chemical transmission of some sort takes place at synapses in the central nervous system, although here the evidence is still very incomplete. These facts sufficiently substantiate our earlier argument that secretion is a fundamental property of the nerve cell, and we can now appreciate the close similarity that exists between the chromaffin cells and adrenergic neurones in this respect.

Thus, fractional centrifugation of homogenates of nervous tissue has yielded granules which contain noradrenaline and which apparently correspond with the synaptic vesicles seen in electron micrographs (see Fig. 80). These vesicles are bounded by a membrane, and their contents

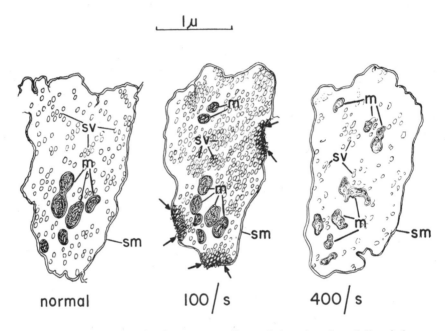

Fig. 80. Diagrams showing nerve endings of the adrenal medulla of the normal rabbit, and after stimulation for 10 min with supramaximal pulses of 100 and 400 per second (cf. Plate XIII). At 100 there is a near maximal output of catechol amines from the gland, and an increase in the number of synaptic vesicles and in their liberation. At 400 there is a diminished output of catechol amines, accompanied by fatigue of the nerve endings and depletion of their synaptic vesicles. cf. Plate IX.
    m, mitochondria; sm, synaptic membrane; sv, synaptic vesicles.
    (From de Robertis, 1959. *Internat. Rev. Cyt.* **8**, 61–96.)

become depleted after discharge of the chemical transmitter substance, so that the situation closely resembles that which we have already noted in the chromaffin cells. The comparison of these with sympathetic neurones can, however, be pressed further than this. For one thing, the former receives a nerve supply, a situation which is very uncommon in the endocrine system, and the functional condition of the nerve endings varies under experimental stimulation in a manner which can be correlated with fluctuations in the output of amines from the gland (Fig. 80). The significant feature of this nerve supply is that it is generally held to consist of preganglionic sympathetic fibres (cf. Fig. 91, p. 269) so that in this respect chromaffin cells could be said to have the same anatomical relationships as have postganglionic sympathetic cells, as well as resembling them in being able to synthesize catechol amines. There is evidence, however, that this innervation is post-ganglionic in elasmobranchs (Fig. 75) but even so the close relationship between the chromaffin cells and the cells of the sympathetic ganglia is demonstrated by their common embryonic origin. The ganglia themselves are derived largely, if not entirely, from the neural crest of the embryo, the remarkable area bordering the neural plate which, by breaking down into migratory cells, becomes the origin not only of these ganglia but also of a wide variety of tissues ranging from pigment cells to the major part of the visceral arch skeleton. An extension of this migration results in cells moving out of the ganglia (Fig. 83) and giving rise to chromaffin tissue, usually in close relationship with the developing adrenocortical rudiment.

In comparing the chromaffin cells with the post-ganglionic neurones, then, we find community of biosynthetic activity and of embryological origin, and perhaps also identity of anatomical relationships. It seems highly probable, therefore, that they have had a common evolutionary origin and since, as we shall now see, their functional relationship is equally close, it becomes helpful to regard them as constituting a sympathetico-chromaffin complex. This makes it easy to accept that chromaffin cells are found in parts of the sympathetic division as well as in the chromaffin tissue itself; groups of such cells, known as paraganglia, are particularly characteristic of immature mammals and tend to disappear later, but isolated cells may persist in the ganglia throughout life. In addition, developing adrenal tissue may give rise to accessory glands, often largely adrenocortical in composition, but sometimes with chromaffin tissue included.

5. The sympathetico-chromaffin complex in mammals

In reviewing the development of the theory of chemical transmitter substances we have noted that there was considerable delay in establishing the presence of acetylcholine in the body. Dale had foreseen that this substance, if present at all, might be very difficult to identify because of its rapid enzymatic destruction, and later work showed that this suggestion was well founded. Loewi himself showed that the activity of his '*Vagus-stuff*' was destroyed by an esterase and that it could be restored by acetylation, and it is known that under physiological conditions acetylcholine is almost instantaneously destroyed by a cholinesterase. By this avoidance of the possibility of wide diffusion of the transmitter substance the precision of control of the cholinergic fibres is safe-guarded; it is, in fact, a bio-chemical parallel to the localization of their synaptic relays close to the end-organs, which localizes the area of discharge of the impulses. The situation as regards noradrenaline is a little different. The existence of the catechol amines in the circulation seems to be short-lived, for the greater part of an intravenous injection of adrenaline is destroyed within a very few minutes, probably as a result of deamination, followed by oxidation. Nevertheless, the rate of destruction is less rapid that that of acetylcholine, so that noradrenaline can certainly escape into the blood and may thus be able to produce effects upon end-organs remote from its point of origin. This again parallels the anatomical organization of the fibres concerned, because their synaptic relays are at some distance from the effectors which they innervate (in, for example, the ganglia of the solar plexus), so that impulses can be propagated over widely diffused paths. It is not, in fact, essential for both divisions of the autonomic system to be equally precise in their action; if, in general, they are antagonistic to each other it will be sufficient if one produces localized modulation of a general condition set up by the other.

Our present conception of the functional significance of these facts derives from an analysis which was developed particularly by Cannon, and which we have already encountered in one of its aspects in our discussion of the homeostatic regulation of metabolism. Animals must maintain their activity in a constantly fluctuating external medium, and they must in consequence be able to respond to those fluctuations with corresponding internal adjustments. It seems evident that this problem became more acute in the vertebrates at the stage when some of these animals left the water and adopted a terrestrial life, with its more rigorous and variable conditions, and it is probably largely in correlation with this that we find the autonomic nervous system in the higher members of the group developing an increasingly well-defined antagonism between its two com-ponents and conferring finally upon the homoiothermous birds and mam-mals a capacity for a remarkably precise control of their internal medium. This development is based upon the same principle that governs the relationship of insulin with its antagonists, the regulation of a dynamic equilibrium by the interaction of opposing systems.

We have seen that the organization of the sympathetic division is adapted to bring about a somewhat diffuse type of response. Included in this are many reactions that increase the capacity of the animal for work and activity at times of emergency, such as the acceleration of the heart-beat, the redistribution of blood, and the dilatation of the bronchioles. Again, during exposure to cold or at a time of emotional excitement, it will bring about erection of hairs or the 'goose flesh' which is its vestigial equivalent in man. All such responses will be accompanied by a release of adrenaline and noradrenaline from the chromaffin tissue because of its sympathetic innervation, and these hormones, released perhaps in proportions dependent upon the nature of the stimulus, will develop and prolong the animal's reaction; thus it is that students sitting their examinations may pass into a transitory hyperglycaemic state. We can therefore regard the sympathetic division and the chromaffin tissue as forming a physiological complex which organizes the body for resisting emergencies by 'fright, flight, or a fight'. This complex is not, however, essential for life in a limited sense, as is shown by the fact that Cannon was able to keep alive for three and a half years a cat from which all parts of the sympathetic nervous system had been removed. Nevertheless, such animals could only hope to survive under carefully controlled laboratory conditions; they have a reduced capacity for work and they lack the ability to respond to emergencies, so that in the long run the complex must be regarded as essential for life in the more realistic use of that word.

The discovery that the chemical transmitter at post-ganglionic sympathetic nerve endings is chiefly, if not exclusively, noradrenaline makes it necessary to assume that the two catechol hormones, differing in their individual properties, must be concerned with more than a simple prolongation of the effects of sympathetic stimulation, and that the differences in their properties must be of some physiological significance. It has been suggested that the release of adrenaline predominates under conditions of emotional stress as, allegedly, in passengers prior to flying in aircraft or in patients suffering from pain or from hypoglycaemia, and that noradrenaline tends to be preferentially released in circumstances involving circulatory stress as, for example, during asphyxia or the carrying out of heavy muscular work. There is certainly evidence that such differential release does occur, and we have seen that there is a histological basis for it, but its significance needs further elucidation. It may be, for example, that adrenaline is concerned with a more general mobilization of the body's resources at times of stress, or it may be, as some have suggested, that it has as one of its functions the stimulation of the release of corticotropin from the pars distalis of the pituitary gland (p. 253).

One of the well-defined effects of the catechol hormones is the production of a rise in metabolic rate, with a consequential elevation in heat output, and this, the so-called calorigenic effect, may be expected to play some part in the regulation of the body temperature of mammals. There is some reason for believing that noradrenaline is of particular importance in this respect, and that it is specifically concerned in cold acclimation, the term given to the adaptive responses of animals to prolonged exposure to low temperatures. Under such circumstances small mammals, which offer little scope for improvement of the insulating value of their fur, seem to rely upon increasing their metabolism without the aid of visible shivering. This non-shivering thermogenesis may lead to a doubling of the heat production in rats, and the result of this is greatly to increase the possibility of the animals remaining active at low temperatures. During such cold acclimation there is an increase in the concentration of catechol amines in the chromaffin tissue and an increased urinary excretion of noradrenaline, and for this and other reasons it is thought that the latter may be the actual mediator of the response, the main tissues to show the increased metabolism being probably the striated muscles (cf. p. 192).

The belief implicit in the above analysis, that the catechol amines are true hormones, rests on the demonstration that they are released into the blood stream from the chromaffin tissue under sympathetic stimulation, and that they are present in the circulation in sufficient quantities to influence the organs over and above the extent to which these would be influenced by sympathetic stimulation alone. This can be shown to be so by observing the reactions of animals in which the heart has been denervated. On exposure of such animals to cold the heart-beat is found to accelerate, and this can only be due to the action of the adrenaline released from the chromaffin tissue, for the latter retains its sympathetic nerve supply while the heart has been deprived of this and cannot, therefore, be stimulated by nerve impulses. It is found, too, that if such an animal is excited for one minute an acceleration of heart-beat may persist for nearly thirty minutes; this prolonged response must be due to the continuous release of the hormone into the circulation, while further confirmatory evidence is that the acceleration fails to occur at all if one medulla is removed (enucleation of the adrenal gland) and the other denervated. It would probably be a mistake, however, to suppose that the chromaffin tissue only secretes in response to emergencies; a healthy man is said to excrete about 30 μg of noradrenaline and 10 μg of adrenaline per day, despite the fact that these substances are so rapidly metabolized, and it seems probable, as already mentioned, that a continuous, if small, secretion is continuously released from the gland.

6. The catechol hormones in other animals

It is now known that both adrenaline and noradrenaline are present in extracts of chromaffin tissue from a wide range of vertebrates, including elasmobranch and teleost fish, and they have also been identified in extracts prepared from the ventral nerve cords of earthworms. In addition, both are present in a variety of insects, more particularly in the larvae and imagos, but they are said to be lacking in a number of other invertebrate groups. The physiological significance of this distribution is not clear, and it cannot be assumed that the catechol amines act as chemical transmitter substances in these groups, for according to von Euler it still remains to be established that adrenergic fibres occur even in fish.

It is well established, however, that adrenaline has a stimulatory influence upon the heart of vertebrates in general and also of many invertebrates, and this property, according to Fänge and Östlund, is shared by noradrenaline. In the isolated and perfused heart of *Raja batis*, for example, both substances produce a marked increase in the amplitude of the beat and a slight increase in its frequency, precisely identical effects being evoked by extracts of the interrenal (chromaffin) tissue of *Squalus acanthias*. A curious feature is a brief initial inhibitory action which,

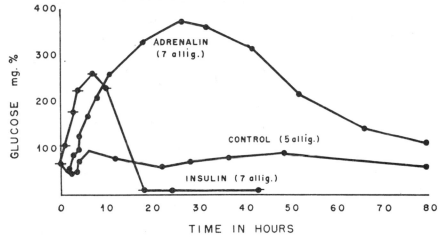

Fig. 81. The effect of adrenaline (2 ml per kg of 1/1000) and commercial insulin (1.0 U/gm) on blood glucose in *Alligator mississippiensis*. The results are qualitatively similar to those obtained with mammals but the response to adrenaline is considerably delayed.

(From Coulson & Hernandez, 1953. *Endocrin.* **53**, 311–20.)

since it can be abolished by treatment with atropine, may possibly result from the release of acetylcholine from the vagal nerve endings.

Equally well established is the metabolic influence of these hormones. Both will promote glycogenolysis in the perfused and isolated liver of the toad, while the injection of adrenaline evokes hyperglycaemia in all groups of vertebrates, but it is by no means clear that such actions contribute to the handling of emergencies. Coulson and Hernandez have remarked in this connexion on the considerable delay in the blood-sugar response of the alligator to the injection of adrenaline (Fig. 81), a delay shown also in the contraction of the pupil, which does not begin until after two hours and then persists for a long time, so that the animal remains nearly blind for several hours. It may be, then, that the functions of the catechol hormones in mammals, as postulated in Cannon's interpretation, are dependent upon high body temperature and consequent speed of response, and that the metabolic influence of these substances in lower forms is of a more generalized nature, although it still remains difficult to determine how far the responses of experimental animals to them are truly physiological or merely pharmacological.

Of particular interest in this connexion, however, is the curious situation in the cyclostomes. The work of Fänge, Östlund, and their colleagues has clearly shown that the hearts of both *Lampetra* and *Myxine* contain exceptionally large amounts of adrenaline and noradrenaline, present both in chromaffin cells and to some extent in the muscle cells themselves. Now in contrast to the typical situation in vertebrates, the isolated hearts of these two animals respond only weakly to these catechols, and it has been suggested that this may be because their metabolism is normally influenced by catechols released from their own tissues. If this is so, a further significant fact is that while the heart of the lamprey is innervated by the vagus nerve, the heart of *Myxine* has no innervation and possesses no nervous tissue at all in its wall. This latter animal is such a remarkable blend of primitive and specialized characters that it is impossible to decide *a priori* the status of this particular condition, but if one considers it in conjunction with the suggestion that the chromaffin tissue of elasmobranchs may receive post-ganglionic innervation (p. 227) there clearly emerges the possibility that this tissue may in some cases have been initially concerned with the peripheral regulation or support of metabolism and that its pre-ganglionic innervation may be a secondary development. This suggestion, of course, runs counter to the widely accepted view that the chromaffin cells have evolved from post-ganglionic sympathetic neurones, and it may well prove to be ill-founded, but we can hardly doubt that much remains to be learned about the evolution of the sympathetico-chromaffin complex in the lower vertebrates, and of the function of the catechol amines in invertebrate animals.

7. Hormones and neurohumours

It may now be appreciated that, despite these uncertainties, the evidence for the hormonal status of the catechol amines is singularly complete, as judged by the criteria which we have earlier suggested. They have been purified and synthesized, their site of origin has been demonstrated, a plausible mode of biosynthesis suggested with some experimental confirmation, and they have been shown to be present in the blood stream and, particularly in mammals, to participate in normal physiological responses of a clearly defined character. We have also encountered an extension of the principle of chemical regulation beyond the limits of the classical definition of a hormone, for the catechol amines are not only transmitted through the blood stream but one at least of them, in conjunction with acetylcholine, functions as a chemical transmitter, at certain nerve endings. Since in so doing it is released from one cell and produces a specific effect in another it is still satisfying the condition of transmission which is one of the elements of the definition (p. 3), although the distance is minute and the route is not provided by the blood stream.

Some writers have sought to deal with this situation by making a distinction between vascular hormones and tissue hormones, thus emphasizing the difference in the mode of transmission, but this is inconvenient in practice since by far the greater part of endocrinological discussion centres around the vascular ones and the adjective tends to become a tautology. We shall here adopt, therefore, the procedure outlined earlier (p. 76), and shall employ the term neurohumour for transmitter agents which are secreted by neurones and used in regulatory processes which demand precise timing and rapid completion. The term hormone remains as we have already defined it (p. 3), which means, of course, that noradrenaline at least must be included both as a neurohumour and a hormone. There should be no need for confusion to arise from this overlap; indeed, it constitutes a situation that will surprise nobody who is familiar with the difficulty of confining biological phenomena within the framework of formal definitions.

X. THE ADRENOCORTICAL TISSUE
OF THE ADRENAL GLAND

1. Physiological effects of adrenocortical secretions

W E have had occasion to note several dates that mark steps of fundamental importance in the development of endocrinology and one that must certainly be included with these is 15 March 1849, which saw the publication by Thomas Addison of a preliminary note on a chronic clinical condition which was later to be called Addison's disease. Six years later he had developed the subject into a monograph entitled *On the Constitutional and Local Effects of Diseases of the Suprarenal Capsules.* Addison's disease comprises a wide-ranging complex of symptoms, including general debility, muscular weakness, low blood pressure, and disturbed ionic balance of the body fluids. The ascription of this Addisonian syndrome to disorder of the adrenal glands was clearly established by Addison's studies, and the condition is now known to be due to destruction of the adrenocortical tissue, but the importance of the distinction between medulla and cortex was not at that time apparent. When, therefore, Oliver and Schäfer discovered in extracts of the gland the active principle that was subsequently identified as adrenaline, it was natural to suppose that this was the agent involved, particularly since it was observed to increase muscular tone and elevate the blood pressure. Nevertheless, this supposition was incorrect.

We have seen that cats can survive the removal of the sympathetic nervous system, and similarly animals can survive the removal of the whole of one adrenal gland and enucleation of the other. The complete removal of both glands, however, is fatal, and it is now known that this result, and the progressive development of Addison's disease, are due to deprivation of adrenocortical hormones, which have a far-reaching and complex influence upon the maintenance of life. The extent of this influence can be judged from the summary made by Ingle of the effects of total adrenalectomy in mammals:

Digestive. Loss of appetite; delayed or incomplete absorption from the intestine; nausea and vomiting; ulceration of the alimentary tract; diarrhoea.

Circulatory. Increased concentration of the blood, and decrease in its pressure, flow and volume; decrease in the sodium, chloride, bicarbonate, and glucose of the serum, and increase in its potassium and non-protein nitrogen.

Tissues. Muscular weakness and reduction in muscle mass; decrease in sodium and increase in potassium and water in muscle; decrease in glycogen in the liver and muscles after fasting.

Kidney. Increased excretion (renal wastage) of sodium, chloride, and bicarbonate; decreased excretion of potassium and total nitrogen; inability to excrete ingested water.

Growth. Hypertrophy of the thymus and lymphoid structures; cessation of body growth; loss of weight; fall in body temperature.

Resistance. Decreased resistance to all forms of stress (e.g. toxins, injury, environmental changes), leading to death in untreated animals.

It is customary to simplify the analysis of adrenocortical functions by grouping them under two main headings, the first including effects exerted upon the metabolism of water and salt-electrolytes, and hence upon the serum concentrations of sodium and potassium, and the second including those exerted upon carbohydrate metabolism. Effects in the former category must presumably result largely from disturbances of the functioning of the kidney, and they are shown, for example, in the increased non-protein nitrogen of the blood which follows adrenalectomy. This can be restored to normal by injection of suitable adrenocortical extracts, and this procedure forms the basis for a bio-assay technique using dogs. The renal wastage of sodium and chloride shown in the above list is another example; injection of adrenocortical extracts in this instance will result in sodium retention, which is reflected in the decrease in the sodium/potassium ratio in the urine, and the measurement of this in rats is the basis for another bio-assay procedure. Such a disturbance of ionic balance, with which is associated disturbance in water metabolism, is doubtless one of the factors contributing to the death of adrenalectomized animals, and their condition can be greatly alleviated by the administration of sodium and chloride, preferably as a mixture of sodium chloride and bicarbonate in order to allow for the fact that sodium is lost at a greater rate than chloride; this treatment will permit the survival of such animals for long periods.

The effects upon carbohydrate metabolism are shown by the importance of the part played by the adrenal steroids in antagonizing the action of insulin (p. 57). They are illustrated, too, by the fall in blood sugar and in liver glycogen which are amongst the consequence of total adrenalectomy in mammals, and this is the basis for another bio-assay procedure, since the glycogen content of the liver can be restored by the injection of adrenocortical extracts. Loss of muscular strength is probably associated with such effects in so far as it may reflect disturbance of glucose metabolism. It is manifested in the rapid development of fatigue after adrenalectomy, and this can be measured quantitatively either by making rats swim in water until they are exhausted, or by making the gastrocnemius muscle contract against a weight in response to faradic stimulation. In an untreated adrenalectomized animal exhaustion of the muscle may occur in less than ten hours, while in one that is appropriately treated with adrenocortical extracts the muscle may be able to continue working for more than twenty-four hours.

2. Corticosteroids

We have seen that the analysis of the function of a supposed endocrine organ ideally involves not only a study of the effects of removing it but also of the possibility of alleviating these by replacement therapy. From 1928 onwards investigators were finding it possible to overcome the normally fatal results of complete adrenalectomy by injecting the animals concerned with extracts of adrenocortical tissue, and in consequence attempts were made to isolate and characterize an active principle. By analogy with what had been learned of other glands it was at first supposed that this would prove to be a single hormone which was provisionally designated as cortin, but this supposition, although properly in accord with the principle of Occam's razor, was ill-founded.

By 1931 it was already apparent that the activity was concentrated in the lipid fractions of the extracts, and its further analysis was a part of the developments in steroid chemistry which we have already encountered (p. 100). Systematic investigation of these fractions, following the isolation of oestrone in 1929, were carried out simultaneously by workers associated with Kendall, Wintersteiner, Pfiffner, and Reichstein, and a large number of adrenocortical steroids were soon isolated and characterized.

It has been said that for some time this work had something of an esoteric character, but a turning point came in May 1949, with the announcement from the Mayo Clinic that one of these substances, cortisone, appeared to be of strikingly beneficial value in the treatment of rheumatoid arthritis. With the large doses that were customary during the early trials some very dramatic results were achieved, patients who had been dependent on others for years being able within forty-eight hours to dress themselves. Further study showed that prolonged treatment with this substance might be associated with undesirable side-effects, such as peptic ulceration, sodium retention (leading to oedema), and increased risk of bone fracture, but the discovery was none the less of fundamental importance. The belief that literally millions of patients might be demanding treatment with a substance at a time when the world supply of it amounted to only a few grams provided an immense stimulus to research into methods for its bulk preparation, particularly since in the early days of insulin therapy some patients had died, owing to shortage of the hormone, after their condition had been temporarily alleviated. Thus it

has been found, for example, that cortisone can be prepared from progesterone, which itself can be prepared from diosgenin, the latter being a
steroid that is present in commercially workable quantities in plant
sources; the fall in the price of cortisone from about £1,500 to £12 per
ounce is a sufficient testimony to the success of such studies.

At the present time, some twenty-nine steroids have been isolated from
adrenocortical material, but, as we have earlier emphasized, the presence
of active substances in tissue extracts is no proof that they are a normal
secretory product of that tissue, or that they are of physiological importance. Many of these steroids are probably intermediary metabolites
or artifacts of the method of extraction, but even so they may be of great
potential importance. For example, they include androgens, oestrogens
and progesterone, and we shall see later how defects of adrenocortical
metabolism may result in the overproduction of these, with remarkable
consequences for the sexual differentiation of the affected individual.
Decisions as to which of these steroids are of major importance in the
normal functioning of the adrenocortical tissue have been greatly aided
by Vogt's demonstration that the quantities of steroids which are secreted
into the blood are large relative to the amounts which are extractable
from the tissue itself. Developments in paper chromatography, the
availability of known reference substances, and the utilization of certain
characteristic reactions of the corticosteroids have made it practicable
to identify and analyse these substances on the micro-scale, so that
it has been possible to determine which of them are actually released in
physiologically significant quantities. A note of caution is needed here,
however, for substances secreted in minute amounts may still be physiologically important if they have a very high biological activity, a point
which, as we shall see, has been well illustrated in the discovery of aldosterone.

Before we review some of these corticosteroids it should be noted
that the biologically active ones have two important features which may
be compared with those which are characteristic of the sex hormones.
Firstly, they carry in ring A an $\alpha\beta$-unsaturated ketone grouping, as also
does testosterone and progesterone (p. 106). Secondly, they are C_{21}
steroids, carrying, that is, two carbon atoms in a side-chain at carbon-17,
carbon-20 with a ketone substitution $(C=O)$ and carbon-21 with a hydroxyl
substitution.

With these facts in mind we may now consider the more important of
the mammalian corticosteroids (Fig. 82), referring to them by their
trivial names, together with the semi-trivial ones which are derived from
these by the addition of prefixes and which indicate related compounds.
We shall refer also to another system of nomenclature, which arises
from the fact that at the time when these compounds were first being

isolated it was customary for the research school concerned to designate them by letters of the alphabet; this system is passing into disuse, but is still encountered in the literature. Finally, those compounds that exert their effects mainly upon carbohydrate metabolism are called gluco-corticoids while those that act mainly upon the metabolism of water and of salt-electrolytes are called mineralocorticoids.

Corticosterone (Kendall's compound B). This compound, first isolated

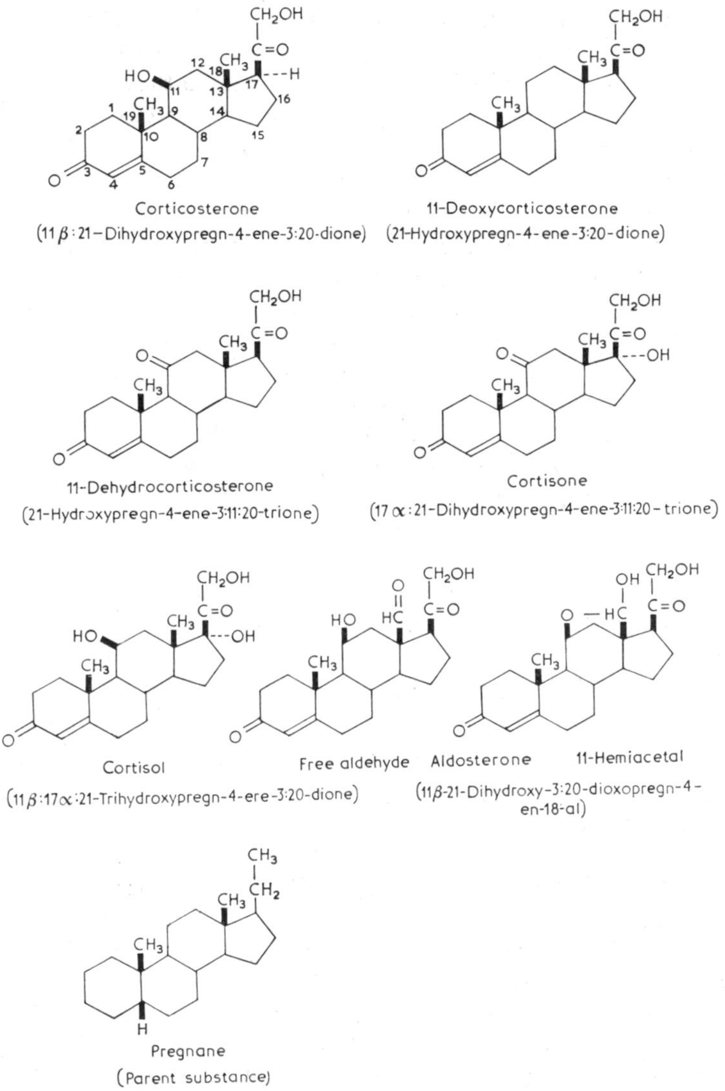

Corticosterone
(11 β : 21 − Dihydroxypregn-4-ene-3:20-dione)

11-Deoxycorticosterone
(21-Hydroxypregn-4-ene-3:20-dione)

11-Dehydrocorticosterone
(21-Hydroxypregn-4-ene-3:11:20-trione)

Cortisone
(17 α : 21-Dihydroxypregn-4-ene-3:11:20- trione)

Cortisol
(11 β :17α :21-Trihydroxypregn-4-ere-3:20-dione)

Free aldehyde   Aldosterone   11-Hemiacetal
(11β-21-Dihydroxy-3:20-dioxopregn-4-
en-18-al)

Pregnane
(Parent substance)

Fig. 82. Corticosteroids.

from bovine glands in 1937, is one of the major secretory products of the mammalian adrenocortical tissue, as judged by its concentration in the adrenal venous blood; together with cortisol (see below) it makes up from 74 per cent. to 100 per cent. of the corticosteroids in various mammalian species, but the proportions of the two differ markedly. Man, the monkey, and the sheep secrete mainly cortisol, the rat and the rabbit mainly corticosterone, while the cow, ferret, dog, and cat secrete more equal mixtures of both. Corticosterone has been regarded as being primarily a glucocorticoid, but it also has a definite, although moderate, action on salt-electrolyte metabolism.

Deoxycorticosterone. This is the accepted trivial name for the 11-deoxy compound, in which the hydroxyl group at carbon-11 is replaced by hydrogen. It is sometimes known as DOC, and its carbon-21 acetate as DCA. Deoxycorticosterone, which was first obtained by partial synthesis in 1937, seems to be secreted in only very small amounts, although it has been prepared from the glandular tissue. It produces some effect upon carbohydrate metabolism, but its main influence is upon water and salt-electrolyte metabolism, so that it has been regarded as belonging to the group of mineralocorticoids.

11-dehydrocorticosterone (Kendall's compound A). First isolated in 1936, this compound is very similar to corticosterone in its activity, and differs from it structurally in the loss of 2H from the CHOH at carbon-11, with the consequent formation of a keto group.

Cortisone (Kendall's compound E). This substance, the first biologically-active compound to be isolated from the adrenal cortex, can be produced from the preceeding one by the addition of a hydroxyl group at carbon-17. It is primarily glucocorticoid in its activity, but it also affects water and salt-electrolyte metabolism, and we have already noted its use in the treatment of rheumatoid arthritis. It does not seem to be one of the major components of the secretion in certain mammals, but it has been identified in the adrenal venous blood of the capon and grass-snake, and is formed by *in vitro* preparations of the adrenocortical tissue of the teleost *Fundulus.*

Cortisol (hydrocortisone, Kendall's compound F). This compound, first isolated in 1937, is the 11-hydroxy derivative corresponding to cortisone and, like it, is a 17-hydroxy compound. It closely resembles cortisone in being primarily glucocorticoid in its activity, but differs from it in being, as we have already noted, one of the major components of the adrenocortical secretion of mammals.

Aldosterone. It will be apparent that the main mammalian secretory products mentioned above are primarily glucocorticoid, while deoxycorticosterone, the only one of the compounds which is markedly mineralocorticoid, is secreted in only very small amounts; in fact, it has often been regarded as an artifact. Thus for some years there seemed to be a piece missing from the jig-saw. However, it was recognized that after active steroids had been extracted from adrenocortical tissue there remained a residue, called the amorphous fraction, which still possessed considerable activity, and the development by Simpson and Tait of an improved technique for the determination of mineralocorticoid activity made it possible to detect this in material which contained the amorphous fraction but which was known not to contain any deoxycorticosterone. This led to the demonstration in 1952 of the existence of another corticosteroid, subsequently called aldosterone, which was synthesized in 1955, and which proved to have a structural formula differing from all the others in possessing at carbon-18 an aldehyde substitution; this is normally masked by acetal formation with the hydroxyl group at carbon-11. It is of particular interest that aldosterone is present in the adrenal venous blood of mammals in only trace amounts, representing less than 1 per cent. to 2·5 per cent. of the total corticosteroid production in the dog. Functionally, however, it is a potent mineralocorticoid and is clearly the one that had been missing from the roster of adrenocortical products, for it has an effect on salt-electrolyte metabolism many times more powerful than that of deoxycorticosterone. It thus strikingly illustrates the principle that biological importance is not to be judged solely in terms of quantitative abundance, while its relatively late discovery reminds us that the apparent absence of an expected secretory product may merely reflect the imperfection of the means available for its detection (p. 176).

3. Development, organization, and histochemistry of adrenocortical tissue

We have seen that chromaffin tissue shares a common embryological origin with the sympathetic nervous system and have commented on the significance of this. Of equal interest is the fact that the adrenocortical tissue and the gonads are closely related in their development, for they share an equally close biosynthetic relationship in being the main sources of steroid hormones in the vertebrates. The situation is well seen in the gymnophionan amphibian, *Hypogeophis*, where, as in other vertebrates, the adrenocortical cells are budded off, like the gonadal tissue, from localized thickenings of the coelomic epithelium (Fig. 83). They lose their connexion with the epithelium and come to lie ventro-lateral to the dorsal aorta, in the angle between it and the median cardinal vein. Tracts of cells growing out from the sympathetic ganglia then connect with these adrenocortical rudiments and give rise to the chromaffin tissue, and in this way the compound gland arises from two entirely separate sets of rudiments.

As finally established in placental mammals, the adrenal gland is surrounded by a connective tissue capsule which extends inwards to ramify amongst the secretory cells of the cortex. It carries blood vessels with it, but, in sharp contrast with the chromaffin tissue, the adreno-cortical cells receive no secreto-motor nerve supply. These cells are arranged mainly in cords which give rise to three distinct zones (Fig. 84). The outermost of these is the zona glomerulosa, characterized by the cells

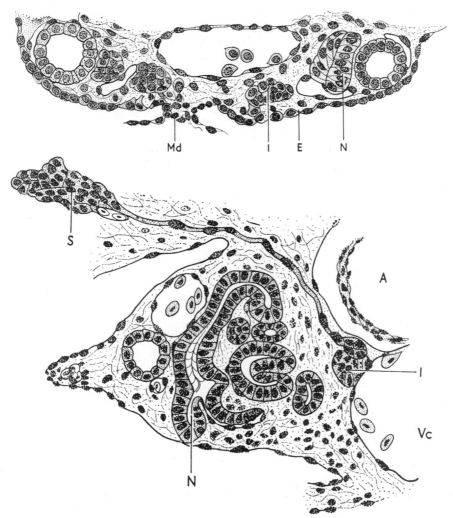

Fig. 83. Transverse sections of embryos of *Hypogeophis* (Amphibia, Gymno-phiona). *A*, aorta; *E*, coelomic epithelium; *I*, adrenocortical rudiment, developing in the upper figure from the coelomic epithelium; *Md*, dorsal mesentery; *N*, mesonephros; *S*, sympathetic ganglion, from which developing chromaffin tissue is extending to the adrenocortical rudiment; *Vc*, cardinal vein.
(From Brachet, 1921. *Embryologie des Vertébrés*, Masson.)

forming loops or clusters, the middle one is the zona fasciculata, where there are long, straight cords, while the innermost is the zone reticularis, where the cords form a network. These zones differ in their histological characteristics, but one significant feature of the adrenocortical tissue as a

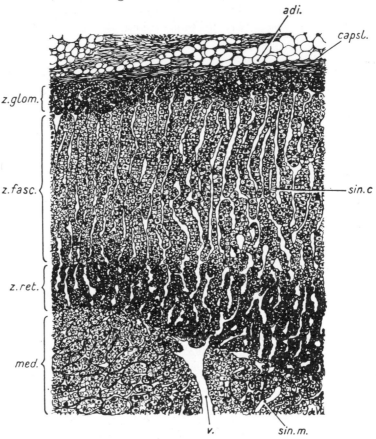

Fig. 84. Section of the adrenal gland of the monkey (*Macacus*).
adi., adipose tissue; *capsl.*, connective tissue capsule; *med.*, medulla (chromaffin tissue); *sin. c.*, sinusoids of the cortex; *sin. m.*, sinusoids of the medulla; *v.*, vein; *z. fasc.*, zona fasciculata; *z. glom.*, zona glomerulosa; *z. ret.*, zona reticularis.
(From Young, 1957. *The Life of Mammals.* Oxford: Clarendon Press.)

whole is the presence in its cells of lipid droplets. These are particularly richly developed in the outer part of the zona fasciculata, while in the zona reticularis they are scarce and, when present, rather large. This latter circumstance, together with the pycnotic appearance of many of the nuclei, gave rise at one time to the belief that new cells originated at the outer side of the cortex, moved inwards, and were finally removed in the reticularis, but this interpretation is disputed and it seems certain that cell proliferation can occur in the reticularis as well as in the fasciculata. Moreover, there is now good evidence that the histological differentiation of the adrenocortical tissue is an expression of a functional differentiation, for it appears from *in vitro* studies that aldosterone (with some corticosterone) is produced in the ox only by the zona glomerulosa, while corticosterone and cortisol are produced by the zona fasciculata and perhaps also by the glomerulosa.

The lipid droplets are readily demonstrated by osmic acid and the Sudan dyes (Plate X E) but it has long been appreciated that they possess certain properties that differentiate them from ordinary fat. They are, for example, more resistant to acids and alkalies, they do not blacken so intensely with osmic acid, and after treatment with the latter they continue to be soluble in xylene and in other fat solvents. With the realization that the hormones of the adrenocortical tissue were steroids it was natural to suppose that they would be associated with the lipid droplets, and that this would account for the distinctive properties of the latter. Attempts have therefore been made to devise histochemical methods that would demonstrate their presence and would make it possible to study variations in the functional status of the gland. Bennett, in particular, was a pioneer in the modifications of the methods of steroid chemistry for this purpose, and techniques recommended by him have been widely used.

Histochemical procedures, however, require the most searching and critical scrutiny before their validity can be accepted. It is essential, for example, that any one method shall be based upon a clearly defined chemical reaction, and that this reaction shall be specific for the particular type of substance which is under investigation. Unfortunately, it is doubtful whether the histochemical methods available for the study of adrenocortical tissue satisfy such conditions. Indeed, there are those who would say that the fat-soluble Sudan dyes are still the best indicator of the functional state of the cortex, but it is also fair to add that the other methods are of great value in following changes in that functional state provided that no more chemical significance is read into the observations than the methods themselves can justly bear. These methods are fully discussed in current works on histochemistry, and we shall here note only the general sense of the criticisms to which they have been subjected.

With the phenylhydrazine reaction the formation of yellow phenylhydrazones indicates the presence of carbonyl groups, but the difficulty here is that some of the carbonyl groups give a positive PAS reaction (p. 284) and must, apparently, be aldehydic in nature, being derived from unsaturated fatty acid residues. On the other hand, some are probably ketonic and may be assumed to be derived from ketosteroids, but since the concentration of these in adrenocortical tissue is exceedingly small, amounting to perhaps 12·5 μg of active material per gm of fresh tissue, it has been questioned whether the phenylhydrazine can in any case be expected to yield a useful positive reaction with such minute amounts. Ashbel and Seligman introduced in 1949 the use of 3-hydroxy-2-napthoic acid hydrazide, with the aim of improving the sensitivity of the reaction. The resulting hydrazone is coupled with diazotized dianisidine to form a blue product, but the specificity of this method has also been questioned, and it is said that aldehydes react even more readily with it than do ketones.

Owing to the supposition, for which there is much evidence, that the biosynthesis of steroid hormones proceeds from acetate through cholesterol, tests for the latter substance have been widely used in studies both of the gonads and of adrenocortical tissue. With Schultz's method a blue-green colour indicates the presence of cholesterol, but it is said that a lipid droplet must contain at least 10 per cent. to give a positive reaction. The presence of birefringent crystals in the lipid droplets of fresh or formalin-fixed material can be observed in frozen sections under a polarizing microscope and is also thought to indicate the presence of cholesterol esters and therefore, perhaps, of hormonal products; it does, in fact, seem that the size of these crystals varies with the condition of the adrenocortical tissue, being smaller, for example, in the rat after the administration of corticotropin (p. 250). The presence of cholesterol can also be demonstrated by the Windaus reaction, in which digitonin is used to precipitate birefringent crystals of a cholesterol-digitonin complex (Plate x c).

Importance has been attached to the fluorescence shown by the lipid droplets in fixed material, but this is of uncertain significance; it is said to parallel the carbonyl reaction, and is possibly a generalized property of unsaturated fats and fatty acids.

Finally, it may be mentioned that considerable amounts of ascorbic acid are present in the cortex, and the reduction of acid silver nitrate has been used to demonstrate this; here again, however, there is doubt as to the specificity of the method, and in any case the significance of the presence of this substance in adrenocortical tissue is quite obscure. Its depletion by corticotropin is, however, the basis of one method of bio-assay of that hormone.

It may be well to add that the application of all of these methods in a particular investigation does not increase the specificity of any one of them! Strength, therefore, is not necessarily gained from numbers, but it does appear to be a fact that areas that react to one of the reagents enumerated above do not necessarily coincide with those reacting to others, and in practice such differences seem to give at least some evidence of fluctuations in the degree of activity in the different parts. On the other hand, it must be remembered that the corticosteroid content of adrenal effluent blood is far in excess of the amount that is actually extractable from the

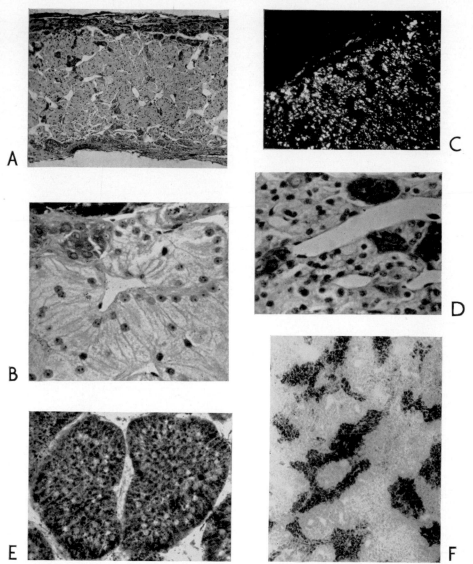

Plate X. *A*. L.S. of the adrenal gland of a male lizard, *Agama*, showing adreno-cortical cords and blood sinuses. The peripheral layer of chromaffin tissue is at the top, and islets of this tissue are seen amongst the adrenocortical cords. (Zenker-formol, Haematoxylin and eosin. × 63.)

B. Part of the same gland at higher magnification. The peripheral chromaffin layer is at the very top, with an islet of this tissue just below. (Heidenhain and van Gieson. × 420.)

C. Part of the gland of a normal animal, showing birefringent material made up of cholesterol digitonides. (Windaus digotonin method. × 40.)

D. Part of the gland of an animal hypophysectomized for 30 days. The chromaffin islets remain normal, but the adrenocortical cells are reduced and their nuclei are pycnotic. (× 420.)

E. Part of the adrenal gland of a normal grass-snake, *Natrix*, showing the sudano-philia of the adrenocortical cells. (Formol, Sudan black. × 280.)
(From Wright & Chester Jones, 1957. *J. Endocrin.* **15**, 83–99.)

F. Frozen section of the adrenal medulla of the cat after treatment for 48 hours with 10% potassium iodate solution. Cells containing noradrenaline are coloured by an insoluble brown oxidation product; those containing adrenaline are uncoloured, the red 2-iodoadrenochrome having been dissolved out during the procedure. (× 35.)
(From Hillarp & Hökfelt, 1955. *J. Hist. Cytochem.* **3**, 1–5.)

gland, so that we can hardly expect the relationship between activity and lipid content to be a simple one.

We have already briefly reviewed the distribution of adrenocortical tissue in the several vertebrate groups, and histochemical investigations along the above-mentioned lines have given results in general agreement with the anatomical evidence. The supposed adrenocortical tissue of cyclostomes awaits adequate study from this point of view, but in tetrapods and elasmobranchs it has been shown that the adrenocortical cells (although not necessarily all of them) do contain sudanophilic and osmiophilic lipid droplets, and that these give positive reactions to the Schultz and phenylhydrazine tests and can form birefringent crystals. A surprising exception is provided by the interrenal tissue of teleosts which, although possessing ascorbic acid, seems to lack the typical lipid droplets of adreno-cortical tissue and is largely negative to the standard tests. Since, as we have explained, the latter are not in any case specific for these steroids this does not necessarily imply any fundamental difference between the secretory products of this tissue and that of the other groups, but it serves to remind us that the teleosts are the product of a specialized line of evolution which is remote from the main line of vertebrate ascent. It is, of course, the Dipnoi and the coelacanth *Latimeria* which of all living fish stand closest to that line, and it is unfortunate that the situation in the lung-fish is not entirely clear owing to the presence (in *Protopterus*) of much fatty tissue which superficially resembles adrenocortical tissue in some of its properties. However, groups of cells lying in the region of the kidney have been shown to contain lipid material and to give positive responses to the cholesterol and phenylhydrazine tests, so that the crossopterygian fish probably resemble the tetrapods more closely than do the teleosts.

4. Corticosteroids and vertebrate evolution

The doubts about the specificity of the histochemical procedures show how unsatisfactory it would be to have to depend solely upon them for establishing the existence of adrenocortical activity in the lower verte-brates, and it is fortunate, therefore, that methods are now available for identifying micro-quantities of corticosteroids in the circulating blood, a consequence, as we have seen, of the technical demands created by the clinical use of cortisone. Ideally, it is desirable that blood should be collected for this purpose as it drains from the cortical tissue, and this has been achieved by Chester Jones in the domestic fowl (*Gallus domesticus*) and in the grass-snake (*Natrix natrix*), while it has been possible to collect a mixture of renal and adrenal blood from amphibians (e.g. *Xenopus laevis* and *Amphiuma tridactyla*). In fish this is technically impossible, so that use must here be made of blood drained from the general circulation, the small quantities available creating, of course, difficult problems

of supply, as may be judged from the fact that the identification of aldosterone in the sockeye salmon required the processing of 8,868 ml of
teleost plasma, obtained from 364 fish. Less exacting from this point of
view is the investigation of the production of corticosteroids by adrenocortical tissue when this is incubated *in vitro*. In this way Phillips and
Mulrow have shown that the head kidney of *Fundulus*, with its embedded
adrenocortical tissue, can convert progesterone to cortisol, cortisone, and
aldosterone, while Nandi and Bern have obtained cortisol and cortisone
by incubating the head kidneys of several other teleosts, in this case without
the addition of progesterone to the medium.

The results of both type of investigation are shown in simplified form
in Table 5. The data are scanty and are drawn from the study of only a

TABLE 5

*Corticosteroids which have been identified in certain species from the major
groups of vertebrates.*

	Corticosterone	Cortisol	Cortisone	Aldosterone
Cyclostomata	+	+		
Elasmobranchii	+	+		+
Actinopterygii	+	+		+
Amphibia	+	+		+
Reptilia	+	+	+	+
Aves	+	+	+	+

very few species, but they suggest, as far as they go, that the adrenocortical
tissue of vertebrates has a uniformity in its synthetic capacity comparable
with that of its histochemical properties. They also provide at least the
beginning of a basis for speculation as to adrenocortical function in these
lower forms. Firstly, the existence in teleost plasma of aldosterone
with other corticosteroids gives some ground for supposing that the
production of mineralocorticoid and glucocorticoid hormones is a fundamental characteristic of the tissue. There is some evidence, too, that they
may be essential for life, for complete adrenalectomy in non-mammalian
vertebrates is often fatal, although seasonal conditions may affect the
result as, for example, in frogs, which are much more resistant to the
operation in winter than they are in summer. It is impossible to enumerate
the results of such operations in more detail, but it appears that the
metabolic symptoms are sometimes of the character that would be associated in mammals with glucocorticoid deprivation, such as muscular weakness, circulatory disturbances, hypoglycaemia, and loss of liver glycogen,
but information in this field is still very incomplete.

That mineralocorticoid symptoms are also present is indicated by
the way in which removal of the adrenocortical tissue from frogs results

in a loss of sodium and accumulation of water; it is significant, too, that the lives of such animals can often be prolonged by immersing them in isotonic saline, which enables them to maintain a more normal water and electrolyte balance. On the other hand, the removal of this tissue from skates has been said to produce no significant change in the electrolytes, although the interpretation of the data of these particular experiments has been questioned. However, the problem can also be approached by injecting corticosteroids into unoperated animals, and rainbow trout (*Salmo gairdnerii*) have been employed in this way. Using fish into which saline had been previously injected in order to establish a salt load, it has been shown that the mineralocorticoid deoxycorticosterone and the glucocorticoid cortisol both evoke a mineralocorticoid type of response, including increased sodium retention by the kidney, increased sodium excretion by the gills, and diminished sodium uptake from the external medium. Here, in exerting an effect upon the gills, the corticosteroids are acting in a manner that has no exact parallel in mammals, thereby illustrating the principle, already noted in our discussion of the hypothalamic polypeptides, that adaptive evolution of a major group must involve a concomitant evolution of the relationship between hormones and their target organs. So also in birds, where cortisol promotes the removal of excess sodium in the secretion of the nasal (supra-orbital) glands. The concentration of the ion in this fluid reaches a higher level than is attainable in mammalian urine, and this, by enabling birds to survive the ingestion of sea water, is presumably of considerable physiological importance in marine species.

A further complication here is that natural selection is able to play upon the whole complex of interacting hormones which makes up the endocrine system. We have already seen that more than one hormone is involved in the regulation of carbohydrate metabolism (p. 56) and that the hypothalamus and neural lobe are involved in the regulation of water balance (p. 85). If we accept the arguments of Robertson, that vertebrates arose in the sea and that the glomerulus was initially concerned with ionic exchange under marine conditions (p. 93), we can venture the speculation that corticosteroids might have evolved early as part of the physiological mechanism for regulating ionic balance. Thereafter they would have constituted a system upon which, in conjunction with other hormonal mechanisms such as the polypeptide secretions of the hypothalamus (p. 92), the vertebrates could have drawn as they progressively improved their homeostatic mechanisms in response to the demands of freshwater and terrestrial life. Meanwhile, glucocorticoid control would presumably have been evolving in conjunction with the establishment of islet tissue, and with the pars distalis of the pituitary gland intimately concerned with both systems (pp. 57, 250).

At this stage such speculations are inevitably rather nebulous, but, however well founded they may eventually prove to be, it seems certain that the adrenocortical hormones are so far-reaching in their effects that they must have provided an essential basis for the adaptive responses of vertebrates to a wide range of environmental pressures. Such adaptive responses have been generalized, under the influence of Selye, into the concept of resistance to stress, a term that may be taken to cover the situation arising when animals are exposed to stimuli that are actually or potentially harmful. Under such circumstances they manifest a complex and generalized response which is termed the Stress Syndrome or General Adaptation Syndrome, and this is regarded, according to Selye's interpretation, as falling into three phases.

The first of these, the alarm reaction, is conceived as a 'generalized call to arms' of the defensive forces of the organism, and it is accompanied by excitation of the sympathetico-chromaffin complex and increased adrenocortical secretion, together with enlargement of the adrenal gland and depletion of its lipid content. If the exposure to the stressful stimulus continues, and if the animal is able to survive, the second stage is established, the stage of resistance. The body now manifests the results of adaptation to the stimulus under the particular influence of the adrenocortical secretions, which may be involved, for example, in the regulation of water balance, carbohydrate metabolism, and neuromuscular irritability. After still more prolonged exposure the animal may lose this acquired adaptation and pass into the third stage, the stage of exhaustion. From this, it is thought, there might result in man certain diseases of adaptation such as gastro-intestinal ulcers, arteriosclerosis, and rheumatoid arthritis, which are thus conceived as arising at least in part from disorders of the endocrine system. Indeed, it has even been suggested that the Stress Syndrome might contribute to the heavy mortality that results from over-crowding in populations of wild mammals.

The extent to which this complex of responses can be adequately interpreted in such a way, and the question how far there may be other causative agents at work in the promotion of diseases of adaptation, are matters that need more discussion than we can accord to them here. It has been said that 'one important key to increased understanding of the nature of man's psyche and emotional behaviour, and the intimate details of complex enzyme systems residing in the liver, brain, heart, kidney and muscles, lies in the study of the response of tissue cells to steroid hormones'. If this is so, the application of the principle will certainly not be restricted to man, and we may expect that future research will disclose increasing evidence that the corticosteroids are involved not only in the day-to-day adjustments of vertebrates to their environment but also in the periods of intense activity and physiological crisis which are a regular feature of their life-cycle (p. 198). Pointers in this direction are reports of increased levels of corticosteroids in the blood of migratory salmon and steelhead trout, and of hyperplasia of their adrenocortical tissue.

Certainly we are now in a position to appreciate that the production of steroid secretions in the gonads and adrenocortical tissue, and the common origin of these and of the kidneys in the coelomic epithelium, are fundamental features of vertebrate organization, and the interpretation of this situation has been discussed by Willmer. He has emphasized the possible evolutionary significance of the obvious tendency of that epithelium to give rise to cords and tubules. This tendency, well seen in the sex cords of the early stages of the gonads and in the characteristic histological pattern of the adrenocortical tissue, may, he suggests, be related phylogenetically to the production by it of coelomoducts. These are thought to have been concerned initially with the removal of the genital products and later to have become involved in excretion and osmo-regulation, and he suggests that all three organs, kidneys, gonads, and adrenal cortex, may be derived from them. He argues that an important function of such tubules in the early stages of their evolution would have been the regulation of the composition of the fluids bathing their walls, and that this activity would have resulted in the formation of metabolites which could later have become modified into hormones. In this way, for example, the release of metabolites arising from the responses of the adrenocortical cells to fluctuation in the sodium/potassium ratio in the blood might have come to serve as a means for evolving an integrated response on the part of those cells of the kidney tubules which are directly concerned with the regulation of this ratio.

Some such explanation of the possible origin of the diverse adrenocortical steroids would certainly make it a little easier to understand the existence of the multiple metabolic pathways which seem to be responsible for their biosynthesis, yet even so it remains difficult to account for the production of two hormones such as corticosterone and cortisol which are so closely similar in their actions. It has been suggested, however, that the very complexity of the metabolic system may be a positive virtue, conferring upon the adrenocortical tissue the capacity for making flexible responses to differing demands and thereby facilitating the maintenance of life in a complex and variable environment. This is a helpful line of thought, and we may find an analogy in the chemical changes which seem to be involved in the adaptation of poikilotherms to life at low temperatures. Such acclimation, it has been suggested, may depend upon differential responses in the components of the relevant enzyme systems, so that those which are unimportant at high temperatures come to have a dominating influence when the tissues are exposed to cold conditions.

5. Corticotropin

It has been known since 1930 that the adrenocortical tissue of mammals is under the control of the pars distalis of the pituitary gland, and it is thoroughly well established that hypophysectomy results in atrophy of the tissue (Plate IX *D*) and that this effect can be counteracted by implants or injections of adenohypophyseal extracts. Since there is experimental evidence for the existence of the same situation in elasmobranch and teleost fish, this relationship may be regarded as typical of the vertebrate endocrine system from those groups upwards, although the condition in cyclostomes is not yet clarified.

The hormone concerned is termed corticotropin or ACTH (for adreno-corticotropic (or -trophic) hormone) and, because of its great clinical interest, it has probably been studied more intensely than any other of the pituitary hormones. In view of the clear-cut responses which it evokes in adrenocortical tissue a number of methods are available both for the determination of the presence of the hormone and for its quantitative assay, including, with hypophysectomized animals, the restoration of the normal lipid content of the secretory cells, the maintenance of the normal weight of the gland, and the reduction of its ascorbic acid content. A lowering of the blood lymphocyte and eosinophil counts can also be used as an index of corticotropin discharge in the intact animal, while use has been made more recently of the direct chemical estimation of the 17-hydroxy-corticosteroids of the blood.

By 1943 extracts of sheep pituitary had yielded a highly purified preparation of corticotropin with less than 0·10 per cent. of gonadotropins and thyrotropin; this material appeared to be a protein with a molecular weight of 20,000 and without a carbohydrate moiety. We have taken note that the biological activity of such complex substances may reside in only a part of their molecular structure, and this principle has been clearly exemplified in subsequent studies of corticotropin, which has now been obtained in a completely pure form and has been shown to be a straight-chain poly-peptide composed of 39 amino-acid residues (Fig. 85).

A comparison of the structure of the corticotropins of the sheep, ox, and pig has shown that they differ from each other in certain details of the arrangement of the amino acids between positions 25 and 39, while fragmentation studies have shown that this region is not essential for the biological activity of the molecule. This activity seems to reside in the portion extending from position 1 to position 24; attempts to degrade this end have resulted in the loss of activity, and it is significant that this region is of identical composition in all three species.

The means by which the secretory activity of the adrenocortical tissue is regulated is by no means fully understood. It is accepted that as far as the zona fasciculata is concerned the most important factor is the influence of corticotropin, but the accumulating evidence for some degree of physiological independence in the zona glomerulosa, related to its production of aldosterone, leaves open the possibility that it may be free of this particular control. In the intact mammal there is thought to be a

H. Ser-Tyr-Ser-Met-Glu-His-Phe-Arg-Try-Gly-Lys-Pro-Val-

Gly-Lys-Lys-Arg-Arg-Pro-Val-Lys-Val-Tyr-Pro-Asp-Gly-Ala-

$$\underset{\displaystyle{\text{Glu-Asp-Glu-Leu-Ala-Glu-Ala-Phe-Pro-Leu-Glu-Phe.OH}}}{\overset{\displaystyle{\text{—NH}_2}}{|}}$$

Fig. 85. Amino-acid sequence of pig corticotropin. For a guide to the amino acids refer to Figs. 12 & 25. (After Shepherd *et al.*, 1956. *J. Amer. Chem. Soc.* **78**, 5067–96.)

constant secretory output from the cortex, with some diurnal rhythm, and it might be supposed that this would depend upon a comparable output of corticotropin. Actually, however, life can be maintained better after hypophysectomy than after adrenalectomy, and this seems to be due to the fact that the cortex continues its activity in the absence of the pars distalis, although at a reduced rate. Presumably, then, it has some capacity for autonomous action (as has the thyroid, for example), although under normal conditions in mammals this may never be realized, since the fact that the cortex is better developed when the pars distalis is present than when it is absent indicates that the former is always under some degree of stimulation from the latter. Such capacity for independence needs to be borne in mind, for it is always possible that it might represent the retention of a more primitive level of organization; if this were so, it might mean that hypophyseal control of the adrenocortical tissue, although certainly present in the lower forms, would prove to be less thoroughly established than it is in the higher ones.

6. The adrenogenital syndrome

We have already noted the capacity of the adrenocortical tissue for producing steroids that can affect the gonads; oestrone and progesterone have been identified amongst the many compounds which have been isolated from tissue extracts, while androgens are known to be secreted in small amounts *in vivo*. It seems doubtful whether such substances have any normal physiological role to play, and we may rather suppose that they arise as an inevitable consequence of the generalized steroid-secreting capacity of the coelomic epithelium which we have already discussed. It is, however, a singular misfortune for the human species that its adreno-cortical tissue produces far more androgenic secretion than does that of any other species which has been investigated, for disturbance in the balance of the activity of the tissue can in consequence have grave results.

It may happen that the cortical tissue of genetic females will produce an excessive amount of androgens, either as the result of the development of a tumour, or sometimes because of an inherited defect in the enzyme equipment of the tissue. The early sexual differentiation follows the pattern appropriate to the genetic sex (p. 161), but signs of masculinization (virili-zation) appear when the androgen production becomes sufficiently great. This condition (the adrenogenital syndrome), which provides an instructive example of hormonal interaction, is characterized by increased excretion of 17-oxosteroids. The disturbance of the normal metabolic pathways of the gland also results in a reduction of cortisol production; this leads to an excessive output of corticotropin, which then stimulates the adrenocortical tissue to an increased output of intermediary metabolites, and thus a condition of adrenal hyperplasia is established.

Tumours can be removed by surgery, while if cases of metabolic defect are detected sufficiently early they can be satisfactorily feminized by treatment with cortisone; the supposition is that this depresses corti-cotropin output, and thereby leads to a lowering of the secretion of the adrenocortical sex steroids, this in its turn promoting the output of pituitary gonadotropin with a consequent restoration of normal ovarian function. If, however, such cases are untreated, they may result in a genetic female coming to attain a completely masculine physique, aptitude, and drive, and actually developing a guilt complex as a result of being sexu-ally attracted towards females. Under such circumstances it has sometimes been found advisable to recommend the acceptance of complete mascu-linity, the 'change of sex' involving a combination of legal action and minor surgical adjustment.

7. The control of corticotropin secretion

Several views have been advanced as to the means by which the secre-tion of corticotropin is regulated, and the considerations involved are in many respects similar to those that we have discussed in connexion with the secretion of thyrotropin and the gonadotropins. One suggestion is that the regulating factor is the concentration of adrenocortical steroids circulating in the blood, it being supposed that increased peripheral utiliza-tion of these at times of stress, for example, will result in a fall in their blood level which will then evoke an increased output of corticotropin. It is certainly true that injection of adrenocortical extracts may result in a reduced output of corticotropin, but here, as with the control of thyroid secretion, it is doubtful whether such a simple feedback relationship can provide a complete explanation for all of the facts. It has been found that pituitary transplants situated at points remote from the hypothalamus cannot maintain an entirely normal adrenal cortex, which should clearly not be so if the only factor involved in its maintenance was the direct action of its circulating adrenocortical steroids upon the pars distalis. Particularly striking in this connexion is the fact that the transfer of a pituitary transplant back to the median eminence, after it has been situated on the kidney for one month (p. 119), will result in restoration of the reduced adrenal cortex to normal size and function.

Equally impressive is the evidence made available as a result of the development of a procedure for assaying the concentration of circulating corticotropin. This evidence confirms the existence in the rat of the direct feedback relationship in that the concentration of circulating corticotropin is substantially increased after adrenalectomy. On the other hand, the application of stress (in the form of exposure to ether, with or without a standardized scald) results within two minutes in an increase in the circulating corticotropin, not only in the intact rat but even in the adrenalectomized animal, from which it follows that the discharge of corticotropin can be evoked in the complete absence of adrenocortical steroids. Possibly, then, the direct feedback relationship is a homeostatic mechanism providing delicate adjustments under normal or basal conditions, as we have suggested also for the thyroid gland (p. 211), and other factors come into play under conditions that present the animal with a marked departure from the normal.

As to the nature of these other factors, one suggestion, which we have already touched upon, is that the output of adrenaline at moments of stress is responsible for evoking an increased secretion of corticotropin, but the evidence for this is not conclusive and there are difficulties in the way of accepting such a view. For example, the stressful stimulus of an injection of histamine can bring about a release of corticotropin within a few seconds, while a single injection of adrenaline would be ineffective under the same circumstances; here, in other words, is an example of a stress that produces a response quicker than the latter can be produced by adrenaline itself.

We are left, then, with another suggestion, that the release of corticotropin is controlled by a neural mechanism located in the hypothalamus, a view propounded by Harris in 1950. As outlined by him, the basis for the suggestion is that rabbits react to emotional stress, such as restraint, by a reduction of lymphocytes (lymphopenia), that this response is abolished by hypophysectomy, and that it can be evoked by the injection of corticotropin into hypophysectomized animals. Using his technique of electrical stimulation by remote control (p. 117), he showed that stimulation of the posterior region of the tuber cinereum or mammillary body resulted in lymphopenia, but that stimulation of other parts of the hypothalamus or of the pituitary had no such effect. Similar results have been obtained by other workers using other animals, including the cat, monkey, and dog, and with the dog it has been possible to measure the concentration of 17-hydroxycorticosteroids in adrenal venous blood and to use this as an index of cortical activity. In this way it has been shown that the output of these steroids in normal dogs which are subjected to surgical stress is over twice that in dogs which are similarly treated after lesions have

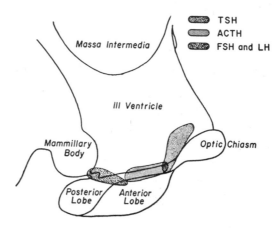

Fig. 86. Areas in the hypothalamus believed to be concerned with the regulation of the secretion of thyrotropin (TSH), corticotropin (ACTH), FSH, and LH in the dog. The diagram represents a sagittal section of the hypothalamus, with the areas superimposed.
(From Ganong, 1959. *Comparative Endocrinology*, ed. Gorbman. Wiley.)

been established in the anterior end of the median eminence, while lesions elsewhere do not have this effect of reducing adrenocortical secretion. The supposition is that the lesions in the anterior median eminence impair the ability to secrete corticotropin, and this has been confirmed by direct measurements of the blood level of the hormone, which rises in normal animals subjected to surgical stress, but does not do so in those with the lesions.

There is thus very convincing evidence that the regulation of corticotropin release in response to stress depends upon the integrity of a functional link between the hypothalamus and the pars distalis, and that this link can be broken by damage to the median eminence. We have already arrived at similar conclusions in relation to the secretion of thyrotropin and the gonadotropins, and, combining these conclusions, it is possible to arrive at a tentative map of the relevant areas (Fig. 86). It will be obvious that such conclusions, important though they are, merely push our questions a stage further back, for we know nothing of the factors by which the hypothalamic centres themselves are activated, nor is it yet agreed how the hypothalamus itself comes to affect the pars distalis. We

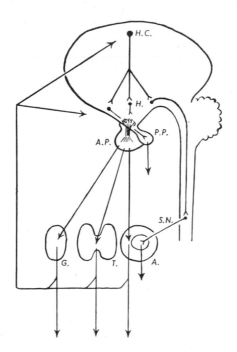

Fig. 87. Diagram to illustrate the reciprocal relationship believed to exist between the central nervous system and endocrine system. *A.*, adrenal gland; *A.P.*, adenohypophysis; *G.*, gonads; *H.*, hypothalamus; *H.C.*, 'higher centres'; *P.P.*, neural lobe; *S.N.*, splanchnic nerves, here shown innervating the adrenal medulla; *T.*, thyroid gland.
(From Harris, 1955. *The Neural Control of the Pituitary Gland*. Arnold.)

have seen, however, that there are strong arguments for regarding the hypophyseal portal vessels as constituting a path for the transmission of chemical mediators concerned with gonadotropin and thyrotropin control; precisely similar arguments apply to corticotropin control and they need not be outlined separately here.

Two features, perhaps, stand out in the picture as it presents itself to us at this point (Fig. 87). Firstly, we begin to grasp the nature of the fundamental relationship which exists between the adenohypophysis and the hypothalamus, which has conditioned, as we shall see, the evolution of the pituitary gland throughout the vertebrates. Secondly, bearing in mind that the hypothalamus is the main directing and co-ordinating centre of the autonomic nervous system (p. 116), we can see a satisfying and inevitable logic in the development in that same region of the centres which regulate much of the activity of the pars distalis and, through that, the greater part of the endocrine activity of the body. This activity, as we now know, influences every aspect of the internal adjustments of the vertebrate animal, overlapping, therefore, the activity of the autonomic system and, in the particular case of the chromaffin tissue, perhaps developing directly out of it.

XI. COLOUR CHANGE IN VERTEBRATES

1. Melanocytes

WE now have to consider one other function of the pituitary gland, its involvement in regulation of the colour changes that are a well-known property of the lower vertebrates from cyclostomes up to and including certain reptiles. This property (Plate XIII) depends upon the presence of cells called chromatophores, which we can define, following Parker, as pigmented cells, with dendritic processes, in which the colouring matter can be dispersed or concentrated with consequent changes in the colour of the animal concerned. These cells, which lie mainly in the epidermis and dermis, but sometimes in the deeper tissues, are of various types, including (in zoological terminology) melanophores, with granules of black or brown melanin, lipophores, with yellow or carotenoid pigments which are soluble in alcohol, allophores, with red or red-brown pigments which are insoluble in alcohol, and guanophores, with granules or crystals of guanine, but most of our knowledge of the physiology of colour change in these animals is based upon the study of the responses of the melanophores, and it is therefore to these that we shall confine our attention.

Since this type of response is not found in mammals it was formerly supposed that they lacked such cells, and that the Malpighian layer of the epidermis was responsible for the pigmentation of the skin, but this is not so. It is now recognized that the epidermis of these animals, like that of other vertebrates, is of dual origin, with a Mapighian or keratinizing system arising from the embryonic ectoderm and a pigmentary system arising from melanoblasts, which migrate from the embryonic neural crest and give rise to the specialized cells known to dermatologists as melanocytes. These constitute a self-maintaining system which is the sole source of the melanins forming the natural pigments of the mammalian skin, and we may therefore define them, following Fitzpatrick and Kukita, as melanin-producing cells of characteristic form, with two or more dendritic processes, and derived from the neural crest. We shall use this term here to include also the melanophores of lower vertebrates, which resemble them in their form and origin, and are presumably homologous with them, but which possess the additional capacity for dispersal and concentration of their pigment.

The mammalian melanocyte, while lacking this property, has its branches closely applied to the cells of the Malpighian layer of the epidermis and transfers its pigment directly into them. The way in which this is effected is not understood, but it is presumably a general property of such cells, for similar transfers have been observed in tissue cultures of amphibian material. As a result, the melanocytes are responsible for variations in the colour of the human skin, as seen in racial differences, for example, or in the effects of sun-tanning. Such variations seem to depend upon the degree of activity of the cells and not upon their number, for their frequency distribution, while showing a good deal of individual variation, shows no significant racial or sexual differences and is independent of the degree of exposure of the skin to light.

The melanins which develop within these cells are a group of pigments of high molecular weight which are believed to be formed by enzymatic oxidation of tyrosine, with dihydroxyphenylalanine (dopa, see p. 223) as an intermediate stage. They are remarkable for their extreme insolubility, a characteristic that is thought to be a result of polymerization and of their close association with protein. It has, indeed, been claimed that melanin granules are not simple aggregations, but organized particles which possess enzymic activity and which, it has been thought, might possibly be derived directly from mitochondria. Another interpretation, however, based upon electron micrographs, prefers to regard them as arising in the Golgi zone of the cell as vesicular pregranules, within which the melanin polymer is laid down upon an initial deposit of protein.

Colour changes based upon the melanins may be of two types, morphological and physiological, the former involving long-term changes in the total amount of pigment while the latter involves short-term changes in the degree of its dispersal or concentration. Morphological changes, which are, presumably, the only ones that can occur in mammals, have been less intensively studied in the lower vertebrates than physiological ones, but they are known to occur under the same experimental conditions as promote the latter. For example, if fish are illuminated on a white background for long periods they suffer a diminution of the total amount of pigment in their skin, and it can be shown that this is associated with a loss of melanophores by degeneration. Under such circumstances individuals of *Fundulus* have been found to lose as much as 59 per cent. of their melanocytes in the course of sixty-nine days. Conversely, fish show an increase in the number of these cells when they are illuminated on black backgrounds, and in both cases visual stimulation of the eye is an essential condition of the response, as it is with the physiological type of change.

The current supposition is that these results are brought about by the action of the same agents, hormones or nerves, as bring about the corresponding physiological response, the morphological one, in other words, being an exaggeration or accentuation of this. There is some evidence, for example, that the pituitary gland can evoke melanin formation in yellow (xanthic) goldfish, although it has been suggested that corticotropin may be the agent rather than the melanocyte-stimulating hormone with which we shall be concerned below. Other hormones may be involved, too, for it is known that thyroid treatment of young salmonid fish (p. 196) will evoke silvering, partly by an increased deposition of guanine and partly by destruction of the melanocytes. It may well be, therefore, that major changes of pigmentation associated with crucial phases of the life-cycle, including the development of breeding colours, are promoted by a complex of nervous and hormonal agencies.

When physiological colour changes are directly observed in the skin of fishes and amphibians it seems superficially as though the melanocytes are expanding and contracting, but it is now generally accepted that this is not so, and that the cells actually preserve a more or less constant form, with delicate branches along which the pigment granules move, these becoming dispersed to give a dark colour or concentrated to give a light one. Despite this, however, the older terms 'expanded' and 'contracted' are still in common use as the respective equivalents of the more accurate 'dispersed' and 'concentrated'.

Much attention has been devoted to determining the mechanism of this movement of the granules, and over a period of some thirty years it has become rather generally accepted that it depends upon sol-gel changes in the cytoplasm of the melanocytes. One illustration of the relevant evidence is afforded by the effects of centrifuging, which differ according to the state of the pigment. If this is dispersed the granules can readily be displaced by a force of 70,000 times that of gravity, whereas if it is concentrated they cannot be displaced by forces of 125,000 times that of gravity acting for as long as twelve minutes. The inference is that concentration of the granules is associated with a more rigid condition of the cell contents, and this has been extended into the supposition that these form a gel framework to which the granules are attached. On this view the process of concentration is brought about by a shrinkage inwards of the framework, sol being squeezed out into the cell processes, while dispersal is effected by a reversal of this, the gel framework unfolding and sol flowing backwards into the cell body. This, however, is a tentative view, and it seems certain that our interpretation of the physiology of the melanocyte will be extended and modified by the application of electron microscopy. Already it has been shown, for instance, that the sacs containing the granules in the cells of *Lebistes* are associated with fibrils, and it has been suggested that contraction of the latter may be an important factor in the process of concentration of the pigment.

2. Melanocyte-stimulating hormone in Amphibia

In examining the physiology of the melanocyte responses it will be convenient to deal first with the Amphibia, for this group has provided much of the foundation of our present knowledge. It is important here to distinguish the two types of response known as primary and secondary. The former is found in young larvae, and results in the animal being pale in complete darkness and dark in bright light; it does not depend upon the functioning of the eyes, for it persists in the blinded animal, and it is generally assumed that it represents a direct response of the melanocytes to the quantity of light falling upon them, and that it is independent of any hormonal control. The secondary response supersedes the primary one in late larval life and throughout the adult phase and depends upon the ratio (or albedo) of the amount of direct incident light to the amount of light reflected from the background. The eyes are the receptors concerned, so that blinded animals no longer show this response and, in fact, often revert to the primary type. It is this secondary response with which we are now concerned, and which has attracted most of the attention of investigators.

Much of the experimental work has involved the study of the effects of transferring animals from one to another of three different types of background, an illuminated white one, an illuminated black one, and a completely dark (i.e. non-illuminated) one. The effects produced in an amphibian by such changes are not very spectacular but are nevertheless well defined, consisting in the development of a pale colour (blanching) when the animal is placed upon an illuminated white background and a dark colour when it is placed on an illuminated dark one. In *Xenopus*, which is a completely aquatic toad, light appears to be the main effective stimulus, but it has long been recognized that in the more terrestrial forms other factors may also be operative. These include temperature and humidity, so that *Rana temporaria*, for example, tends to be pale in a warm and dry environment and dark in a cold and moist one.

It is characteristic of amphibians that these colour changes are slow processes, their completion involving hours or days rather than minutes, and this at once suggests that the mechanism is hormonal rather than nervous, although it was inevitable that this could not be appreciated by the nineteenth-century workers. They recognized that the presence of the eyes was an essential condition for the manifestation of these responses, and because of this, and because of the overriding importance attached at that time to nervous co-ordination, it was supposed that these colour changes must be regulated by nervous reflexes, an interpretation closely analogous to that which developed in connexion with studies of the control of alimentary activity (p. 10). The demonstration in 1898 that injection into frogs of extracts of the adrenal gland resulted in the development of pallor suggested that glandular activity might also be involved, but this possibility did not attract serious attention until the introduction of experiments involving the hypophysectomy of tadpoles in connexion with studies of the regulation of their metamorphosis. It quickly emerged that tadpoles lacking a pituitary gland were permanently colourless, and it was this fact that led Hogben in 1922 to initiate his important series of investigations of the pigmentary effector system.

In order to reduce the subjective element involved in estimates of

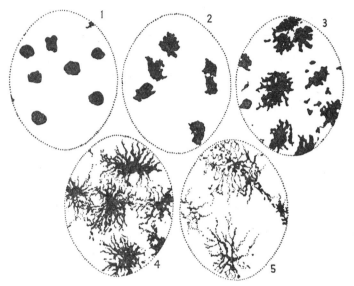

Fig. 88. The melanophore (melanocyte) index of Hogben and Slome (diagrammatic).
(From Young, 1950. *The Life of Vertebrates*. Oxford: Clarendon Press.)

relative pallor and darkness of the skin he and Slome later introduced a quantitative method of expression which depends upon distinguishing five melanocyte phases, ranging from fully concentrated to fully dispersed, and giving to each an arbitrary numerical value. On this basis it is possible to express the mean condition of the melanocytes of a particular animal as a 'melanophore (melanocyte) index' which will lie between 1 and 5 (Fig. 88). More recently, quantitative studies have been helped by the development of a photo-electric procedure which allows the recording of the melanocyte responses in pieces of excised frog skin. These can be stretched over a ring and placed in the test fluid on the stage of a microscope, the colour change being recorded by means of a photo-electric cell inserted in place of the eyepiece.

The first conclusion which emerged from Hogben's work, and one which has never been seriously questioned, is that darkening is brought about by the release of a hormone from the pituitary gland. Initially this hormone, which was referred to as the B-substance, was regarded simply as a secretion of the 'posterior lobe', but it will be recalled that this region has included in practice both the pars nervosa and the pars intermedia, and that both of these are extracted in the commercial preparation of 'posterior lobe' extracts which have been commonly employed in this type of investigation. It is now accepted that the hormone concerned is actually a product of the pars intermedia, and it has therefore been generally referred to in zoological literature as intermedin (but see below).

The evidence for this hormonal control has been discussed so often that it will not be necessary here to do more than recapitulate briefly the salient steps of the argument. Firstly, it has repeatedly been demonstrated in both anurans and urodeles that removal of the pituitary results in permanent pallor even under conditions, such as the provision of a dark background, which favour darkening in the intact animal. Secondly, the injection of pituitary extracts into animals which are pale, either because they are on a pale background or because they have been hypophysectomized, results in darkening, the effect then slowly wearing off as the hormone is metabolized and excreted. In such experiments the pituitary of one frog has been found to contain sufficient stored hormone to induce melanocyte darkening in at least fifty other animals. Thirdly, the presence of the hormone in the blood can be demonstrated by introducing into a pale frog some blood drawn from a dark one, the result being the expansion of the melanocytes of the former. The separation of the parts of the pituitary is not always very easy, but it has been possible to darken a hypophysectomized tadpole by implanting into it a pars intermedia, and albino tadpoles of the tree-toad *Hyla* have been produced by experimental treatment which inhibits the development of that region while allowing the rest of the pituitary to grow normally. That the hormone is acting directly upon the melanocytes is shown by the fact that isolated pieces of amphibian skin in Ringer's fluid will react to the presence of pituitary extracts in the latter, and that the reactions are not affected by the presence of nerve paralysants such as atropine.

We shall see that there is good reason for believing the nervous system to be involved in the regulation of colour change in certain vertebrates, and from time to time there has been put forward histological evidence for the innervation of the melanocytes of amphibians. This has inevitably led to the suggestion that such fibres may influence their colour responses, but Parker, who was not given to minimizing this aspect of nervous function in other groups, concluded that the possible extent of this had been exaggerated by some of those who had advocated it and that the amphibian melanocytes were certainly excited in the main by hormonal means. The innervation of the skin may well merit further study, but conclusions drawn from such work must always demand the support of experimental investigation, and it should be remembered that Hogben was of the emphatic opinion that neither section nor stimulation of the peripheral nerves produced any local pigmentary responses in the amphibians studied by him in his pioneer work.

As regards the nature of the melanocyte-stimulating hormone, there was at first a period when it was suspected that it might be identical with

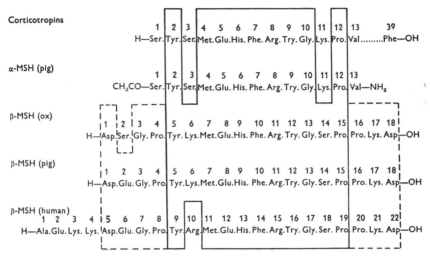

Fig. 89. Amino acid sequences of corticotropin and melanocyte-stimulating hormones from mammalian pituitary glands. Refer to Figs. 12 and 25 for a guide to the amino acids.
(From Harris, 1960. *Brit. Med. Bull.* **16**, 189–195).

oxytocin, but it was later shown that its activity remained in 'posterior lobe' extracts from which vasopressor and oxytocic properties had been removed, and that it actually originated in the pars intermedia. It has now proved possible to isolate this hormone from certain mammals in a pure form known as β-melanocyte-stimulating hormone (Fig. 89). As obtained from the ox and pig this has been found to be a polypeptide consisting of a straight chain of eighteen amino acids, while in the form obtained from man it consists of twenty-two. All three, however, possess an identical group of eighteen, except that arginine is substituted for one of the lysine residues in man (recalling the analogous substitution which we have found in the hypothalamic polypeptides), and serine for a glutamic acid residue in the ox.

The name melanocyte-stimulating hormone (MSH) is now used for these polypeptides in preference to intermedin, on the grounds that it is normal practice to name a hormone by reference to its point of action rather than its point of origin, and this term will be adopted here. It must be realized, however, that the situation is an unusual one in that we are discussing a hormone that is chemically characterized as a mammalian preparation but physiologically characterized and assayed by its action on the isolated skin of frogs. Nevertheless, there is already some reason for believing that the α- and β-melanocyte-stimulating hormones, and perhaps others still uncharacterized, may prove to be present together in the secretion of many species, not only in mammals but also in lower forms. Intermedin, then, is probably a hormone complex which, by analogy with other polypeptide hormones, may well be prone to molecular variation (p. 91). Its function in mammals remains obscure; it has been shown, however, that injections of the α and β hormones into human subjects produce a darkening of the skin, and this has led to the suggestion that it may be concerned in the regulation of melanin synthesis.

The melanocyte-stimulating hormones described above as obtained from the ox, pig, and man are known as β-melanocyte-stimulating hormone because there has been isolated from the pig a second hormone, called α-melanocyte-stimulating hormone, which differs from the other three in consisting of only thirteen amino acids (Fig. 89). Comparison of the structural formulae of the four shows, however, that they all possess a common group of seven amino acids (positions 4 to 10 in the α-hormone formula), and it is concluded that their biological activity resides in this particular grouping. Interesting confirmation of this is seen in the fact that the corticotropin molecule (Figs. 85, 89) also carries this same set of seven residues, for this hormone has long been known to show a small degree of melanocyte-stimulating activity, amounting, in the pure preparation, to about 1 per cent. of that of the β-melanocyte-stimulating hormone of the pig. It is supposed, therefore, that this activity results from the presence of the characteristic grouping, its full potency being perhaps masked by the remaining structural features of the molecule. Further confirmation is supplied by the observation that a small amount of activity (estimated to be 10^5 to 10^6 times less than that of the natural hormone) is present in a synthetic pentapeptide corresponding to positions 6 to 10 of the α-hormone of the pig.

These structural studies, like those of the hypothalamic polypeptides, evidently have an important bearing upon the interpretation of evolutionary history, for the resemblances of the corticotropic and melanocyte-stimulating hormones suggest that they may have originated in a primitive synthetic capacity of adenohypophyseal tissue, and that this has been subsequently subjected to adaptive evolutionary change. Evidence for some physiological interrelationship between the two is seen in the fact that corticotropin normally inhibits the release of melanocyte-stimulating hormone. This may be the cause of the darkening of the skin which is a characteristic of Addison's disease, for it is suggested that the adrenocortical insufficiency is associated with a lack of corticotropin and hence with a loss of this inhibiting action.

Our experience with the hypothalamic polypeptides shows that the course of the history of these two hormones will not be unravelled until it has been possible to study their chemistry in the lower vertebrates. The substitutions that differentiate the melanocyte-stimulating hormones of the mammalian species so far studied indicate that they also must have been influenced by genetic mutation, and it is particularly interesting to observe that such substitutions do not occur within the supposedly active group of seven residues. This suggests, within the limits of our present meagre knowledge, that counter-selection may have operated to keep this group stable, which in its turn suggest that it may still be of physiological importance in mammals. It looks, therefore, as though the melanocyte-stimulating hormones may have some hitherto-undiscovered function in this group, although in the past it has often been assumed that the absence of the power of physiological colour change in mammals has left these hormones as biochemical vestiges.

3. Cyclostomata

The ammocoete larvae of lampreys show a well-marked diurnal colour change as a result of which they are pale by night and dark by day (Fig. 90). Adult brook lampreys (*Lampetra planeri*) behave similarly, their dorsal surface being dark by day and becoming pale at night like the belly, but adult river lampreys (*Lampetra fluviatilis*) show little change. J. Z. Young showed that this rhythm is undoubtedly influenced by external stimulation, for it can be stopped by reversing, with artificial illumination, the normal diurnal alternation of light and darkness (Fig. 90). The effect of continuous darkness is less clearly defined, and under this condition there may be some persistence of the diurnal rhythm, so that we seem to have here an example of the interaction of exogenous and endogenous factors analogous to what we have encountered in our analysis of sexual cycles.

This colour change, like the changes that we have been considering in amphibians, is due to the movement of pigment granules in melanocytes, and it has been shown that these cells are uninfluenced by section of the spinal nerves and by faradic stimulation of these or of the spinal cord. Hypophysectomy by cauterization, however, results in permanent pallor, which suggests that the melanocytes are under the control of a melanocyte-stimulating hormone similar to that of amphibians, and regional destruction of the pituitary has shown that this hormone is contained in either the pars intermedia or pars nervosa, the assumption, by analogy with other vertebrates, being that it is actually secreted in the former. Confirmation of this interpretation is given by the fact that intraperitoneal injection of mammalian 'posterior lobe' extracts will cause dispersal of pigment in these animals.

Ammocoete larvae are blind, with imperfectly developed eyes buried beneath the skin, and it has been shown by Young that the pineal eyes serve as the external receptor agent, for if these are destroyed the animals lose all capacity for colour change and become permanently dark. This suggests that the resting phase of the melanocytes is the state of concentration (which is, in fact, the state into which they pass after death),

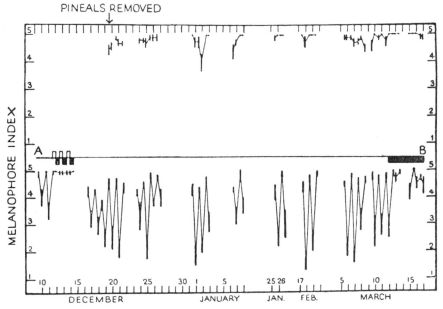

Fig. 90. Colour changes of larval lampreys. Animals kept out of doors except as shown along the line *AB*, where rectangles above the line show illumination with electric light and below the line total darkness. Normal animals show a regular daily rhythm which stops when the normal diurnal alternation of light and darkness is reversed. On 19 December the pineal eyes were removed from five out of the ten individuals and these thereafter remained dark (upper chart); the other five continued to show the normal rhythm, until placed in total darkness.

(From Young, 1950. *The Life of Vertebrates.* Oxford: Clarendon Press.)

that secretion of the melanocyte-stimulating hormone promotes darkening, and that this is regulated by the sensory activity of the pineal eyes; in adults, in which the paired eyes are well developed, these also become involved in co-operation with the pineal complex. The exact path of communication between the central nervous system and the pars intermedia is not known, but it seems certain that the neurohypophysis must be involved, and we shall return to this point. In the meantime we can take note that there is no evidence for innervation of the melanocytes in these animals, and that the regulation of colour change by means of an adeno-hypophyseal secretion is evidently a very primitive feature of vertebrate organization. Whether this is the only hormone involved, however, is a question that merits reconsideration in the light of the recent extraction of a pigment-concentrating substance from the pineal organ of mammals (p. 280).

4. Elasmobranchii

Elasmobranchs show a type of colour change essentially similar to that found in amphibians, although there are considerable variations in the degree of response. *Mustelus canis*, for example, changes from a grey colour on a black background to a pale colour on a white one in some two days, the reverse change taking only half an hour to two hours, while *Raja erinacea* will develop pallor on a white background in twelve hours and will darken on a black one in nine hours. On the other hand, there are many elasmobranchs which are extremely sluggish in their responses; examples of this are the common dogfishes, *Scyllium catulus*, *Squalus acanthias*, and *Scyliorhinus canicula*, the last-named requiring from eighty to one hundred hours to change from its pale-background response to the dark one, and vice versa. The ray *Raja clavata* has been said not to show any colour change when it is transferred from a black background to a white one and, like the dogfish, is normally dark. However, when it is hypophysectomized it develops a pallor, which shows that its melanocytes have certainly not lost their capacity for pigment movement, and the assumption is that its normal colour is maintained by a steady production of melanocyte-stimulating hormone by the pituitary, and that the activity of the gland is not markedly influenced by incident light.

The conclusion that the dark phase in the responses of these fish is evoked by the secretion of a melanocyte-stimulating hormone by the pars intermedia may be regarded as thoroughly well established. It derives initially from the studies of Lundstrom and Bard on *Mustelus canis*. They showed that removal of the pituitary gland resulted in blanching, which reached a maximum in twelve hours and which, as with the corresponding phenomenon in amphibians, could be temporarily overcome by the injection of mammalian 'posterior lobe' extracts. They further showed that removal of the 'neuro-intermediate lobe' (p. 297) also resulted in blanching, and that removal of the 'anterior lobe' did not, while injections of extracts of the former into such experimentally blanched fish produced a temporary darkening. Thus they concluded that the 'neuro-intermediate lobe' must be the source of the supposed hormone. A further important step in the analysis was taken later when other workers showed that the injection into a pale dogfish of blood from a dark one resulted in the development of a dark area at the site of the injection, whereas the injection of such blood into a dark fish, or of blood from a pale fish into either a dark or pale one, had no such effect. There was thus some evidence for the presence of the hormone in the blood stream.

As regards the possibility of an innervation of the melanocytes in this group, it is doubtful whether there is any completely convincing evidence for this, although Parker has argued that nerve fibres bring about concentration of the pigment in certain species. His interpretation hinges upon the significance to be attached to caudal bands similar to those that have been obtained in teleosts, and the arguments against it are substantially the same as those outlined below, with the additional consideration that such bands have only been observed in *Mustelus canis* and *Squalus acanthias* and that they have not been found in at least six other species of rays and dogfish in which investigators have looked for them. If we add to this the fact, often overlooked, that no grey rami arise from the sympathetic ganglia in elasmobranchs and that there is, in consequence, no outflow of sympathetic fibres from the sympathetic chain to the skin, it becomes difficult to justify a belief in autonomic innervation of the melanocytes in this group.

5. Teleostei

It is very well known that the colour changes of teleosts are more complex than those of the groups that we have so far discussed. For one thing, their equipment of chromatophores is much more elaborate, including all the types mentioned earlier, together with associations of chromatophores in complexes termed chromatosomes. In addition, their background responses may be varied and remarkably rapid, a matter of seconds or at most minutes, while some species, such as the bottom-dwelling flat-fish, can contrive a creditable imitation of the actual pattern of their background in a manner that clearly depends upon regional differences in the response of the cells. Such characteristics suggest the intervention of the nervous system at the level of the actual effectors, and we shall see that this suggestion is well founded, but in addition it seems reasonably certain that a pituitary hormone is also operative in certain species.

Part of the evidence for the presence of this hormone depends on the fact that pigment dispersion is produced in amphibians on the injection or implantation of pituitary material from a variety of teleost donors. This is not, of course, evidence that the supposed hormone has any physiological action in the donor, and reciprocal tests, in which pituitary preparations from various vertebrate donors are introduced into teleosts, do, in fact, give varied and puzzling results. These have been conveniently summarized by Pickford and Atz, and it will be sufficient now to note that the effect is dispersion in some species but concentration in others, examples being, respectively, *Ameiurus nebulosus* (the catfish) and *Fundulus heteroclitus.* Concentration can be produced in the latter animal by pituitary material from individuals of its own species, or from other teleosts, but the injection of purified mammalian preparations into it will produce no effect at all, so that the situation is not a simple one. Equally varied are the results of removal of the pituitaries; neither in *Ameiurus* nor in *Fundulus* are the effects as striking as in elasmobranchs or amphibians, and, indeed, teleosts commonly do not develop a permanent pallor as a result of this

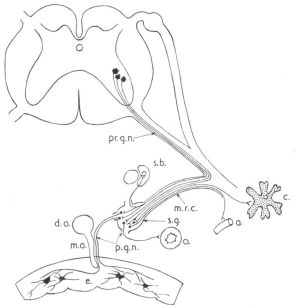

Fig. 91. Diagram of some sympathetic pathways in a teleost fish. *a.*, artery; *c.*, chromatophore; *d.a.*, dorsal aorta; *e.*, intestine; *m.a.*, mesenteric artery; *m.r.c.*, mixed (white and grey) ramus communicans; *o.*, oviduct; *p.g.n.*, post-ganglionic neurones; *pr.g.n.*, pre-ganglionic neurone; *s.b.*, chromaffin tissue; *s.g.*, sympathetic ganglion.
(From Nicol, 1952. *Biol. Rev.* **27**, 1–49.)

operation. The effect in *Ameiurus* is to produce some impairment of the capacity for dispersion, but in *Fundulus* it is doubtful whether the background responses are in any way affected. This might seem to suggest that hormonal regulation plays no part in the responses of the latter species, yet it appears that its blood must contain a hormone, for injection of it into hypophysectomized *Rana pipiens* has been shown to produce pigment dispersion. Such a negative assumption is, in fact, always a difficult one to justify, and it is worth noting that in *Phoxinus* the removal of the pituitary does not seem to affect adversely the rapid adaptations of the animal to its background, but that in the absence of the pars intermedia it has difficulty in maintaining the response to black backgrounds.

It is evident that such data do not lend themselves to any very simple generalization, but it is probably safe to conclude that a pituitary hormone is a factor in the colour responses of some teleosts, although we are hardly justified in assuming that it is necessarily identical with the corresponding hormone of amphibians. Indeed, we cannot exclude the possibility that part at least of the variability in the responses of melanocytes may result from specific variation in the molecular pattern of the hormone concerned.

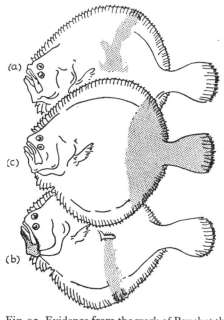

Fig. 92. Evidence from the work of Pouchet that nerve impulses cause concentration in the chromatophores of the turbot, *Scophthalamus* (*Rhombus*) *maximus*. The darkening results from (*a*) cutting spinal nerve branches, (*b*) cutting spinal nerve branches and the inferior maxillary branch of the trigeminus, (*c*) destroying the sympathetic chain in the posterior haemal canal.

(From Nicol, 1960. *The Biology of Marine Animals*. Pitman.)

However, this is in any case only one of the factors involved in colour response in this group of fish, for it is agreed that the nervous system is also of the greatest importance. This results from the fact that the skin of teleosts differs from that of elasmobranchs in being innervated by the autonomic system, the fibres concerned running in recurrent grey rami (Fig. 91) which, as we have seen, are absent from the latter group. Here, then (and we shall see that this also true of certain reptiles), we have a combination of endocrine and nervous regulation which presents an interesting parallel with the mechanism of control of alimentary functions which we considered in Chapter II.

It has been known since 1893 from histological evidence that the melanocytes of teleosts are innervated, and even earlier than that, in 1872 to 1876, it was demonstrated by Pouchet that the colour responses of flat-fish were under the control of the autonomic nervous system, characteristic patterns of localized darkening being produced by nerve section or by destruction of the sympathetic chain (Fig. 92). Subsequently this aspect was investigated with particular thoroughness by von Frisch, who established the course of the sympathetic fibres in *Phoxinus* by studying the effect of nerve section on the background responses of the fish and on the reaction of its melanocytes to electrical stimulation of the nervous system.

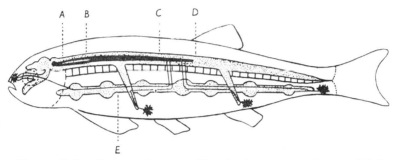

Fig. 93. Paths of aggregating nerve fibres in the minnow, after von Frisch. (From Healey, 1954. *J. exp. Biol.* **31**, 473–90.)

He was able to show, as have many subsequent workers, that concentration of pigment takes place when the nerve fibres supplying a particular group of melanocytes are stimulated; the response is a localized one, and does not spread to adjacent areas that have been denervated by section of their nerves, so that it must result from the direct action of the nerve fibres upon their effector cells and cannot be due to a hormone distributed in the blood.

In *Phoxinus* von Frisch was able to trace the preganglionic melanocyte fibres from the medulla down the spinal cord, which they leave to pass into the sympathetic chain at about the level of the fifteenth vertebra (Fig. 93). The sympathetic chain in these animals extends also into the head, and according to von Frisch the melanocytes of that region are innervated by sympathetic fibres running in the trigeminal nerve. The effect of this arrangement is, of course, that section of only a few spinal nerve roots, at the particular level at which the melanocyte fibres leave the spinal cord (between C and D in Fig. 93), will influence the colour of the whole body surface.

The immediate result of denervation of the melanocytes is a dispersion of their pigment, although later some concentration occurs, and it has been very generally supposed that the dispersion is a condition of relaxation or paralysis of the effector. Against this, however, stands the view of Parker, based upon many years of intensive study of this problem, according to which the melanocytes have a double innervation, consisting of antagonistic concentrating and dispersing fibres. This view has been exhaustively discussed in the literature, and a full review of it would be irrelevant to our present purpose. It must suffice to say that it is largely based upon a study of the 'caudal bands' of darkening which are produced as temporary phenomena by cutting across a bundle of the nerve fibres which radiate out over the caudal fin. This darkening, which results from pigment dispersion on the distal side of the cut, was held by Parker to be produced by the action of nerve impulses transmitted along dispersing fibres and initiated by the irritation set up at the cut ends of the fibres. This view seems to be based upon the classical conception of antagonistic components of the autonomic nervous system but, as we have seen earlier, it is doubtful whether these exist at the level of evolution of fish; certainly Young's analysis of the responses of the alimentary tract provides little evidence for them and affords no justification for assuming their existence in the skin. Other objections have also been brought against Parker's interpretation, such as the unlikelihood that the cutting of nerve fibres would initiate the propagation of nerve impulses over a period of several days, and it has never been generally accepted, although the facts described by him seem clear enough and certainly demand some explanation. It has been suggested that this should be sought in such possibilities as vasomotor disturbances arising from the incision, or an intrinsic response of the melanocyte to its release from nervous control.

6. Reptilia

The only group of reptiles which shows marked colour changes is the Lacertilia, although some snakes and the alligator are said to have a slight capacity for this. Within the Lacertilia there is evidently great variation in the nature and extent of the response, ranging from simple background reactions to the spectacular performances of *Chamaeleo*, which is said to be able to show responses involving an immense variety of combinations of green, yellow, brown, black, and white. It is thus unfortunate that the group as a whole has been much less intensely studied than have the other three, and mention will therefore be made here of only one or two particular species.

A simple example is provided by *Phrynosoma*, in which the capacity for colour change is substantially restricted to blanching and darkening in response respectively to light and dark surroundings. There seems no reason to doubt that this reaction is dependent upon melanocyte-stimulating hormone in the same manner as that of elasmobranchs and amphibians. Hypophysectomy of this animal is followed by the development of pallor, which is known to have been maintained for at least as long as five weeks, and it is known also that such an animal can be temporarily darkened by the injection of pituitary preparations. The presence of the hormone in the circulation is indicated by the fact that blood from a dark animal induces a dark spot when injected subcutaneously into a pale animal, whereas a similar injection into a dark animal is without effect.

There is, therefore, good evidence that the melanocytes of *Phrynosoma* are under hormonal control, but the situation is complicated, as it is in teleosts, by the fact that they also appear to be under the control of the nervous system (cf. Fig. 94). This was demonstrated by Redfield, who found that a dark individual could be completely blanched within a few minutes by electrical stimulation of the roof or floor of the buccal cavity or of the surfaces of the cloaca. Further, if the spinal cord of a dark animal is cut at about the middle of its length, the portion anterior to the level of the cut becomes paler, and, most convincing of all, will become fully blanched if the roof of the mouth is stimulated electrically, the portion of the body behind the cut meanwhile remaining dark. Later, after perhaps some fifteen minutes, the anterior portion becomes pale again, and the inference would seem to be that the hormone is re-establishing its influence after the withdrawal of the nervous stimulation.

According to Redfield this colour change is also involved in an easily observable diurnal rhythm, the animal being dark in the early morning, pale at midday, dark in the evening, and pale during the night. It is now known that lizards, although poikilothermal, have a remarkably well-developed pattern of behavioural thermo-regulation which enables them, by taking full advantage of all the physical conditions of their environment, to maintain a surprisingly constant temperature during their hours of activity, and it seems likely that colour changes could make an important contribution to this. The rhythm of *Phrynosoma* may well serve to facilitate the absorption of heat from the sun's radiation during the early morning and late evening and to reflect more of it during the middle of the day, and it is interesting that a similar suggestion has been made in respect of the diurnal colour change of the fiddler crab *Uca* (p. 311).

Two other examples may be briefly mentioned. *Anolis carolinensis* has a much more elaborate play of colours than is found in the preceding species, ranging from brown to green through shades of light brown and yellow. Here again there is evidence for the operation of the hormonal mechanism, for hypophysectomy is followed by a permanent assumption of the green colour, representing the pale phase, while the injection of extracts of the pituitary of *Fundulus* results in a temporary assumption of the brown colour. According to Kleinholz, however, there is no evidence for innervation of the melanocytes of this animal, a conclusion that he bases upon the results of experiments similar to those previously carried out by Redfield on *Phrynosoma*. Cutting of the spinal cord and sympathetic chains has no effect upon the background responses, and even when the posterior part of the cord is further destroyed by pithing the animal can still respond as a whole to light and dark backgrounds by assuming respectively the green and brown phase. It is true that electrical stimulation of the cloaca, muscles, or spinal cord evokes a generalized pallor, but Kleinholz found that this was shown by denervated regions of the body as well as by intact ones, and he therefore concluded that the melanocytes were not directly controlled in any way by the nervous system. As for the chameleon, relatively little is known regarding the regulation of its colour change, although it is certain that its melanocytes are innervated by sympathetic fibres which are responsible for bringing about concentration of the pigment. The distribution of these fibres (Fig. 94) is somewhat like that in *Fundulus* (p. 271), so that the effect of cutting the nerve cord depends upon the level at which this is carried out (Fig. 95).

7. The unihumoral and bihumoral theories

We must now turn to deal with a complication in the analysis of the hormonal aspect of regulation which first arose from the studies of Hogben and Slome on *Xenopus*, and which led them to conclude that the existence of the one hormone (melanocyte-stimulating hormone, intermedin, or B-substance) was not sufficient by itself to explain the responses of that animal, but that a second hormone, which they called W-substance, must also be involved, this being responsible for inducing pallor. This interpretation has become known as the bihumoral hypothesis, as compared with the unihumoral one involving melanocyte-stimulating hormone alone, and it was later applied also by Hogben and Waring to certain elasmobranchs. A few examples must serve to indicate the reasoning upon which these conclusions are based.

Firstly, Hogben and Slome found that the result of injecting extracts containing melanocyte-stimulating hormone into pale toads differed according to whether they were intact animals, pale because of a background response, or hypophysectomized ones, pale because of the lack of pituitary secretion (Fig. 96). Both categories darkened as a result of the injection, but the former became pale again quite quickly while the latter remained dark for much longer and blanched only slowly and incompletely. Technically, the former are said to show a greater tolerance for the hormone, and they ascribed this to the presence in the blood of the hypothetical W-substance, secreted by the pituitary, and tending by its pallor-inducing property to neutralize the effect of the B-substance. The hypophysectomized toads would lack this secretion, with the result that the

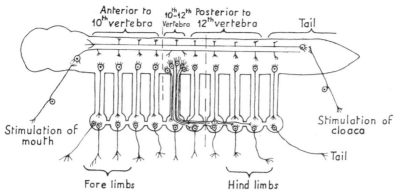

Fig. 94. Diagrammatic representation of the nerve paths involved in the control of the pigmentary effector system of the chameleon (cf. Fig. 92.) (From Hogben & Mirvish, 1928. *J. exp. Biol.* **5**, 295–308.)

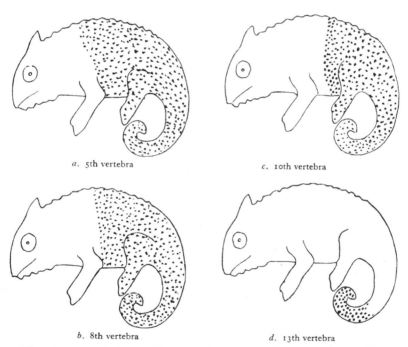

a. 5th vertebra

c. 10th vertebra

b. 8th vertebra

d. 13th vertebra

Fig. 95. Demonstration of the direct innervation of the pigmentary effector system of the chameleon through the central nervous and sympathetic systems. Section of the nerve cord anterior to the 11th vertebra restricts the pallor following faradic stimulation of the mouth to the region in front of the cut (*a, b, c*). Section of the cord at the 13th vertebra results in generalized pallor as a result of impulses being distributed to posterior parts of the body through pre-ganglionic fibres leaving the cord at about the level of the 10th to 12th vertebrae (*d*). (Cf. Fig. 94.)

(From Hogben & Mirvish, 1928. *J. exp. Biol.* **5**, 295–308.)

effect of the injection of melanocyte-stimulating hormone (B-substance) would persist for a much longer period.

The differential release of two such hormones under different conditions of illumination implies some degree of differentiation in the receptor organ, and Hogben and Slome investigated this by making use of the fact that *Xenopus*, being a fully aquatic animal, with its eyes directed upwards, could be arranged in a tank of water in such a way that the eyes could receive light either from all sides or only from above. The former condition was secured by illuminating the animal from above in a tank with white sides, and the latter by illuminating it from above in a tank with black sides; the portion of the retina which received light only from above

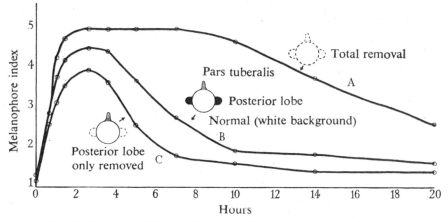

Fig. 96. Tolerance of *Xenopus* (3 series of 6 animals, normal, and operated as indicated) to similar injections of 'posterior lobe' extract.
(From Hogben & Slome, 1936. *Proc. Roy. Soc.* B **120**, 158–73.)

was termed the floor, and the remainder the periphery. Using this method they were able to show that the melanophore index was 4·5 when the floor alone was illuminated, 1·3 when the periphery alone was illuminated, 1·8 when both were, and 3·0 when neither was, the animal being then in complete darkness. From these results they inferred that illumination either of the floor or of the periphery resulted respectively in the release either of B-substance or of W-substance, that if both were illuminated simultaneously both substances were released, with W-substance being prepotent over B-substance, and that in the absence of any illumination there was no release of either substance and that the melanocyte then passed into an intermediate condition of rest.

Hogben and Landgrebe later applied a similar analysis to *Gasterosteus*, and showed that overhead illumination on a white background would stimulate one localized area of the retina (*PQ* in Fig. 97) and on a black background would stimulate another (*QR* in Fig. 97, and perhaps the area immediately ventral to it). The situation differs from that in *Xenopus* in that the white background response of *Gasterosteus* is known to be mediated by the nervous system, in accordance with the common situation in teleosts, but they believed that their data gave evidence that this was superimposed on the more archaic hormonal mechanism. In this connexion Waring has tentatively suggested that the interpretation of the

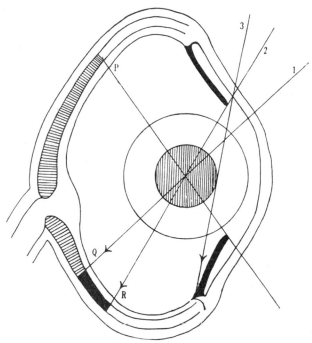

Fig. 97. Image formation in the eye of the stickleback, *Gasterosteus aculeatus*. The optical properties of the eye are such that region *QR* forms images of terrestrial objects and *PQ* images of subaquatic ones and the bottom, while the peripheral zone forms no clear images.
(From Hogben & Landgrebe, 1940. *Proc. Roy. Soc.* B **128**, 317–53.)

nervous mechanism as being historically more recent than the hormonal one is supported by the relative geological ages of the various groups of fish concerned.

Now Hogben and his colleagues well recognized that the data obtained from *Xenopus* could also be explained in terms of a unihumoral theory, involving, that is, only one hormone, if it were assumed that illumination of one area of the retina excited its release while illumination of the other area inhibited this. They therefore extended their analysis in order to secure further evidence for the bihumoral interpretation. As an example of this extension, they compared the effect of injecting melanocyte-stimu-lating hormone preparations into three groups of toads, one consisting of intact animals, the second of animals with the pituitary completely re-moved, and the third of ones with only the 'posterior lobe' (including the pars intermedia) removed. They found, as before, that Group 1 showed a greater tolerance than Group 2, but that Group 3 showed a greater tolerance than either of the others. To account for this they assumed that the W-substance was secreted by the 'anterior lobe'; thus Group 1 would possess both this and the B-substance, Group 2 would possess neither, while Group 3, possessing the W-substance but not the B-substance, would be in the best position to neutralize the effect of the injected hormone (Fig. 96).

They also drew support for the bihumoral theory from a study of the time relations of colour change in intact *Xenopus*, in which they recorded the time taken for the melanocytes to achieve equilibrium on transference of the animal from one type of background to another. The argument involved is a complicated one, but it depends upon the fact that the mel-anocytes of *Xenopus* show dispersion when the animal is on an illuminated black background, concentration when it is on an illuminated white background, and an intermediate condition when it is in complete dark-ness. This is taken to mean that transfer from a black background to a white one, for example, must involve the destruction (or excretion) of more of a dispersing hormone than would transfer from a black background to com-plete darkness. If, then, only the one hormone were concerned, the colour change resulting from the former transfer would take longer than that resulting from the latter transfer. It was found, however, that the time relations actually recorded were not explicable in terms of the unihumoral theory but rather supported the view that two hormones were interacting.

It will be evident that the bihumoral theory has been carefully considered and that it is founded upon a substantial body of observation, but it remains difficult to accept it as thoroughly established, partly because much of the evidence is essentially indirect, and also because, as Kent has pointed out, the facts relating to the time relationships of colour change are susceptible of more than one interpretation. Moreover, the operative treatment involved in such experiments may have consequences which are difficult to assess. For example, there is evidence that the activity of the pars intermedia is inhibited by hypothalamic nerve fibres; any injury to these might therefore result in an increased output of melanocyte-stimulating hormone which could give the misleading im-pression of the removal of an antagonistic hormone.

However, some recent observations of Enami have shown that if extracts of the pituitary or hypothalamus of the catfish *Parasilurus asotus* are injected into dark-adapted and hypophysectomized animals of the same species there results a pallor at the site of injection and very occasionally a generalized pallor of the whole body. This he ascribed to the presence of a pigment-concentrating substance which was apparently distinct from the melanocyte-stimulating hormone, since he found it to be located most abundantly in the meso-adenohypophysis (p. 292) and in the nucleus lateralis tuberis of the hypothalamus. He was unable to find any trace of the substance in either the pituitary or the hypothalamus of the dog and rat, nor, unfortunately, was he able to identify it in the frog *Rana nigromaculata*, nor is there yet any evidence for its presence in elasmobranchs.

Enami's observations, together with the suggestion of Parry and Holliday that the pseudobranch may be involved in the regulation of colour change (p. 168), show that much remains to be learned about this process. Account needs to be taken, too, of the well-known fact that the catechol hormones are active agents in evoking concentration of pigment in the melanocytes. In elasmobranchs it has sometimes been necessary to use enormous doses, ranging up to 2 mg of adrenaline per 200 g of body weight, to produce this response, and results obtained in such a way must obviously be regarded as of little more than pharmacological interest. In general, however, melanocytes readily respond to this substance, a solution of one part in a million being sufficient to produce concentration in the isolated scales of *Fundulus*, while the injection of 1 ml of a 1 in 10,000 dilution will establish pallor in *Rana pipiens*. The interpretation of these responses is uncertain, but it may well be that they are a consequence of the neurohumoral function of the catechol hormones, and that they are only of physiological significance in colour change when the melanocytes are directly innervated. It has been commonly supposed that in fish they are the cause of the pallor which so often develops when these animals are excited by handling or in other ways.

Even more uncertain at present is the interpretation to be placed upon the function of the pineal gland. Extracts of this organ have long been known to influence colour change, one example of this being its action in the sockeye salmon, *Oncorhynchus nerka* (Plate XIII *A*). Hoar has shown that simultaneous destruction of the eyes and pineal complex in the smolt will result in the animals becoming jet black (except for their silvery ventral surface) when kept against an aluminium-painted background, as compared with the light colour of unoperated control animals and the intermediate colour of those in which the eyes only are destroyed. Such animals also lose their negative phototaxis, both by night and by day. This influence of the pineal complex upon colour is similar to that found by Young in the ammocoete, but the interpretation is here complicated by the involvement of the nervous system in the colour changes of teleosts; evidently the pineal complex in the salmon is concerned in some way with the promotion of lightening of the colour, but it is not clear whether this is due to the direct action of a hormone upon the chromatophores or to some functional relationship of the organ with the nervous system.

The likelihood that a pineal secretion may be able to act directly upon melanocytes in the vertebrates has, however, been increased by the isolation from the pineal of the ox of a substance with a strong pigment-concentrating property. This substance, now called melatonin (Fig. 98)

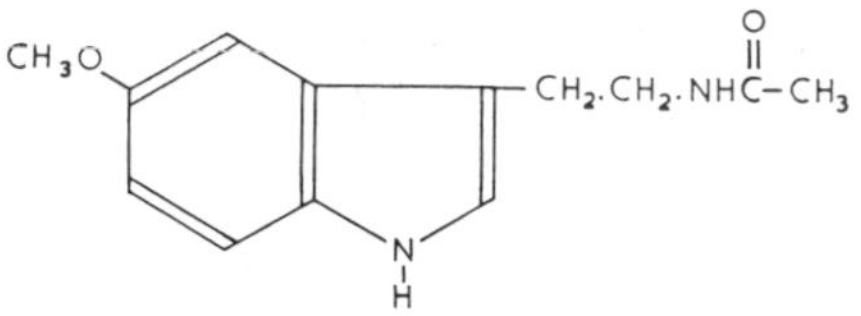

Fig. 98. Melatonin (*N*-acetyl-5-methoxytrypta-mine).
          (From Lerner & Case, 1959. *J. Amer. Chem. Soc.* **81**, 6084.)

is by far the most effective of the various agents known to be capable of lightening the skin of the frog. Thus it is at least 100 times as active, on a weight basis, as the catechol hormones, 200 times as active as triiodothyronine, and 5,000 times as active as serotonin. Melatonin, acetylcholine, hydrocortisone, and the catechol hormones will produce *in vitro* some reversal of the dispersing effect of melanocyte-stimulating hormone, and it has been suggested that they may all be acting upon cell permeability or some other fundamental element of cell organization, with an effect perhaps comparable with the changes in permeability which accompany the transmission of nerve impulses. Evidence for the presence of melatonin in peripheral nervous tissue, and the fact that serotonin (p. 326), suspected by some to be a neurohumoral agent, influences melanocytes, would agree with such an interpretation, but this awaits further exploration.

8. Some evolutionary considerations

In looking back over the problems of colour control in vertebrates it must be appreciated that the examples which we have discussed represent a small fraction of the wealth of investigation which has been devoted to the field; generalizations, therefore, are difficult to frame and may well be unfair to the views of those who have an intimate knowledge of the responses of particular species. We can see, however, that melanocytes are already present in the Agnatha and must, therefore, have been established very early in vertebrate evolution. This is understandable, for the fossil Agnatha from the Silurian and Devonian seem mostly to have been heavily armoured forms, probably rather sluggish and almost certainly feeding on the detritus at the bottom of lakes and streams. Under such circumstances a simple form of background response may well have had a substantial survival value, and the same consideration applies to the heavily armoured gnathostomes that succeeded them. The colour change of modern cyclostomes, which is of no very obvious value to them, may thus be a relic of those archaic times.

These colour responses were evidently mediated initially by a simple hormonal mechanism, which we may ascribe to the action of melanocyte-stimulating hormone, although further studies are needed to establish how far the structure of this remains uniform throughout the vertebrate series. The regulation of the responses through a light-sensitive receptor mechanism must have been needed from an early stage. This would have demanded a control of the responsible endocrine tissue by the central nervous system, and this must have been one factor in the evolution of the particularly close association of the pars intermedia, or its homologue, with the neurohypophysis, an association which is already established in the Cyclostomata and which remains a characteristic feature of the organization of the pituitary gland (see Chapter XII).

The exact nature of the physiological connexion between those two regions demands further study. We have seen that the polypeptide secretions of the hypothalamus have been mentioned as one of the possible means by which the activity of the pars distalis might be controlled (p. 120), and there seems, therefore, to be an obvious possibility that similar secretions might control the pars intermedia. Some observations of Oztan and Gorbman that exposure of ammocoete larvae to continuous illumination results in depletion of the neurosecretory content of the nucleus preopticus (p. 291) may be evidence for the involvement of the hypothalamus in the control of the colour responses of cyclostomes, and it has been suggested that in them the blood vessels of the pituitary could provide the functional link (p. 291). In the frog, on the other hand, there is some evidence that the neurosecretory fibres actually enter the pars intermedia from the neural lobe, so that here the link may be a direct nervous one. All of this, of course, is part of the general problem of the regulation of adenohypophyseal secretory activity, and it needs to be considered together with the other aspects of this which we discuss elsewhere. In this connexion we clearly need to know more about the functioning of the brain in the regulation of melanocyte responses, especially in view of von Frisch's suggestion that *Phoxinus* may have a paling centre in the medulla and a darkening centre in the diencephalon. Equally relevant is evidence implying the presence of light-sensitive cells in the diencephalon of the ammocoete larva and of *Phoxinus*; it is, of course, from this region of the brain that the eye develops (as also the pineal and parapineal organs), and it may be that this has itself been a factor in determining the establishment at this point of the association between the adenohypophysis and neurohypophysis.

With advances in vertebrate organization, the mechanism of regulation of colour responses clearly becomes more complex, and it is certain that nervous control is incorporated into the system in teleosts and reptiles. This particular advance may well have taken place independently in the two groups, the teleosts having specialized along lines remote from the path that led to tetrapods, but we can see that nervous regulation in this particular respect confers a speed and precision of response which is in line with their general level of activity and efficiency. We noted similar advantages in reviewing the development of the closely analogous association of hormonal and nervous control in the regulation of alimentary function.

With the appearance of terrestrial vertebrates we become aware that other factors than visual ones may influence colour response. Warmth, dryness, and bright light contribute to evoke pallor in amphibians, for example, while cold, moisture, and shade evoke darkening. The full significance of this merits further study, but it is clear that it provides an illustration of the bearing of ecological problems upon endocrinological ones, and we have noted already in discussing reptiles that thermo-regulation may be a relevant factor. Certainly wide fluctuations of temperature provided one of the crucial problems encountered by vertebrates when they abandoned the thermostable properties of a fully aquatic environment, and it may be that their chromatophore mechanism made a valuable contribution in bridging the transition. Soon, however, with the development of feathers and hairs as part of the machinery of homoiothermy, the chromatophores seem to have lost some of their original value. The melanocytes retain their old prerogative of being the source of melanin, but this comes to represent the limit of their usefulness, and they lose their capacity for dispersion and concentration of this material, despite the continued formation in the mammalian pituitary of melanocyte-stimulating hormone. The function of the latter remains in doubt, but its diminished importance may well account for the lack of the pars intermedia in the pituitary gland of birds and of certain mammals. This does not mean, however, the loss of melanocyte-stimulating hormone, for in such forms the hormone is said to be extractable from the pars distalis. In man, for example, where the pars intermedia is later replaced by an invasion of basiphil cells from the pars distalis, the hormone is extractable both from the latter and also from the zone of invasion. We can accept such facts as being a natural consequence of the close embryological and functional relationships between the pars distalis and pars intermedia, a relationship already noted in our discussion of the molecular structure of corticotropin and the melanocyte-stimulating hormones.

XII. ORGANIZATION AND EVOLUTION OF THE PITUITARY GLAND

OUR analysis of the functional organization of the endocrine system of the vertebrates has repeatedly drawn our attention to the special significance of the part played by the pituitary gland. It is true that, as far as the tropic hormones of the latter are concerned, the reciprocity of action which is now known to exist between it and the other glands has modified earlier conceptions of it as 'the leader of the endocrine orchestra'. In association with the hypothalamus, however, it remains an element of central importance in the regulation and co-ordination of endocrine activity, and we must now draw some threads together by examining certain features of it in more detail and by attempting to assess something of its evolutionary history.

1. Histology of the pars distalis of mammals

We have seen that the mammalian adenohypophysis secretes six hormones, thyrotropin, FSH, ICSH, prolactin, corticotropin, and growth hormone. We have further considered the means by which the discharge of certain of these hormones is regulated, but it is evident that an essential element in our understanding of this is information regarding the location within the gland of the cells concerned with the production of each one of them; in particular we require to know whether each is secreted within a distinctive type of cell or whether two or more are likely to be released simultaneously from the same one. For this reason a great deal of attention has been focused upon the problem of the cytological organization of the pars distalis, the interest in this having, in fact, long antedated our current information as to the chemical characteristics of the hormones; in consequence, the techniques employed show an evolutionary history no less instructive than that of the organ itself. Unfortunately, despite the number of procedures that have been applied to this problem it remains very difficult indeed to present any useful generalizations, the reason being that different techniques are not always equally applicable to the same species. As a result, it is almost impossible, particularly with the more recently developed techniques, to establish valid comparisons between one species and another. Because of this we shall attempt no more here than to illustrate the possibilities of such studies by referring mainly to the pituitary gland of the rat, a species that has probably been more intensely investigated from this point of view than any other.

Earlier studies of the pars distalis, up to the 1930's, were based upon the use of such staining mixtures as Mann's methyl blue-eosin or the methylene blue and eosin mixtures of Giemsa and of Romanowsky. It has been customary to classify the cells into those with a stainable cytoplasm (chromophils) and those with a non-staining one (chromophobes), and with these mixtures it was possible to differentiate the former into basiphils (*basis*, base; *philein*, to love) and acidophils (*acidus*, sour), according to their affinity for basic and acidic dyes. With advances in our understanding of cell chemistry it then became apparent that the basiphilia largely resulted from the presence of ribonucleic acid and could be removed by preliminary treatment of the sections with ribonuclease, so that this terminology was seen to contribute little of value to the differentiation of the cell products. As a result, and despite the claim that with careful control of pH it is still possible to demonstrate some degree of basiphilia and acidophilia of the cell contents, these terms have fallen increasingly into disuse, to be replaced by a new terminology arising from the use of the Azan technique of Heidenhain. With this method the acidophils will stain either with orange G or with azocarmine, and the basiphils with aniline blue, so that it becomes possible to refer to the two types as acidophils and cyanophils (*kyanos*, blue).

With studies of the pituitary hormones making it increasingly likely that the cyanophils might be secreting more than one kind of product, attempts were made to introduce staining methods that would make it possible to subdivide this category. Some success was achieved in 1940 by Romeis, who, using resorcin-fuchsin combined with the Azan method, found it possible to distinguish two types of cyanophil which he termed beta and delta cells. Others, however, were less successful with this technique, and little progress was made along these lines until Halmi, in 1950, substituted Gomori's aldehyde-fuchsin for the resorcin-fuchsin and followed this by counter-staining with a modified Azan procedure in which light green replaced the aniline blue. With this method he was able to distinguish in the pars distalis of the rat two types of 'basiphil' which corresponded with the beta and delta cells of Romeis. Aldehyde-fuchsin has since proved to be a valuable stain for pituitary studies, not only for the adenohypophysis but also for revealing the neurosecretory fibres of the hypothalamus, but it suffers from the disadvantage that its use is purely empirical, so that the basis of its affinity for particular cell products remains obscure.

It is all the more important, then, that a valuable histochemical procedure is available for pituitary studies in the form of the periodic acid/Schiff (PAS) reaction, developed by McManus in 1946 and Hotchkiss in 1948. This is a specific test for 1,2-glycol groups (CHOH-CHOH), which are converted into dialdehydes (CHO-CHO) as a result of the

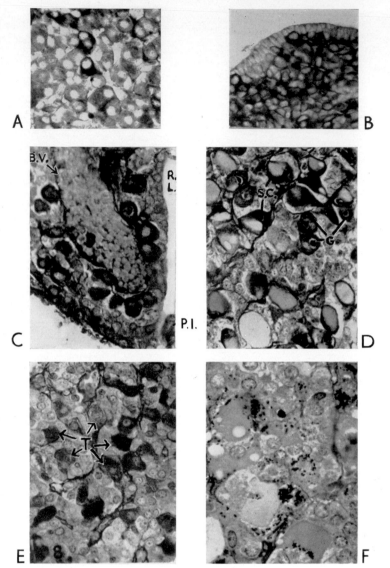

Plate XI. *A*. Section of the pars distalis of a normal mouse, stained by the combined aldehyde-fuchsin periodic acid-Schiff orange G stain and photographed through a green filter. A typical thyrotropic cell occupies the centre of the figure and is very dark. Nestling beneath a process of this cell is a round acidophil with grey cytoplasm which contrasts with the dark grey cytoplasm of the large gonadotropic cell just below it.

B. Section of the pars distalis of a mouse of the genetic dwarf strain, stained with aldehyde-fuchsin and orange G after permanganate oxidation. Numerous gonadotropic cells (dark) are present, but there is a deficiency both of acidophils and of thyrotropic cells. (×425.)

(From Elftman & Wegelius, 1959. *Anat. Rec.* **135**, 43–47.)

C to *F*. Cytology of the pars distalis of the rat (PAS and haematoxylin). *C*, at the anterior border in a normal animal, showing round or oval gonadotropic cells, with PAS-positive granules, surrounding a blood vessel. *D*, a similar region in a male rat, 15 months after castration; the majority of the gonadotropic cells have been converted into signet-ring cells, with vacuoles containing a hyaline substance, which stains a faint pink. *E*, In the central region in a normal animal, showing polygonal thyrotropic cells with PAS-positive granules. *F*, a similar region in a male 66 days after thyroidectomy; the thyrotropic cells have an extensive accumulation of hyaline substance which contains vacuoles. *B.V.*, blood vessel; *G*, gonadotropic cells; *P.I.*, pars intermedia; *R.L.*, residual lumen of Rathke's pouch; *S.C.*, signet-ring cells; *T*, thyrotropic cells (cf. Fig. 99, p. 286). (C, D, E, ×415.)

(From Purves & Griesbach, 1951. *Endocrin.* **49**, 244–64.)

oxidation of the C-C bonds by the periodic acid. Owing to the fact that this substance, unlike some other oxidizing agents, does not carry the oxidation any further, these dialdehydes can be visualized by the application of Schiff's reagent, which reacts with them to give a compound with a magenta-red colour. The method is fully reviewed in current textbooks of histochemistry and will not be further discussed here beyond pointing out that it will reveal four main types of biologically important materials: (a) glycogen; (b) acid mucopolysaccharides, which can also be identified by staining them with Alcian blue, and by the reddish response (gamma metachromasia) which they give when stained with toluidine blue; (c) mucoproteins, glycoproteins, and neutral mucopolysaccharides; (d) various lipids, including sphingomyelin and certain glycolipids.

Studies of the pituitary of the rat have shown that cyanophilia and the aldehyde-fuchsin staining of the cells of the pars distalis is a property of the cell granules, and that the PAS method evokes from these a positive response which, in conjunction with appropriate controls, indicates that they contain material belonging to category c, thereby establishing a strong presumption that they are concerned with the secretion of the glycoprotein (or mucoprotein) hormones (FSH, ICSH, thyrotropin). By itself this evidence would not be conclusive, but by combining it with the application of certain experimental procedures it has been strengthened to a point where it carries reasonably complete conviction.

These procedures are devised to correlate cytological changes with changes in hormonal content, and the results show that some cells secrete thyrotropin (thyrotropic or thyrotroph cells) while others secrete gonadotropins (gonadotropic or gonadotroph cells). These are respectively the beta and delta cells of Halmi's terminology, but, owing to a confusion of nomenclature, correspond respectively to the delta and beta cells of Romeis. The two types can be identified by their form and their position in the gland (Fig. 99). The gonadotropic cells are rounded in shape, with large granules, and are situated predominantly in a ventral zone (the 'sex zone') and in a narrow zone dorsally; they tend to be clustered closely around the larger portal vessels. The thyrotropic cells are somewhat larger, polygonal in shape, with fine granules, and are situated more centrally where they show no particular relationship with the large vessels. The experimental evidence for their identification rests upon the following procedures (Plate XI C–F):

Firstly, if either male or female rats are castrated there is found, within one or two days, a marked increase in the size and number of the gonadotropic cells, with many mitotic stages, beginning in the sex zone and spreading to all parts of the pars distalis. After several weeks many of these cells contain a hyaline vacuole, which is coloured a faint pink by the PAS reaction and which is surrounded by deeply stained granules, giving a characteristic appearance known as the 'signet-ring stage'. This reaction can be correlated with an increased gonadotropin content of the gland, and is the result of the disturbance of the feedback balance by the withdrawal

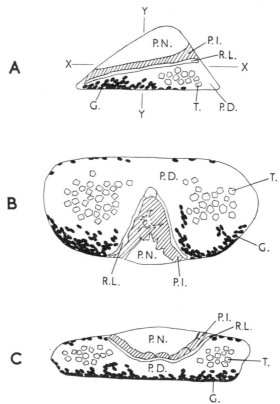

Fig. 99. The distribution of thyrotropic and gonadotropic cells in the pars distalis of the male rat (cf. Plate x). *A*, Sagittal section of the pituitary gland; *B*, horizontal section in the plane marked *X——X* in *A*; *C*, transverse section in the plane marked *Y——Y* in *A*; *G.*, gonadotropic cells; *P.D.*, pars distalis; *P.I.*, pars intermedia; *P.N.*, neural lobe; *R.L.*, residual lumen; *T.*, thyrotropic cells.
(From Purves and Griesbach, 1951. *Endocrin.* **49**, 244–64.)

of the influence of the gonadal steroids. Conversely, the injection of oestrogen into the male will produce degranulation of the gonadotropic cells, leading sometimes to their degeneration.

Secondly, thyroidectomy or goitrogen treatment causes the appearance of large numbers of 'thyroidectomy cells' (Plate XI *F*), originating in the thyrotropic region and again accompanied by many mitoses. These cells later develop hyaline vacuoles, which give a stronger PAS response than the vacuoles of the castration cells, and later still there may be an extensive accumulation of hyaline material which may itself contain vacuoles and also some granules of a peculiar character. Despite this increase in the number of these cells the thyrotropin content of the gland is found by bio-assay to be low, and this is reflected in the fact that the fine granulation of the cells responds only faintly to the PAS test. This means that in this case the disturbance of the feedback balance results in an increased production of thyrotropin which, however, is discharged so vigorously that the hormonal content of the gland is actually lower than under normal working conditions. Such a circumstance, incidentally, is of interest for the interpretation of the secretory status of any gland, for it shows how the condition of the cells depends upon the balance between synthesis and discharge; cells with conspicuous stores of secretion may be relatively inactive, while those with sparse contents may be highly active but may be losing their product as quickly as they succeed in making it. It is important, therefore, in evaluating the secretory status of any gland, and particularly so with one as complex as the pars distalis, to check one staining method against another, to use histochemical procedures wherever possible, and to check these in their turn against experimentally modified or pathologically disturbed glands, or, better still, against direct estimations of hormone contents by suitable assay procedures. It is because these conditions have so seldom been met that it is at present impossible to generalize very widely about pituitary organization, although there is, according to Pearse, some reason for thinking that thyrotropic and gonadotropic cells can be distinguished in the human pituitary by the application of the performic acid-Alcian blue, PAS and orange G procedure of Adams.

The above analysis does not make any distinction between the secretion of FSH and ICSH, nor is such a distinction easily made, for the activities of these, as we have seen, are very closely interlinked. However, it has been found that if adult female rats are treated with testosterone the pituitary shows an increased content of FSH and a decrease and eventual disappearance of ICSH. Cytological study of the glands from such rats shows that in addition to the more peripherally situated gonadotropic cells, with coarse granules, there are also some which are centrally situated and which possess a finer granulation. After twenty-eight days of treatment the former are filled with granules while the latter have regressed to a point at which they can no longer be distinguished. This suggests that the two types may be functionally distinct, with the more peripheral ones secreting FSH and the more central ones ICSH.

So convenient is the rat for laboratory studies that these observations do not exhaust the possibilities of functional analysis of its pituitary gland, and useful information has been obtained by studying its development.

Thyrotropic cells are recognizable by their shape at least from the first day after birth, and they become progressively filled with granules which reach their maximum by twenty-eight days. The gonadotropic cells are also distinguishable from an early stage, but at about thirty-five days they become degranulated in the female, and thereafter the ones in the sex zone are no longer distinguishable in that sex, although they remain visible in males of all ages. This change can be correlated precisely with the onset of oestrous cycles, which begin at an age of between thirty-two and forty-eight days, and it is clear that thereafter in these animals, with their continuous sequence of cycles, there is a greatly reduced storage of gonadotropins. The situation as regards the centrally situated gonadotropic cells is less clear, but the acidophils are easily recognizable from soon after birth, although they reach their maturity rather more slowly.

It is generally supposed that growth hormone arises from the acidophil cells, for these are known to be absent from the pituitaries of a strain of dwarf mice in which there is a genetically determined arrest of growth (Plate XI A, B). Moreover, in cattle, where cyanophil and acidophil regions of the pars distalis are readily separated, this hormone is known to be associated with the latter region. The source of prolactin and corticotropin is less clear, although what is known of their chemistry suggests that they are more likely to be produced by acidophils, but some light is shed on this by observations made on other species. In the rabbit, acidophils and cyanophils are readily distinguishable, but it seems to be impossible to subdivide the latter category on cytological criteria. The acidophils are PAS-negative, and are of two types, one with an intense affinity for azocarmine, and the other giving up this stain readily on differentiation and staining with orange G. The former, which occur also in the cat, are generally termed carminophils.

It will be recalled that both the cat and the rabbit ovulate only after coitus, and that there is involved here an important time relationship which bears directly upon the functional analysis of the pituitary. We know that in the rabbit a stimulus is conveyed through the mediation of the sympathetic division of the autonomic system to the pars distalis via the hypothalamus within three minutes of coitus, for during that period alone is it possible to inhibit ovulation by the injection of an adrenergic blocking agent. We know, too, that ovulation in the rabbit can be inhibited by hypophysectomy, but only if this is carried out within one hour of coitus; this means that by the end of that period the pars distalis must have discharged sufficient ICSH to stimulate ovulation, and that no further discharge of it is necessary. Now it has been observed that during that first hour there is a well-defined reaction in the cyanophils, involving nuclear changes and cytoplasmic degranulation, which reaches a maximum by one and a half hours, and that degranulation of the carminophils begins

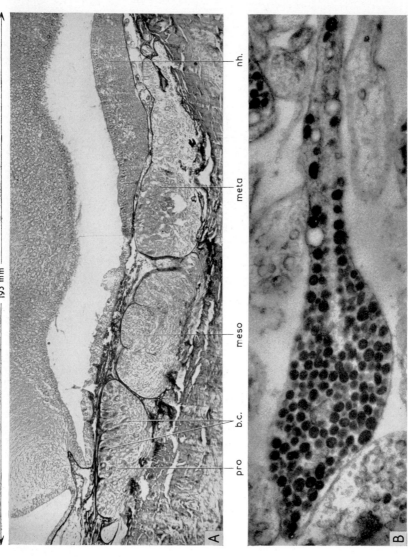

Plate XII. *A.* Sagittal section of the pituitary region of a pre-metamorphic ammocoete larva. *pro.*, *meso.*, *meta.*, pro-, meso-, meta-adenohypophysis; *nh.*, neurohypophysis (infundibulum); *b.c.*, basiphil cell. (×218.)

(From van de Kamer & Schreurs, 1959). *Z. Zellforsch.* **49**, 605–30.)

B. Electron micrograph showing numerous neurosecretory granules in a nerve fibre in the neurohypophysis of the cod (*Gadus callarias*). Clumps of such granules form the neurosecretion revealed by light microscopy (cf. Plate XV. *D*). (×23,760.)

(From Bargmann and Knoop, 1960. *Z. Zellforsch.* **52**, 256–77.)

later, at about three hours after coitus. The conclusion which Pearse has drawn from these data is that ICSH is secreted by the cyanophils, which conforms to the fact that their contents are PAS-positive, and that the carminophils probably secrete prolactin, which conforms to the fact that these are found to be plentiful during late pregnancy and early lactation.

2. The pituitary gland of the Cyclostomata

The organization of the pituitary of cyclostomes (Fig. 100) has been most closely studied in the larval and adult lamprey, but much remains to be learned, even in these forms. The adenohypophysis develops as a solid ingrowth which is at first connected with the olfactory sac by a solid nasohypophyseal stalk. Later it separates from this, and at metamorphosis the stalk hollows out to form a sac which passes back from the olfactory organ to underlie the pituitary. This sac has often been regarded as a persistent hypophyseal cavity which, if it were correctly so interpreted, would be unique in its complete separation from the adenohypophysis, but the facts of its development indicate that it may be a secondary feature of the organization of these animals.

The adenohypophysis (Plate XII *A*) becomes a flattened organ, divided by connective tissue septa into three regions, anterior, median, and posterior, for which the names pro-, meso-, and meta-adenohypophysis have been suggested (see below). The anterior region comes to contain many cyanophil cells which are PAS-positive, and which are stained also by aldehyde-fuchsin; these are very probably gonadotropic since they show increased activity with the approach of sexual maturity and we have seen that the results of hypophysectomy indicate that the pituitary exerts some degree of control over gonadal development. The posterior region is probably homologous with the pars intermedia, for its destruction induces permanent pallor (p. 262), but nothing very definite is known about other possible adenohypophyseal functions. Cells staining with aldehyde-fuchsin are present in the meso-adenohypophysis, but in general the cytological differentiation seems to be less advanced than in higher vertebrates, and the existence of other hormones remains to be established.

A neurohypophysis can be identified in both larva and adult, and to preserve uniformity of nomenclature (pp. 67, 293) is best termed an infundibulum. It exists in a very simple form, with no differentiated infundibular process, as a depression of the floor of the third ventricle, which in this region is formed of a layer of elongated ependymal cells. Amongst these run nerve fibres which contain material stainable by chrome-alum-haematoxylin, and which are hypothalamic neurosecretory fibres, presumably responsible for the transport of the arginine vasotocin (p. 90)

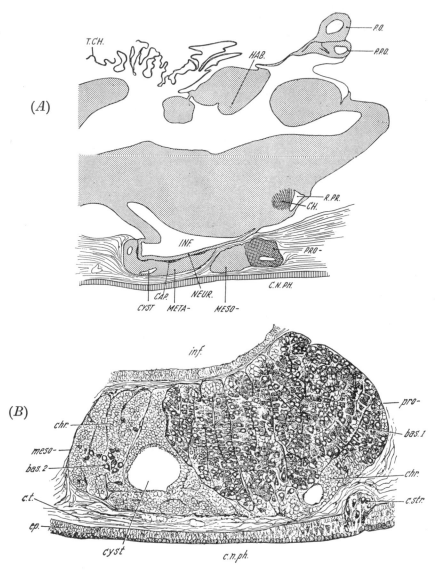

Fig. 100. *A.* Diagrammatic sagittal section through the head of a lamprey (*Lampetra fluviatilis*), to show the localization of the pituitary gland. *cap.*, capillary; *ch.*, optic chiasma; *c.n.ph.*, nasopharyngeal canal; *cyst*, cyst in pituitary; *hab.*, habenular commissure; *inf.*, infundibular recess; *meso-*, meso-adenohypophysis; *meta-*, meta-adenohypophysis; *neur.*, neurohypophysis; *p.o.*, pineal organ; *p.p.o.*, parapineal organ; *pro-*, pro-adenohypophysis; *r.pr.*, recessus preopticus; *t.ch.*, choroid plexus. *B.* Pro- and meso-adenohypophysis of the lamprey; the dark cells (*bas 1, bas 2*) are those containing granules which react positively with the aldehyde-fuchsin stain. *chr.*, chromophobe cell; *c.str*, cell strand connecting epithelium of nasopharyngeal pouch with pituitary; *c.t.*, connective tissue; *ep.*, epithelium of nasopharyngeal pouch. Other abbreviations as above.

(From Lanzing, 1959. *Uitgeversmaatschappij Neerlandia*, Utrecht.)

that is believed present in this gland. Such fibres are largely derived in lower vertebrates from the preoptic nuclei, which are the homologues of the separate supraoptic and paraventricular nuclei of mammals, but a small posterior nucleus is also present in the ammocoete.

The adenohypophysis is closely applied to the neurohypophysis, which suggests that the close functional association between these two regions, so fundamental in importance in mammals, is already established at this

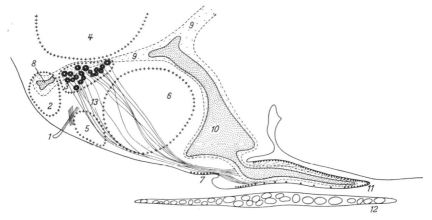

Fig. 101. Diagrammatic median reconstruction of the hypothalamus and pituitary gland of *Myxine glutinosa*. 1, optic tract; 2, preoptic nucleus (region parvocellularis anterior); 3, preoptic nucleus (region magnocellularis); 7, presumed median eminence; 10, ventricle of hypothalamus; 11, infundibular process; 12, adenohypophysis.
(From Olsson, 1959. *Zeitschr. Zellforsch*, **51**, 97–107.)

early stage of vertebrate evolution. The two regions are separated by connective tissue, apparently at its thinnest posteriorly, and in this run blood vessels which supply the ventral surface of the neurohypophysis and also penetrate into the adenohypophysis. These vessels would seem adequate for providing chemical communication between the two regions of the type which we have discussed earlier, and hence would constitute a basis for neural regulation of the adenohypophysis, always assuming that the cells of the latter lack secreto-motor innervation, which has yet to be proved. That some control of the adenohypophysis by the central nervous system must exist is clearly indicated by the melanocyte responses in these animals (p. 265), but we lack as yet the evidence needed for a clear understanding of the mechanism by which this control is exerted.

As regards *Myxine* (Fig. 101), it is of interest that in this animal the neurohypophysis is better developed, projecting backwards as a hollow lobe in a manner recalling the embryonic condition of the infundibular process of higher forms. It receives the product of neurosecretory fibres running from the preoptic nuclei, but some of their product is released in the floor of the hypothalamus immediately anterior to the infundibular process. The outer surface is conspicuously folded and vascularized at this point, and Olsson has speculated that this may be a rudimentary median eminence, a structure that has not otherwise been identified in cyclostomes. From this region small vessels penetrate the connective tissue that separates the adenohypophysis from the neurohypophysis, so that a basis for a vascular link exists here as in the lamprey.

3. The pituitary gland of fish

In dealing with the fish it is important to bear in mind that the modern representatives of these animals are highly specialized and, with the exception of *Latimeria* and the Dipnoi, are remote from the main line of vertebrate ascent. For this reason our present purpose will be sufficiently served by examining only the general principles which appear to govern the organization of their pituitaries and avoiding discussion of details of specialization which are amply recorded in the current literature.

The adenohypophysis of teleosts is usually said to develop as a solid ingrowth, as in the lamprey and in Amphibia, although the immature herring has an open Rathke's pouch which later becomes reduced to a strand of tissue (Fig. 56). In the more primitive sturgeon a hypophyseal cavity remains conspicuous even in the adult, and tubular extensions of it penetrate into the glandular tissue (Fig. 102). In the lower Actinopterygii, as also in teleosts, the adenohypophysis becomes differentiated into three regions, anterior, median, and posterior, and for these, as in the cyclostomes, the terms pro-, meso-, and meta-adenohypophysis have been proposed (Fig. 103). These terms will be used here for descriptive convenience, but it should be understood that they carry no implication that similarly named regions are necessarily homologous, nor can we feel sure that they indicate a clear-cut functional differentiation in any particular gland.

As in the lamprey, however, the posterior region probably represents the pars intermedia, being the region that is in closest contact with that part of the neurohypophysis in which neurosecretion is deposited, and being probably the source of melanocyte-stimulating hormone. The remainder probably corresponds with the pars distalis, and several types of cell have been identified in it. These include two types of cyanophil, one probably thyrotropic and the other gonadotropic, and acidophils of which some stain mainly with azocarmine and the others with orange G. On the whole, and as far as our limited knowledge goes, this adenohypophysis seems to be a highly differentiated organ and one that is fully adequate for the production of the extensive complement of hormones which is believed to be secreted by it.

In the present state of our knowledge it is well to be cautious in applying to the pituitary of fish the system of nomenclature that we use for the mammalian organ, and it is easy to press comparisons too far when they concern such widely separated groups. With this reservation in mind, however, we may regard the infundibulum of teleosts as giving rise to a

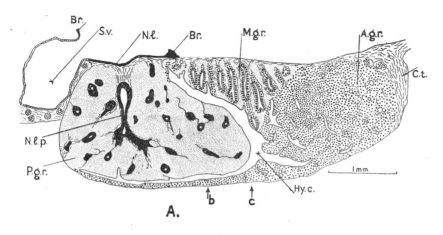

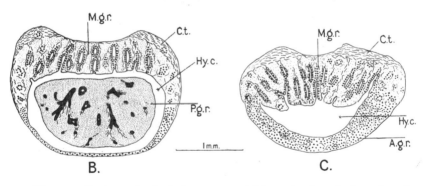

Fig. 102. Pituitary gland of the sturgeon (*Acipenser*). *A*, sagittal section of gland. *B*, transverse section through level '*b*' in '*A*'. *C*, transverse section through level '*c*' in '*A*'. *A.g.r.*, pro-adenohypophysis; *Br.*, brain; *C.t.*, connective tissue with blood-vessels; *Hy.c.*, hypophyseal cavity; *M.g.r.*, meso-adenohypophysis; *N.l.*, neurohypophysis; *N.l.p.*, process of neurohypophysis with central cavity; *P.g.r.*, meta-adenohypophysis; *S.v.*, main chamber of saccus vasculosus. (From Kerr, 1949. *Proc. Zool. Soc. Lond.* **118**, 973–83.)

neurohypophysis in which the infundibular process and stem are not separately identifiable, and in which a true neural lobe, with independent vascularization (p. 72), is not differentiated. Anterior to it lies what Wingstrand has called the post-optic ventricular floor, a region that extends to the optic chiasma (Fig. 104). Within this region there develops in the higher vertebrates the median eminence; this also is not fully differentiated in the cyclostomes and fish, although it is probably foreshadowed in some of them and has been thought to be functionally represented in others.

In fish there is usually to be found attached to the floor of the brain the organ called the saccus vasculosus, which arises in general from the dorsal wall of the infundibulum and a pair of lateral diverticula of it, but since this is not apparently endocrine in function we need not consider it further. It is the ventral wall of the infundibulum which gives rise in these

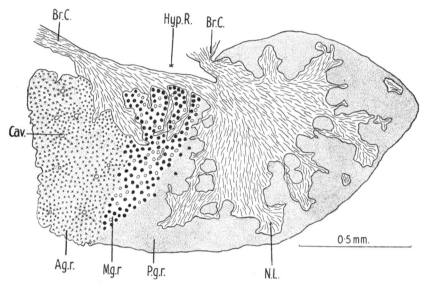

Fig. 103. Longitudinal section of the pituitary gland of the trout (*Salmo trutta*). *Ag.r.*, pro-adenohypophysis, represented by crosses, with stippling in addition to show distribution of acidophils; *Br.C.*, pituitary stalk; *Cav.*, cavity in pro-adenohypophysis; *Hyp.R.*, infundibular recess; *M.g.r.*, meso-adeno-hypophysis, with acidophils represented by solid circles and basiphils (cyanophils) by empty circles; *N.L.*, neurohypophysis, represented by short wavy lines; *P.g.r.*, meta-adenohypophysis, represented by stippling.
(From Kerr, 1942. *Proc. Zool. Soc. Lond.* **112A,** 37–56.)

animals to the definitive neurohypophysis; sometimes, as in elasmobranchs, this preserves its close relationship with the saccus vasculosus while in many teleosts the two become widely separated.

Neurosecretory fibres run in all parts of the neurohypophysis of teleosts (Plate XII *B*), but their secretory products accumulate mainly in the posterior region, which to this limited extent may be compared with the neural lobe of higher forms, although it lacks its characteristic vascularization (p. 72). The whole of the organ is in close relationship with the adenohypophysis and the boundary between them is highly folded in a manner suggesting that it is physiologically important to have as large a surface of contact as possible. The significance of this is to be understood partly in terms of the blood supply (Fig. 106), which here, as in other groups, is derived from the internal carotid arteries. Some of this blood may enter directly into the adenohypophysis, but most (and probably often all) of it reaches the latter after having first passed through the neuro-hypophysis. It will thus be seen that in these fish there is a common

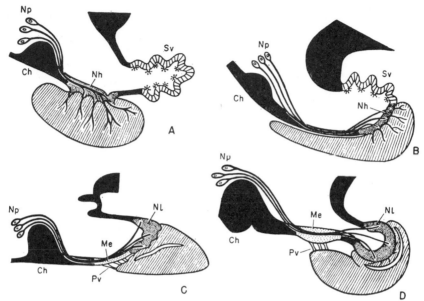

Fig. 104. Diagrams of median sagittal sections of the pituitary glands of *A*, the teleost *Anguilla*; *B*, the elasmobranch *Scyliorhinus*; *C*, the lungfish *Protopterus*; *D*, an amniote. *Ch*, optic chiasma; *Me*, median eminence; *Nh*, neuro-hypophysis; *Nl*, neural lobe; *Np*, nucleus preopticus; *Pv*, portal vessels (there is reason to believe that these may also be present in elasmobranchs); *Sv*, saccus vasculosus.

(From Wingstrand, 1959. In *Comparative Endocrinology*, ed. Gorbman. Wiley.)

vascularization for both the main components of the pituitary, and that there cannot, therefore, be a median eminence in the sense in which this exists in the mammals (p. 72). If, however, we accept Green's alternative definition of this as being that part of the neurohypophysis which has a common vascularization with the adenohypophysis, we can, as he suggests, regard the median eminence of higher forms as being represented in teleosts by the whole of the neurohypophysis, or at least by that part which is in contact with the pro- and meso-adenohypophysis. We thus have the basis for a vascular link between the central nervous system and the adenohypophysis, just as in the cyclostomes but much more elaborately developed, and it is of interest to speculate on what the nature of that link might be, remembering, however, that the absence of secreto-motor innervation from the adenohypophysis has still to be proved.

We have seen that there has been some suggestion that in the mammals chemical mediators might arise in the neurosecretory cells of the hypothalamus and be transmitted through the hypothalamico-hypophyseal tracts, becoming available to the capillaries of the median eminence, with which some of the fibres of those tracts are in close relationship. It has further been suggested that such mediators might be identical with, or chemically related to, the polypeptide hormones of the tracts. Now we have seen that the neurohypophysis of teleosts has not yet been shown to be involved in the regulation of water-balance (p. 92), nor has it been possible to establish other hormonal functions for the hypothalamic polypeptides in those animals, and this, in conjunction with the extensive distribution of the neurosecretory fibres throughout the neurohypophysis, sometimes in very close relationship with the adenohypophyseal cells, has led to the suggestion that the hypothalamus/neurohypophysis complex of these animals may be mainly concerned with the control of adenohypophyseal function.

The implication of this is that the hormonal functions of that complex, which we see fully deployed in the higher vertebrates, would have arisen as later developments of a more primitive regulatory function of its polypeptide secretions, and that the pharmacological properties of these might, in cyclostomes and fish, be a by-product of their molecular structure rather than an indication of their primary functions. It would, of course, be wholly premature to conclude at this stage that peripheral hormonal functions of these secretions are completely non-existent in fish, nor is the complete absence of these functions a necessary feature of the hypothesis. At the morphological level, however, the neural lobe and median eminence differentiate by stages out of the hypothalamus, and it is worth speculating that this might have been paralleled by a biochemical evolution of polypeptide secretions directed in part to hypophyseal regulation and in part to peripheral action, with the latter, perhaps, increasing in relative importance with the demands of adaptation to terrestrial life.

It has, indeed, been suggested that the polypeptide hormones may themselves act as chemical mediators in the control of the adenohypophysis. There is some evidence, for example, that the stimulus of suckling results in the release of prolactin as well as of the oxytocin that brings about milk-ejection, and it has been suggested that these two responses are associated in this way in the rat because oxytocin, in addition to its action upon the mammary gland, also promotes the discharge of prolactin from the adenohypophysis. It is too early to form a final opinion on such views, but if such a dual function of the polypeptide hormones could be substantiated it would afford an interesting parallel with the mode of action of the catechol amines.

The pituitary of elasmobranchs (Fig. 106), while having morphological features of its own, raises no problems substantially different from those discussed above, perhaps because at present it has been less thoroughly studied. The adenohypophysis develops as a hollow Rathke's pouch, just anterior to the oral plate; its tip gives rise to the region that is generally held to be the pars intermedia, and this closely interdigitates with the neurohypophysis, the result being the formation of what is often called the 'neuro-intermediate lobe'; although, as in teleosts, no true neural lobe is differentiated. According to Dodd, the remainder of the adenohypophyseal functions are likely to be centred in the 'ventral lobe', in which considerable traces of the hypophyseal cavity persist, and it is difficult therefore, to say what is the function of the 'rostral lobe', a peculiar region that projects forward beneath the hypothalamus as far as the optic chiasma. Equally puzzling to interpret is a suggestion of Meurling that certain elasmobranchs have a median eminence with a hypophyseal portal system which discharges into the 'rostral lobe' in *Squalus acanthias* and, surprisingly, into the 'neuro-intermediate lobe' in *Raja* and in *Scyliorhinus canicula*. Evidently we need to know a great deal more about the functional organization of this gland. An interesting developmental feature is the existence in the embryo of *Torpedo* of open communications between Rathke's pouch and the anterior pair of mesodermal somites, the premandibular somites; we shall see that these may be of importance in the assessment of the evolutionary history of the gland.

As we have emphasized already, neither the teleosts nor the elasmobranchs are on the direct line of vertebrate ascent, and this introduces some uncertainty in correlating the organization of their pituitaries with those of tetrapods, but the situation should be otherwise with the Class Choanichthyes, for here we have a group divisible into two sub-classes, one of which, the Crossopterygii, was certainly ancestral to the terrestrial vertebrates, while the other, the Dipnoi, is sufficiently close to the latter to parallel them in many features of organization. It is thus fortunate that we are well informed regarding the organization of the pituitary of at least one of the Dipnoi, the African lung-fish *Protopterus* (Fig. 105). The adenohypophysis here arises as a solid ingrowth, which then develops a cavity by splitting, this cavity persisting in the fully formed gland. The pars distalis, which lies below this cavity, contains cyanophil and acidophil cells, the latter being of two types, one staining with orange G and the other with azocarmine. The supposed pars intermedia lies above the cavity and is penetrated by outgrowths from the neurohypophysis; the infundibulum gives off the pair of diverticula that we have mentioned earlier, but these do not develop the cellular structure characteristic of a true saccus vasculosus, so that the region from which the latter structure arises may be said to have become merged into the main pituitary, as it has in tetrapods.

The most interesting feature of this gland, however, is the presence of what Wingstrand believes to be a true median eminence. This is constituted by a region in the post-optic ventricular floor, at which point the external surface is indented by capillaries which are in close relation to ependymal cells containing a few granules of neurosecretory material. It does not appear that these capillaries run close to the preoptic-hypophyseal tract, which lies deeper in the wall of the ventricle, but Wingstrand places much weight on the fact that they communicate with sinusoids in the adjacent tip of the adenohypophysis. The cells here have distinctive characteristics which lead him to suggest that they may be a homologue

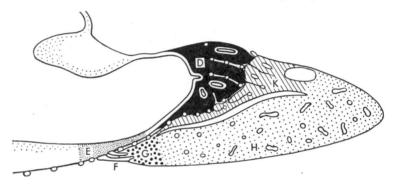

Fig. 105. Diagram of a median sagittal section of the pituitary of *Protopterus*. *D*, neurohypophysis; *E*, median eminence; *F*, portal vessels; *G*, 'pars tuberalis'; *H*, pars distalis; *K*, pars intermedia.
(From Wingstrand, 1956. *Vidensk. Medd. fra Dansk naturh. Foren.* **118**, 193–210.)

of the pars tuberalis, a region that is not clearly recognizable in the pituitaries of other fish. On his interpretation, in fact, this gland is almost identical in its organization with that of a urodele such as *Necturus*, a resemblance that is all the more striking in that the pituitaries of the more primitive Actinopterygii, such as *Acipenser*, *Polypterus*, *Amia*, and *Lepidosteus*, conform so closely to the teleost type.

4. The pituitary gland of Tetrapoda

In Amphibia, as in the lampreys and some Actinopterygii, the adenohypophysis arises as a solid ingrowth, a convenient circumstance which has made possible the numerous experiments involving the adenohypophysectomy of tadpoles at an early stage of their development. The more dorsal part of this rudiment becomes closely applied to the floor of the diencephalon and develops into the pars intermedia, while the remainder forms the pars distalis in such a way that this comes to form the more posterior part of the gland. There seems to be some doubt as to how far a pars tuberalis is developed in this group; it is said it is probably often present, but perhaps sometimes reduced or absent. The adenohypophyseal cells reach a stage of cytological differentiation which seems fully comparable with that of other vertebrate groups; one account of *Rana pipiens*, for example, refers to two types of acidophils and three types of PAS-positive cyanophils, but, again as in other groups, much remains to be learned as to their function.

The neurohypophysis seems superficially to be simpler than that of fish, for much of the floor of the infundibular recess remains as a thin lamina, but closer examination shows that important advances in organization are taking place in the group, reaching different stages in different genera. Morphologically, these advances are expressed firstly in a thickening of the postero-dorsal region of the infundibular process to form the beginning of a true neural lobe (Fig. 106), a term which is justified here, according to Green's analysis, by the fact that this region receives from the basilar artery a blood supply which is separate from that to the adenohypophysis. Secondly, there is another thickening in the floor of the infundibulum, this time immediately anterior to the pars distalis, and thus lying at the hinder end of the region which we have called the post-optic ventricular floor. This thickening is a well-defined median eminence (Frontispiece), a structure which was at one time thought to make its first appearance in Amphibia, although we have now seen that there is increasing evidence of its representation in cyclostomes and fish.

The justification of this identification again rests on the blood supply, for the hypophyseal artery, distinct from that supplying the neural lobe, sends most of its branches into the median eminence, where they form a primary capillary plexus in its thick outer layer. From this arise portal vessels which run into the pars distalis, giving rise there to a secondary capillary plexus, with which, according to Dawson, one type of cyanophil is particularly associated. Thus the blood supply of the pars distalis is derived almost entirely from the median eminence, although the vessels of the neural lobe do have some small degree of communication with the latter and also, through the pars intermedia, with the pars distalis.

As regards neurosecretory fibres, cells in the nucleus preopticus give rise to a preoptico-hypophyseal tract (Fig. 107) which is at first divided into two sections, these uniting into one median tract which passes backwards through the thin inner layer of the median eminence to enter the neural lobe, where the fibres end around its blood vessels. Some of these fibres, however, enter the outer layer of the median eminence, where their endings, and also neurosecretory material presumably derived from these, are oriented in a very clearly defined radial pattern around the capillaries of the primary plexus.

Indications of the functional significance of the median eminence in these animals are given by some results of experimental studies on the

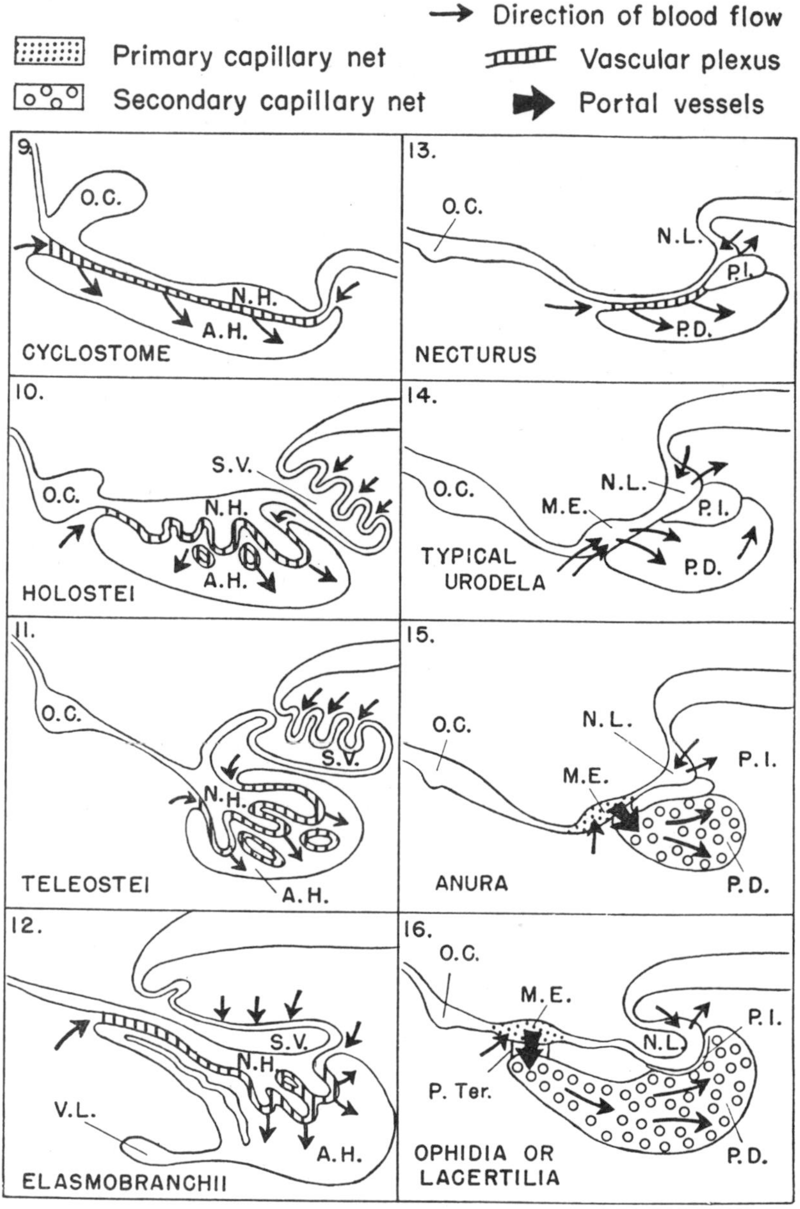

Fig. 106. Phylogenetic development of the hypophyseal portal system. *A.H.*, adenohypophysis; *N.H.*, neurohypophysis; *N.L.*, neural lobe; *M.E.*, median eminence; *O.C.*, optic chiasma; *P.D.*, pars distalis; *P.I.*, pars intermedia; *P.Ter.*, pars terminalis (tissue connecting median eminence with pars distalis); *S.V.*, saccus vasculosus; *V.L.*, ventral lobe.

(From Green, 1951. *Amer. J. Anat.* **88**, 225–90.)

potency of grafted pituitaries. Thus it has been shown that the pars distalis of the toad will remain functional if it is grafted on to the median eminence, but will regress into inactivity if grafted on to other parts of the brain. Clearly this provides support for the supposition that the eminence is concerned with the transmission of some chemical stimulation to the pars distalis, and the evidence of the distribution of neurosecretory material suggests that this may well originate in the preoptic nucleus. This idea receives support from the further observation that if the median eminence is removed and the pars distalis grafted into its place the latter will become

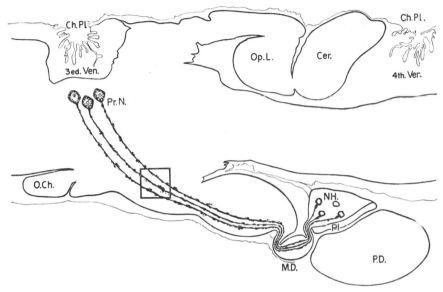

Fig. 107. Diagram of the hypothalamico-neurohypophyseal system in the toad (*Bufo arenarum*). *Cer.*, cerebellum; *Ch.Pl.*, choroid plexus; *M.D.*, median eminence; *NH.*, neural lobe; *O.Ch.*, optic chiasma; *Op.L.*, optic lobe; *P.D.*, pars distalis; *PI*, pars intermedia; *Pr.N.*, nucleus preopticus (*cf.* Frontispiece). (From Gerschenfeld *et al.*, 1960. *Endocrin.* **66**, 741–62.)

functional, presumably as a result of the receiving of stimulating influences which would seem most likely to be derived from the cut ends of the nerve fibres associated originally with the eminence. In general, then, it appears that the specialization of the infundibulum into a median eminence and neural lobe has become well established in the Amphibia, and it is perhaps significant that this parallels, on our present information, the first appearance of a well-defined influence of 'posterior lobe' hormones upon water metabolism. In this connexion it is of interest that the neural lobe is relatively smaller in completely aquatic urodeles such as *Necturus*, although this may, of course, be causally related to the neoteny which is the basis of the secondary return of these animals to water. The same consideration applies to the median eminence, which is absent from *Necturus*, the adenohypophyseal blood supply in this animal, although distinct from that of the neural lobe, being merely carried in vessels along the surface of the proximal part of the unspecialized neurohypophysis. An intermediate stage is seen in other urodeles, such as *Ambystoma*, where these vessels enter this region and then pass on to the pars distalis without actually giving rise to a primary plexus. Although these variations should not be interpreted as constituting an evolutionary sequence, they

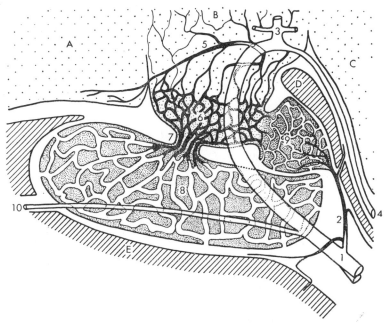

Fig. 108. Diagram of the blood supply of the pituitary gland of *Columba livia*. *1*, internal carotid artery; *2*, inferior hypophyseal artery; *3* & *4*, anterior and posterior branches of the carotid artery; *5*, infundibular artery; *6*, primary plexus in the median eminence; *7*, portal vessels; *8*, secondary plexus in the pars distalis; *9*, capillary bed of the neural lobe; *10*, internal ophthalmic artery.
(From Wingstrand, 1951. *The structure and development of the avian pituitary*. Gleerup: Lund.)

do show us different degrees of the association of the adenohypophyseal blood supply with the hypothalamus, and we may reasonably feel that these illustrate how a physiological mechanism could have been progressively elaborated to reach its full development in the amniotes.

The pituitary of the latter has already been considered in some detail in its mammalian form, and in the amniotes as a whole it exhibits from our present point of view a rather uniform organization in principle, apart from the fact that birds (Fig. 108) lack a differentiated pars intermedia, as also do certain mammals, including whales. A pars tuberalis develops from lateral processes of the hypophysis, although not in snakes, and, as we have seen earlier, this is closely associated with the median eminence. The neural lobe is independently vascularized, a portal system is present, and in the birds all blood entering the pars distalis must pass through that system (Fig. 108). In some reptiles, however, the pars distalis may receive in addition a direct blood supply, as may also occur in the mammals (p. 71).

Of interest from the evolutionary standpoint are the varying degrees of histological differentiation shown by the neurohypophysis, which have been extensively reviewed by Wingstrand. In it simplest form, as found in *Sphenodon* and in certain lacertilians and chelonians, its organization is virtually uniform throughout its length, with a continuous lumen and with little difference between the neural lobe and the median eminence. Its wall at this stage is composed of an internal lining of ependyma, a neuro-secretory layer of fibres, and an outer glandular layer in which a colloid-like secretion is seen; pituicytes are absent and the blood vessels confined to the outer surface. In other reptiles, including various snakes, the neural lobe becomes compact and solid, the median eminence is thickened, and the capillary vessels sink into it, while pituicytes become conspicuous, perhaps derived from ependymal cells and perhaps sharing some secretory function with them.

Somewhat similar variations are found in birds, but in mammals the neurohypophysis is always of a more complex type of organization. The Monotremata, as might be expected, have the simplest and presumably most primitive structure, but even in them the neural lobe is well defined with thickened walls, and its lumen may be much reduced. Not the least important aspect of such variations of pattern is that they remind us that the relatively few mammalian types on which most research effort has been concentrated are the end result of lengthy evolutionary developments and that our generalizations regarding pituitary organization and function will be insecurely based until simpler and more primitive stages have been taken fully into account.

5. The pituitary gland and the Protochordata

Our survey of the pituitary gland throughout the vertebrates has shown that, despite the progressive specialization which it undergoes, the cyclo-stomes already possess an adenohypophysis and a neurohypophysis which are closely associated with each other. We must turn, then, to the protochordates, as we did in considering the thyroid gland, to inquire if anything more can be learned from these animals regarding the origin of these two components.

As far as amphioxus is concerned, there are two organs which merit some consideration, Hatschek's pit (Fig. 109) and the infundibular organ (Fig. 110). The former, an invagination situated just in front of the velum, forms part of the animal's filter-feeding mechanism, but the suggestion that it might also be the homologue of the adenohypophysis was first clearly formulated by Goodrich, who pointed out that it takes its origin in part from the preoral pit, an ectodermal depression which develops in the early larva on the left side of the head and acquires an opening into the left member of the first pair of coelomic sacs. At metamorphosis this opening is lost, and the preoral pit spreads out to for.n the wheel organ, while

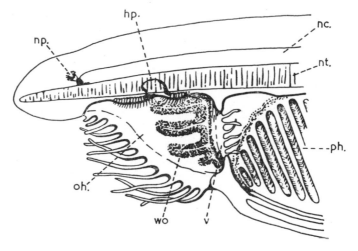

Fig. 109. Hatschek's pit. Left side view of the head of a young amphioxus, with the left body-wall, oral hood, and wall of pharynx cut away; *hp.*, Hatschek's pit (seen by transparency); *nc.*, nerve cord; *np.*, olfactory pit; *nt.*, notochord; *oh.*, right oral hood; *ph.*, pharynx; *v*, velum; *wo*, wheel organ.
(From Goodrich, 1917. *Quart. J. micr. Sci.* **62**, 539–53.)

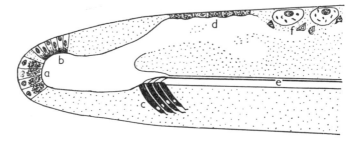

Fig. 110. Diagram of the anterior end of the nervous system of amphioxus. *a*, pigment spot; *b*, secretory ependyma; *c*, infundibular organ; *d*, granular ependyma; *e*, Reissner's fibre in the central canal; *f*, large ganglion cells with some granules.
(From Olsson & Wingstrand, 1954. *Univ. Bergen Arbok*, **14**.)

at the same time contributing to Hatschek's pit, which seems to be derived partly from the original pit and partly from its temporary connexion with the coelomic sac. The asymmetry of the preoral pit is a secondary consequence of the asymmetry of the larva, and it is clear that if normal bilateral symmetry were restored the pit would lie in essentially the position of Rathke's pouch in the vertebrate embryo, while it would presumably have connexions with both left and right members of the anterior pair of coelomic pouches. It is this latter feature which provides the most cogent argument for homologizing the pit with Rathke's pouch, for we have seen that open connexions exist between this and the first pair of coelomic cavities in the embryo of *Torpedo*. This can hardly be a chance coincidence, and the fact that closed vestiges of such connexions can even be identified in the embryo of the duck shows that it is a deep-seated feature of vertebrate organization.

As regards the infundibular organ, this is situated in the floor of the cerebral vesicle towards its posterior end (Fig. 110). It consists of slender cells which are believed to be primary sense cells, having one or two flagella at their free ends and being continued basally into nerve fibres. They contain granules, which stain with chrome-alum-haematoxylin, and which are thought to be secreted into the cavity of the vesicle and also to be transmitted along the fibres, although it is not possible to follow these very far. One function of this secretion seems to be the formation of Reissner's fibre, a structure that is characteristic of the central canal of the vertebrate nervous system (Fig. 134) and which is thought possibly to be concerned with the detoxication of the cerebro-spinal fluid. In vertebrates it is derived from a dorsally situated subcommissural organ, but the situation in amphioxus may indicate the more primitive mode of origin, since in teleost embryos it has been shown to arise first from another group of cells, the flexural organ, situated ventrally in the mid-brain, and to establish later its permanent dorsal relationship. All of these cells, those of the subcommissural organ and of the flexural organ as well as those of the infundibular organ of amphioxus, possess granules which stain with chrome-alum-haematoxylin, and the suggestion has been made by Olsson that they may be the surviving parts of an originally more widely distributed secretory region in the vertebrate brain. Furthermore, it has been suggested that the neurosecretory cells of the hypothalamus might also have been derived in this way, the implication here being that cells originally ependymal in position and secretory in function might have passed inwards, away from the ventricular lining, and have added nervous functions to their original secretory one.

This conception is not lacking in supporting evidence, but there is a very substantial element of speculation in it, and it must always be remembered that the staining of cell inclusions with chrome-alum-haematoxylin is no evidence at all for their homology or, indeed, for their secretory nature. Nevertheless, it is of interest to find such widespread evidence of secretory activity in the central nervous system, and to find it already established at the protochordate level, and Olsson has developed the idea of a parallelism between the history of the thyroid and that suggested for the subcommissural organ and its associated areas. The cells of the latter, he suggests, may be thought of as beginning their history by secreting into a cavity a product that forms a fibrous structure; this is passed continuously along the length of the central nervous system in connexion with its suggested function of detoxication, but later the mechanism becomes superfluous, the cells withdraw inwards, and begin to secrete into the blood stream. On this hypothesis, and it is no more than that, an endocrine centre could arise in the wall of the brain in a manner closely analogous to the withdrawal of iodine-binding cells from the lining of the pharynx.

It is, however, the situation in the Tunicata which has in the past attracted the greater amount of attention from investigators. The evolutionary interpretation of these animals is complicated by the fact that they undergo a profound metamorphosis from a free-swimming larva, and a much-favoured view as to the origin of vertebrates would derive these animals from this larval stage by a process of neoteny. Leaving this difficult issue on one side, however, we may take note that the nerve ganglion of the adult tunicate is commonly associated with a neural gland, which opens into the anterior end of the pharynx by means of a short duct (Fig. 111). A number of investigators, impressed by the superficial resemblance between this neural complex and the pituitary complex of vertebrates, have tested the former for the presence of pituitary hormones and have claimed to have obtained evidence for the presence of oxytocic, vasopressor, antidiuretic, and melanocyte-stimulating principles, but unfortunately these claims have not survived critical examination by more recent workers. Dodd and Sawyer are in agreement that such effects can be obtained from other tissues of tunicates and also from other animals, and that such oxytocin-like principle as may be present differs in its chemical and pharmacological properties from true oxytocin. To take only one other illustration, given by Sawyer, the supposed antidiuretic activity of dried extract of the ascidian *Pyura* is only one two-hundred-thousandth of that of mammalian dried powder, so that it can hardly be regarded as a specific physiological property of the material. In short, the earlier reports seem not to have paid sufficient regard to the fact that all tissue extracts may be expected to display some degree of pharmacological activity, a source of error on which we have already had occasion to comment. While, therefore, the homology of the neural complex with the pituitary complex is not actually disproved by these results it still awaits experimental confirmation. This, however, need not exclude it from our present consideration, for speculation regarding its possible relationship with the pituitary can be approached from another point of view

The histological structure of Hatschek's pit is complex, and it has been suggested more than once that both it and the neural gland of tunicates might be sensitive to materials in the sea-water passing into the pharynx, and that by responding in some way to secretions of other individuals of

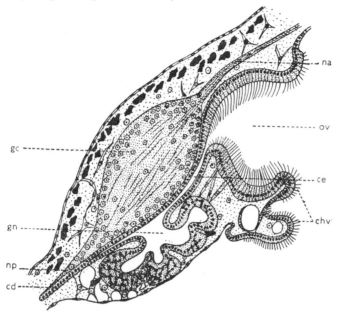

Fig. 111. Vertical section of neural complex of *Clavelina lepadiformis*. *cd*, dorsal cord (posterior extension of neural gland); *ce*, duct of gland; *chv*, ciliated epithelium of dorsal tubercle; *gc*, cerebral ganglion; *gn*, neural gland; *na*, *np*, anterior and posterior nerves; *ov*, ciliated tubercle.

(From Grassé, 1948. *Traité de Zoologie*, **11**. Paris. After Seeliger, 1893–1911. *Bronn's Tierreich*, **3**, Suppl. Tunicata.)

the species they might regulate sexual maturation and spawning. We comment elsewhere (pp. 1, 364) on this type of communication system and it is attractive to reflect that an organ so concerned might have become closed off from the outside world and have evolved into an internally secreting gland responding to chemical influences received now from the central nervous system. It would not be difficult to elaborate such a speculation in some detail, but it seems wiser for the present to treat it as no more than a general guide for future investigation. The presence of a preoral ciliary organ at the base of the proboscis of the Enteropneusta, another group of protochordates, suggests that a tendency for the development of a sensory invagination in this region may well have been common to all the early chordate groups, and may then have been inherited by the vertebrates. Such a common inheritance might have expressed itself in markedly divergent ways in different groups, depending upon their adaptive needs, and because of this, and because our knowledge of the early chordates is at best fragmentary, it is perhaps unlikely that we shall ever achieve a satisfactory interpretation of the early history of the pituitary gland. Further research, however, should certainly be directed towards testing the hypotheses outlined above, and, if necessary, suggesting alternatives to take their place.

XIII. HORMONES IN CRUSTACEA

1. Homology and analogy

In our analysis of the problems of comparative endocrinology as they are manifested within the organization of one major Phylum, the Chordata, we have been developing interpretations based upon the concept of homology. In its classical form this regards certain resemblances between different but related species as resulting from a derivation of the parts concerned from corresponding parts in a common ancestor. With advancing knowledge, however, this concept has become elaborated to include resemblances which do not have a common origin but which have developed independently in related species. Such examples of what is called parallel evolution are regarded as a consequence of a common mode of expression of related genotypes, these rather than the parts themselves having been derived from the common ancestor, and such resemblances are sometimes described as homoplastic instead of homologous. The comparative approach to the analysis of animal organization tends, therefore, to become increasingly complex, even in a group as closely integrated as the Chordata, and this needs to be borne in mind as we turn now to extend our analysis to the Phylum Arthropoda, for here we enter upon much more uncertain ground.

Tiegs and Manton, in their review of arthropodan evolution, have expressed the view that a diphyletic origin of the Phylum is a possibility, and even without this complication it is clear that the two major groups with which we shall be concerned, the Crustacea and the Insecta, must have become separated at a very early stage, possibly in the pre-Cambrian, for the former group is already highly organized in the Lower Cambrian, and its subsequent history, with its failure to make effective use of the possibilities of terrestrial life, shows it setting a course widely divergent from that of insects. In comparing the organization of these two groups, then, the concept of homology needs to be applied with caution, while in comparing both of them with vertebrates we shall necessarily be drawing largely upon the concept of analogy, of resemblances resulting from community of function instead of from a common evolutionary origin. It follows that while some of the comparisons that we shall be able to make will be exciting ones, it will be prudent to be cautious in pressing them any further than can be justified by the classical principles of comparative zoology, although, for reasons explained earlier (p. 6), the analysis may be at times a subtle one, and classical principles not always a sufficient basis for it.

2. Colour change

Investigations of crustacean endocrinology have already disclosed extra-ordinary divergences in matters of detail, even though attention has been largely restricted to the Malacostraca. In the present context, however, we shall be concerned only with fundamental principles, and these we shall illustrate by reference to a few selected examples, taking these initially from researches into the mechanism of the control of colour change (Plate XIII) from which our present understanding of crustacean hormones can fairly be said to originate. We are thus at once in a field that invites direct comparison with the problems that we were considering in Chapter XI.

Several groups of Crustacea, and particularly the Decapoda, possess chromatophores which are similar to those of vertebrates, being highly branched cells in which pigment granules can be either dispersed or concentrated. They lie under the hypodermis or in the deeper part of the body, but details of their arrangement and colour vary greatly from species to species. The pigments are of several kinds, including red, yellow, brown, and white, and these can respond independently of each other; it is thought that this is because each is in a separate cell, two or more of which may, however, unite to form a syncitial complex which is then, as in teleosts, called a chromatosome. Whether these cells are in any way homologous with those of the vertebrates is not clear; conceivably they might all have been derived from some primitive pigmentary effector, for colour change is reported to occur sporadically in other groups of invertebrates, in-cluding polychaetes, leeches, and echinoderms, but it is certain that this property has been the centre of much independent and unrelated evolution.

The insect *Carausius* (*Dixippus*) *morosus* (p. 351), for example, is able to change its colour without possessing true chromatophores, but best known from this point of view are the peculiar chromatophores of the cephalopod molluscs, each of which is a single cell to which smooth muscle fibres are attached. The action of the latter brings about changes of colour by causing the cell to range in its form from a contracted spherical body to an expanded and very thin disk, but they do not create an endocrinological problem, for these fibres have a direct innervation.

The first experimental study of crustacean colour change seems to have been due to Pouchet, whose work on the teleosts we have already con-sidered. He made the fundamental discovery that the adaptive responses of shrimps to the colour of their background could be eliminated by the removal of the animals' eye-stalks. He had also shown that blinded teleosts failed to show these background responses, and had rightly drawn from this, and from the results of experimental sectioning of nerves, the conclusion that the chromatophores of these animals were innervated

B

C

D

Plate XIII. *A.* Influence of the eyes and pineal complex on the colour of sockeye salmon smolt placed on an aluminium-painted background. *Bottom left,* unoperated control, light brown with dark spots. *Top right,* blinded fish, dark green-brown with black spots. *Centre,* eyes and pineal complex destroyed, jet black except for silver ventral surface. *Extreme right,* pineal complex alone destroyed, colour variable.

B, C, & E. Influence of the eye-stalk, and the circumoesophageal and tritocerebral commissures, on the colour of the shrimp, *Crangon.*

B. Eyestalk-less animals; *left,* after injection of sea-water, *right,* after injection of an extract of *Crangon* circumoesophageal commissure, which has darkened the tail. *C.* The same two animals as in *B; left,* after injection of sea-water, *right,* after injection of an extract of *Crangon* eye-stalk, which has blanched the tail.

(From Brown & Ederstrom, 1940. *J. exp. Zool.* **85,** 53–69.)

D. Eyestalk-less animals; *left,* after injection of sea-water, *centre,* after injection of one-sixth of the sea-water-soluble contents of one *Crangon* tritocerebral commissure, *right,* after injection of one-sixth of the alchohol-insoluble contents of one *Crangon* tritocerebral commissure. All three animals were matched and resembled the left specimens before the injections, which were made about nine minutes before the photograph was taken. The results indicate that the sea-water extract contains a body-lightening and a tail-darkening principle, the latter alone being present in the alcohol-insoluble fraction.

(From Brown & Klotz, 1947. *Proc. Soc. Exp. Biol. Med.* **64,** 310–13.)

A

(p. 271), but he now went on to infer that a similar mode of control existed in crustaceans. This is an example, however, of too-readily assuming the existence of similar organization in unrelated groups, although it was a reasonable interpretation at a time when the principles of endocrinology had still to be established. In fact, this type of control does not exist in crustaceans, and Pouchet, not surprisingly, failed to demonstrate in that group any effects of nerve section of the sort that were evident in teleosts.

Our current understanding of these matters dates from the work of Perkins and of Koller who, in 1928, published the results of independent work carried out respectively on the shrimps *Palaemonetes* and *Crangon*. Both of these animals have a range of pigments, the independent responses of which enable them to adapt to a diversity of background colours, the former to white, grey, black, yellow, red, green, and blue, and the latter to white, grey, black, yellow, orange, and red. Such reactions, as in the vertebrates, are albedo responses, dependent upon the ratio of incident and reflected light which enters the eye (p. 260), and it is these which have been widely studied, although they are not the only possible types of colour change. For example, many crustaceans show a response to an increase in the total illumination to which they are exposed, the general tendency being for the pigments to disperse with increasing illumination. Some also show rhythmical colour change, a well-known example of this being the fiddler-crab *Uca*, which shows little capacity for background adaptation but which is pale at night and dark during the day. This 24-hour rhythm is independent of the nature of the background or of the intensity of illumination, but the situation is curiously complicated by the superimposition of a 12·4-hour rhythm which is correlated with the tidal cycle.

Amongst the facts established by Perkins and Koller were firstly that section of the ventral nerve cord had no effect upon the background response, but that if the dorsal blood vessel was cut or interrupted the chromatophores lying posterior to the point of interruption passed into the dispersed state and remained so. If the cut was restricted to a lateral branch of the dorsal vessel, then the chromatophores supplied by that branch would become permanently dispersed while the remainder would continue to show normal colour changes. Since there was no sign of any nerve fibres accompanying the vessels these observations were presumptive evidence of hormonal control and a further indication of this was the fact that if blood from a dark *Crangon* was injected into a pale one the latter would darken even though it was lying on a light background; this went some way to meeting the classical requirement that the hormone should be shown to be present in the circulation.

Following up Pouchet's observation, it was found that the chromatophores would pass into the dispersed state in animals that had been blinded by removal of the eye-stalks, but that they could be made to concentrate by injecting into these an extract prepared from crushed eye-stalks taken from pale animals. This indicated that the eye-stalks were the source of a concentrating hormone, and Koller also believed that there was evidence for the production of a dispersing hormone in the rostral region of *Crangon*, a result which appeared puzzling at the time but which can now be seen as perhaps the first indication of the remarkable complexity of the endocrine control involved. Later work showed that the eye-stalks were equally important in the maintenance of rhythmical colour change, for removal of these from *Uca* abolished the rhythm and the animal became permanently pale. The existence of such rhythms raises the question, which we have already met in other contexts, of the relative importance of exogenous and endogenous factors in their maintenance. The issue is not yet resolved, but the fact that the diurnal colour change of *Uca* has been maintained unchanged for up to twenty-six days in constant darkness indicates an endogenous component of some precision, for during that time there was no discernible drift away from the normal relationship of the rhythm with the solar day and night. Moreover, it has been shown that the tidal rhythm of colour change can be maintained under laboratory conditions, and in this connexion we shall consider later some evidence that rhythmical activity may originate spontaneously within the central nervous system of insects. It would appear, however, that exogenous factors are also involved in the *Uca* colour rhythm, for Brown and his colleagues were able to shift the phases of it by subjecting the animals to abnormal illumination (Fig. 112).

With the recognition of the physiological importance of the eye-stalk a search was initiated for the secretory tissue that was the source of its activity, and within a few years Hanström had drawn attention to two such structures. One of these was at first called the blood gland, but was later given the name by which it is now known, the sinus gland, a term that emphasizes the significance of its situation in the wall of a blood sinus. In its simplest form, as seen in the Mysidacea, this structure is a disk-shaped thickening of the neurilemma of the eye-stalk ganglia, but it becomes elaborated in other groups by folding and by separation from the neurilemma, although it retains its close association with the sinus.

Extraction experiments showed that this sinus gland was undoubtedly a potent source of chromatophore-activating material, but the interpretation was complicated by the fact that the other structure, called the X organ, also seemed to have secretory potentialities. The importance of these was particularly suggested by the results obtained with the cumacean *Diastylis*. Extracts of the head of this animal were found to be able to affect pigment concentration, and it was shown that while the X organ was present in the region extracted the sinus gland was apparently absent. Another puzzling feature was the difficulty experienced in arriving at any histological interpretation of the latter organ, for while it could be seen to

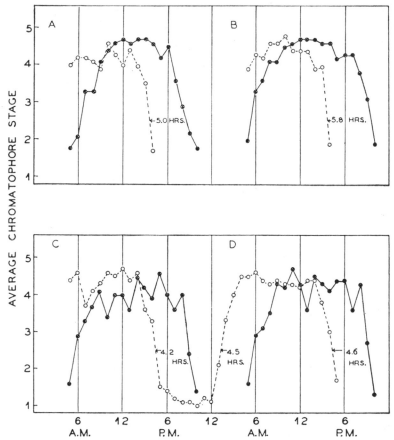

Fig. 112. The diurnal colour rhythm in control specimens of *Uca* (solid line) and those with the rhythm shifted backwards (broken line) by three periods of midnight to 6 a.m. illumination; *A* & *B* from one experiment, and *C* & *D* from another. Taking a melanophore index of 2·5 as a reference point, the rhythm is shifted back about 5·4 hours in the first experiment and about 4·4 hours in the second.
(From Brown *et al.*, 1953. *J. exp. Zool.* **123**, 29–60.)

contain numerous stainable droplets, and to have indications also of what looked like delicate canals, it proved impossible to establish any certain evidence for the presence of secretory cells. It was, in fact, difficult to justify the application of the term gland to it at all, although its physio- logical importance was not in doubt, and there was good evidence that it was innervated by the central nervous system.

The resolution of these difficulties provided a powerful demonstration of the value of comparative studies, for it was directly linked with the analysis by Bargmann and the Scharrers in 1949 and 1950 of the neuro-endocrine activity of the hypothalamus and of the nature of the relationship of this with the neurohypophysis. It became evident, in the work of Enami and many others, that this was the key to the interpretation of the secretory activities of the eye-stalk, and this has led to the recognition that it is the nervous system of the Crustacea which is their most important endocrine tissue. Within the eye-stalk it is now possible to recognize many groups of neurosecretory cells, but their anatomical interrelationships are complex and vary from species to species. We shall not attempt to describe these variations in detail, but shall examine the situation in one or two selected examples.

3. The X organs and the sinus gland

The nervous tissue of the eye-stalk is concentrated into three lobes. The most proximal is a brain centre, the medulla terminalis (Fig. 114), which is connected with the rest of the protocerebrum by the peduncle of the optic lobe, while the other two are primary optic centres, the medulla interna and the medulla externa, the latter being directly connected with the most distal optic centre, the lamina ganglionaris. It seems clear that an important source of neurosecretory material is to be found in one or more groups of cells which lie in the medulla terminalis, for stainable droplets have been identified in these cells, and also in the axons which arise from them (Fig. 113). Unfortunately, the term X organ has been applied to these cell groups in the mistaken belief that they are the homologue of the X organ described earlier by Hanström and other workers of the 1930's, but in fact the two are quite distinct. Carlisle and Knowles therefore emphasize the importance of giving to the medullary cell group the separate designation of ganglionic X organ, and further differentiating them, should that be necessary, according to the particular medulla with which they are associated.

Many nerve fibres from the ganglionic X organ run to the sinus gland, a structure which is now known also to be largely and perhaps exclusively a storage and release centre for neurohormonal products arising elsewhere, mainly in the ganglionic X organ; the two structures thus form a functional unit which can conveniently be called the ganglionic X organ/sinus gland complex, the sinus gland being the neurohaemal organ of the unit. This, of course, is the explanation of the puzzling histological structure of the gland, for, like the neural lobe of vertebrates, it consists largely of the terminations of neurosecretory axons. We shall see that it is not the only neurohaemal organ in crustaceans, and there is some reason for thinking that such centres may have arisen at first simply as local thickenings of the neurilemma, as is still seen today in the mysids (p. 312), the development of more elaborate forms serving to facilitate the release of their contained secretions into the circulation.

The presence of neurosecretory material gives to the sinus gland in the living animal a characteristic opalescence, a circumstance which greatly facilitates its experimental removal. In the fixed gland this material shows a diversity of staining reactions, responding positively both to acidic and to basic dyes, and this presumably reflects a corresponding diversity of

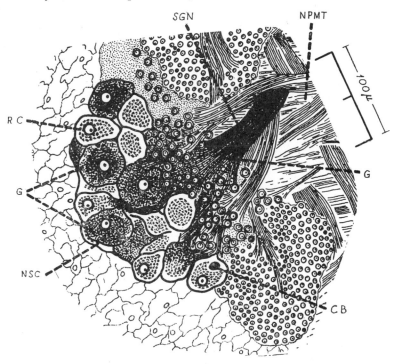

Fig. 113. A section which indicates the passage of secretory granules from giant neurosecretory cells of the medulla terminalis of the crab *Sesarma* into the sinus gland and which provided a clue to the understanding of crustacean endocrine mechanisms. *CB*, central body formed in the cell; *G*, secretory granules; *NPMT*, neuropile of the medulla terminalis; *NSC*, cell in secretory activity; *RC*, resting cell; *SGN*, sinus gland nerve.
(From Enami, 1951. *Biol. Bull.* **101**, 241–58.)

constitution, although the possibility that some transformation or processing of these secretions takes place within the sinus gland cannot be excluded. The question whether cells are present in it is still a matter of dispute, but even if they are it is doubtful whether they make any contribution in the form of an actual synthesis of secretion; on our present information, then, the term gland is something of a misnomer in its application to this structure. What does seem certain, however, is that the products released from it are of a varied nature and this, as we shall see, is in line with the results of physiological studies.

In the blue crab, *Callinectes sapidus*, for example, it has been found possible to differentiate no less than six distinct types of neurosecretory fibres on the basis of their staining reactions, some staining red with azocarmine, others yellow with orange G, blue with aniline blue, or red with aldehyde-fuchsin, a situation reminiscent of the complexity of the staining reactions of the pars distalis. We need to know much more about the significance of these reactions, but they provide some evidence that each fibre may carry one particular type of secretion, for the colours can be traced back to the individual cells from which the fibres presumably take their origin. It has thus been possible to unravel something of the pattern of distribution of nerve connexions, and this has shown not only that the sinus gland undoubtedly receives neurosecretory fibres from the ganglionic X organ (Fig. 114), but that other structures are also involved in this particular system.

We have seen that the ganglionic X organ is not the same as the X organ of Hanström. The latter (Fig. 114) is typically associated with a sensory papilla or with a sensory pore derived from this by reduction, and for this reason it has come to be distinguished as the sensory papilla X organ or sensory pore X organ. Its histological organization seems to be more complex than that of the other structures so far mentioned, for while it is composed in part of the club-shaped endings of neurosecretory fibres, sensory cells are also present, together with epithelial secretory cells and neurosecretory cell bodies, at least in some species. Thus in the natantian *Lysmata*, as described by Carlisle, the sensory papilla X organ is widely separated from the medulla terminalis ganglionic X organ and receives neurosecretory fibres from it (cf. Fig. 114), so that it evidently acts in part as a neurohaemal release organ. In addition, however, axons of its sensory cells unite to form a nerve which runs to the medulla terminalis, so that at this stage of its evolution it is clearly an organ of mixed function, a situation that has some interesting evolutionary implications (p. 364).

The degree of separation of the two types of X organ varies a good deal in the decapods, ranging from the condition just described to that found in the Brachyura, where the two form a single complex lying mainly within the medulla terminalis. This latter arrangement is associated with the loss of the sensory papilla and, if it can be regarded as an evolutionary trend, implies an increasing concentration upon the neurosecretory functions of an originally heterogeneous organ. As yet, however, we lack an assured basis for the determination of the evolutionary history of the endocrine complex of the eye-stalk.

4. Chromatophore-activating hormones and the central nervous system

Our emphasis so far has been upon the presence of neurosecretory tissue within the limits of the eye-stalk, but throughout the 1930's there was accumulating evidence that secretions influencing the chromatophores might not be restricted to that region. Brown, for example, found that extracts of the circum-oesophageal commissures (or connectives) of *Crangon* would darken the telson and uropods, the effect being antagonized by extracts of the eye-stalks (Plate XIII *B*, *C*). There was evidence for some localization of this activity within the commissures, and this aspect has been studied by Knowles, who has established the crucial importance of the tritocerebral (post-oesophageal) commissure which connects the circum-oesophageal commissures immediately behind the oeso-phagus.

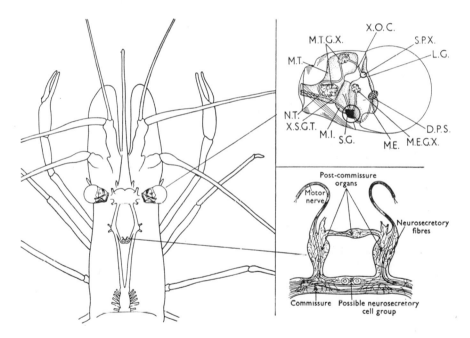

Fig. 114. Diagrams illustrating the approximate positions of the sinus gland, X organs, and post-commissural organ of *Palaemon (Leander) serratus*. In this species the sensory pore has been lost but the sensory pore X organ retained. *D.P.S.*, accessory pigment spot; *L.G.*, lamina ganglionaris; *M.E.*, medulla externa; *M.E.G.X.*, medulla externa ganglionic X organ; *M.I.*, medulla interna; *M.T.G.X.*, medulla terminalis ganglionic X organ; *N.T.*, tract of neurosecretory fibres from brain to sinus gland; *S.G.*, sinus gland; *S.P.X.*, sensory pore X organ; *X.O.C.*, X organ connective; *X.S.G.T.*, X organ-sinus gland tract.

(From Knowles *et al.*, 1955. *J. mar. biol. Assoc. U.K.* **34**, 611–35, and Carlisle & Knowles, 1959. *Endocrine Control in Crustaceans*. Cambridge.)

According to his account (Figs. 114, 115) there are two fine nerves leaving the tritocerebral commisure and in *Penaeus braziliensis, Squilla mantis*, and *Palaemon (Leander) serratus* these each bear a flattened lamella which differs in its exact position in the several species but is formed in all three by an extension of the epineurium. Nerve fibres and chromophil droplets are found in these lamellae, which thus closely resemble the

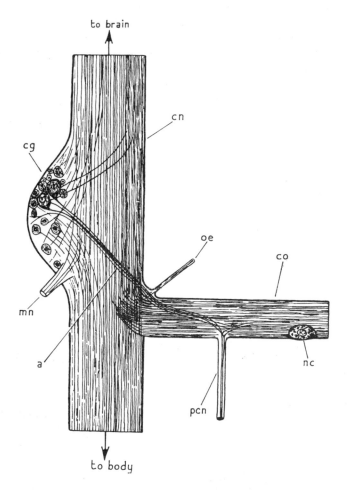

Fig. 115. Left connective ganglion and left half of the trito-cerebral commissure of *Palaemon (Leander) serratus*. The fibres and cell bodies shown were seen in preparations stained by methylene blue. *a*, fibres from the connective ganglion to the post-commissure nerve; *cg*, connective ganglion; *cn*, circum-oesophageal commissive (connective); *co*, tritocerebral commis-sure; *mn*, mandibular nerve; *nc*, cell suspected of neurosecretion; *oe*, oesophageal nerve; *pcn*, post-commissure nerve.
(From Knowles, 1953. *Proc. Roy. Soc.* B **141**, 248–67.)

sinus gland in their organization. This resemblance is heightened by the fact that extracts of them are especially potent sources of chromatophore-activating material, and it seems certain that these structures, which have been called the post-commissure organs, are neurohaemal release organs. The fibres that enter them probably arise in the brain, and it is thought that the material that they release is formed in neurosecretory cells in the tritocerebrum, and transported down the fibres into them. The function of neurosecretory-like cells in the commissure remains uncertain.

We thus begin to see that a characteristic feature of the endocrine system of Crustacea is a widespread distribution of neurosecretory cells in the nervous system. Our present information suggests that these dominate the organization of these animals to an extent far exceeding anything that we find in vertebrates, and we can feel certain that other examples await detailed analysis. Cells of supposed neurosecretory character have been found in other sites, as, for example, in the commissural and thoracic ganglia of crabs, and the variety of their staining reactions suggests that they constitute a variety of cell types which may eventually be found to be concerned with a wide range of regulatory functions, fully comparable with the range of activities which are now thought to be under hormonal control in these animals.

Our discussion of similar problems in vertebrate endocrinology has already shown, however, that the analysis of endocrine systems is fraught with difficulties unless supposed hormonal functions can be securely related to knowledge of the properties of highly purified materials. One need only recall in this connexion the way in which the actions of growth hormone were at one time attributed to individual but hypothetical secretions. Clearly a similar approach needs to be adopted towards crustacean problems, and work on such lines is in active progress. Brown, in pioneer investigations of the properties of extracts of the sinus gland of various species, made use of differential solubility methods, and was able to separate a '*Uca*-darkening' principle (dispersing the dark pigment of *Uca*) from a '*Palaemonetes*-lightening' one (concentrating the red pigment of *Palaemonetes*). He also found evidence for the existence of two principles in the tritocerebral commissure of *Crangon*; the effect of one was to lighten the body while the other darkened the body and tail (Plate XIII *O*). A more recent example, dependent upon the use of paper electrophoresis, has been the separation from the sinus gland and post-commissure organs of *Palaemon (Leander) serratus* of an A-substance, with a concentrating effect on the large and small red chromatophores. This contrasts with a B-substance which can be extracted from the post-commissure organs of the same animal and which has a concentrating effect on the large chromatophores but a dispersing one on the red chromatophores of the body and tail (see also p. 354).

Another illustration of the results of electrophoretic studies is seen in Fig. 116. This shows that extracts of the eye-stalks of the dwarf crayfish, *Cambarellus*, contain a fraction which disperses dark-red pigment and which migrates towards the negative pole, whereas extracts of the combined

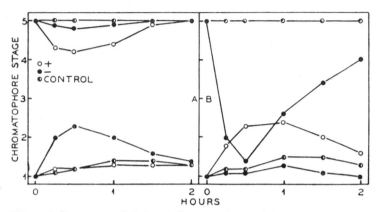

Fig. 116. Responses of dark red chromatophores of dwarf crayfish on white and on black backgrounds to extracts of (*A*) eye-stalks, and (*B*) supra-oeso-phageal ganglia with the circum-oesophageal connectives attached. Filter paper electrophoresis was carried out on the extracts before injection. *Circles*, fraction that migrated towards positive pole; *dots*, fraction that migrated towards negative pole; *half-filled circles*, control.
(From Fingerman & Aoto, 1958. *J. exp. Zool.* **138**, 25–50.)

supra-ocsophageal ganglia and circum-oesophageal commissures contain a fraction which has a similar effect but which migrates towards the positive pole. The inference is that we may here be concerned with two substances which are chemically different yet similar in their physiological action, and an analogus contrast is seen between the concentrating fractions of the two extracts. A continuation of such work should make it possible eventually to determine whether these fractions are indeed separate hormones, and whether, if so, they share a common pattern of molecular structure. This could lead in its turn to the answering of the question how far similar endocrine functions in vertebrates and invertebrates, such as the control of colour change, are mediated by similar hormones; already there has been a tentative suggestion that the melanophore-dispersing hormone extracted from the eye-stalk of *Uca* may bear some resemblance to the melanocyte-stimulating hormone of vertebrates, although their properties are known not to be identical.

Nevertheless it would be unwise to ignore the very real difficulties which are presented by these invertebrate problems, and which have been emphasized by Kleinholz. Injection experiments unaccompanied by the parallel study of the results of ablation and replacement therapy leave open the possibility that the actions of extracts may be of pharmacological rather than physiological significance. For example, the injected material may be acting upon the secretory or neurohaemal centres rather than upon the chromatophores, and may merely be promoting the release of a hormone instead of acting as one itself. If we add to this the risk that the experimental procedures may themselves produce chemical artifacts, and the fact that some of the extracts are unstable, the need for a cautious approach to these matters becomes sufficiently clear.

In connexion with this possibility of comparing the endocrine equipment of crustaceans and vertebrates we may note one difficulty which arises from the widespread distribution of neurosecretory cells in the central nervous system of the former. We have emphasized earlier that the classical criteria for demonstrating the existence of an endocrine organ includes the study of the effects of its removal and of replacement therapy, but this is clearly not practicable when the supposed sources of the secretion are distributed in this way. This difficulty is frankly accepted by Carlisle and Knowles, who argue that crustacean endocrinology demands an approach different from that appropriate to vertebrate studies, and that this approach must place emphasis upon a precise correlation of histological observations with experimental procedures, and a careful analysis of the activity of purified extracts of the supposed secretory regions. The restriction of the B-substance of *Palaemon* (*Leander*), mentioned above, to the post-commissure organs and neighbouring regions of the nervous system, and its absence from the eye-stalk, is an example of the type of evidence upon which reliance will have to be placed in establishing the localization of endocrine centres in the Crustacea. It is, in fact, arguable that this does not imply any very substantial gap between the contemporary techniques of vertebrate and invertebrate endocrinology, for with increasing refinement of analysis such an approach is also becoming of increasing significance in the vertebrate field.

5. Retinal pigment migration

It is a matter of historical accident and experimental convenience that the study of colour change has played such a conspicuous part in the development of crustacean endocrinology, but many other functions are now known also to be under endocrine regulation. Closely related to colour control is the adaptive migration of the pigment of the compound eye, which takes place in response to the intensity of light which falls upon the organ. Each eye consists of a large number of units called ommatidia (Fig. 117), with which are associated characteristic groupings of pigment cells. The crystalline cone is surrounded by distal pigment cells, the inner portions of which (e.g. in *Palaemon* (*Leander*) *serratus*, according to Knowles's account) contain dark pigment and are continuous distally with the cornea and proximally with the retinular cells. The latter give rise at their bases to nerve fibres, but their cell bodies contain further pigment known as the proximal pigment. Finally, a group of tapetal cells at the base of the ommatidium contains a white reflecting pigment.

There is some variation in the pattern both of the pigment cells and of their responses, but it seems to be common for the proximal pigment to

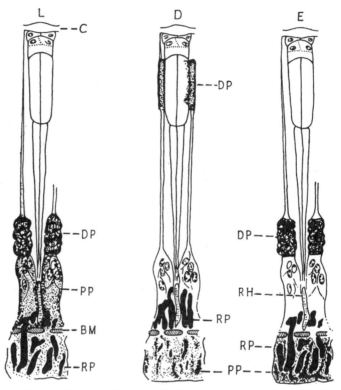

Fig. 117. Ommatidia from the eyes of *Palaemonetes vulgaris*. *L*, light-adapted; *D*, dark-adapted; *E*, light-adapted position of distal pigment in an eye of an animal which, after adaptation to darkness, was injected with eye-stalk extract prepared from light-adapted animals. *BM*, basement membrane; *C*, cornea; *DP*, distal pigment; *PP*, proximal pigment; *RP*, reflecting pigment; *RH*, rhabdome.

(From Kleinholz, 1936. *Biol. Bull.* **70**, 159–84.)

move upwards in illuminated conditions and downwards in darkness; these two reactions are known respectively as light adaptation and dark adaptation, and they have the effect respectively of either screening the photoreceptor cells or exposing them to maximum illumination. There is no convincing evidence that these movements are under hormonal control, and they may well be direct responses to illumination, but this is certainly not true of the responses of the distal pigment cells, in which light adaptation involves a proximal movement and dark adaptation a distal one.

It was first shown by Kleinholz in 1936 that injection of *Palaemonetes* with eye-stalk extracts would bring about light adaptation of the distal pigment in dark-adapted animals, and it was subsequently demonstrated that *Palaemon* (*Leander*) would remain permanently dark-adapted after removal of the sinus glands, even though the eyes themselves were left quite undamaged. It is now well established that these light-adaptive movements of the distal pigment are under hormonal control, but it remains to be determined whether the hormone concerned is distinct from the chromatophore-activating hormones, nor is it yet clear how the dark-adaptive movements are controlled, although the action of a separate hormone has been suggested.

6. Hormones and the moulting cycle

It has long been known that the eye-stalks have some influence on the moulting of crustaceans, and it has been natural in recent years to look for evidence of hormonal regulation analogous with that demonstrated in insects. In dealing with this process it is convenient for descriptive purposes to follow a well-defined terminology, suggested by Carlisle and Dohrn, who distinguish four stages. These comprise (i) proecdysis (premoult) in which preparations for moulting take place, including the removal of calcium from the exoskeleton; (ii) ecdysis (moult), the short stage during which the exoskeleton is shed; (iii) metecdysis (post-moult), a gradual return to normal during which the skeleton hardens; and (iv) intermoult, the normal condition. The intermoult may consist either of a long period called anecdysis in those animals that have a seasonal moult, or of a short period called diecdysis in those that have a succession of moults throughout the year. In either case it is the period of maximal growth, in the sense of protein synthesis and the formation of new tissue, for the apparent growth that marks the moult stage is a swelling that results from the absorption of water (or of air in terrestrial forms).

One aspect of the hormonal control of the moulting cycle is demonstrated by the observation that removal of the eye-stalks from decapods during the intermoult stage will initiate proecdysis, and that this effect can be counteracted by the implantation of sinus glands into such animals. In effect, then, the eye-stalks, and more particularly the sinus glands, appear to be the source of a moult-inhibiting hormone, but it can be shown that the effect of this is strictly confined to delaying the inception of proecdysis, for if the eye-stalks are removed after the beginning of that stage there is no accelerating effect upon the remainder of the course of the moult.

The experiments upon which these conclusions were initially based antedated the unravelling of the true nature of the sinus gland, and some confusion was at first caused when it was found that removal of this gland by itself had no effect at all, whereas removal of the complete eye-stalk in the same species clearly accelerated the onset of proecdysis. The explanation of this apparent paradox is now seen to lie in the organization of the neurosecretory system of the eye-stalk which we have just outlined, and it was Passano who in 1953 demonstrated that the accelerating effect could be obtained if, instead of removing the sinus glands by themselves, these organs were removed together with the neurosecretory cells in the ganglionic X organs which supply them. The importance of this functional relationship, already seen in our analysis of the physiology of colour change, was further emphasized by the demonstration that the precocious moulting which resulted from eye-stalk removal could be completely eliminated by implanting both the sinus gland and the ganglionic X organ with their nervous connexions intact; if, however, they were implanted separately, or with their connexions cut, the elimination was only partial. It is now generally agreed that a moult-inhibiting hormone is secreted in the ganglionic X organ and is transmitted through neurosecretory fibres to the sinus gland for storage and release, and such a system is said to have been found in all Malacostraca in which it has so far been sought.

The moult-inhibiting hormone may be thought of as responsible for the control of the duration of the intermoult, at least in those species in which that stage is prolonged as a result of moulting being seasonally restricted. The end of the intermoult presumably results from a withdrawal of this hormone, but nothing is known of the factors, exogenous or endogenous, which determine this change of activity. Carlisle, however, has suggested that there may be another hormone, the moult-accelerating hormone, which comes into operation when proecdysis has, for whatever reason, been initiated. This hormone is believed to be secreted in the brain and central nervous system and also, in animals such as *Palaemon (Leander)* where a sensory pore X organ is well developed, in the ganglionic X organ; from the latter it is supposedly passed for release not into the sinus gland but into the sensory pore X organ (cf. Fig. 114). The effect of this hormone is thought to be an acceleration of the completion (as distinct from the initiation) of proecdysis and where, as in *Palaemon*, both this and the moult-inhibiting hormone are secreted in the eye-stalk, the results of removal of this structure can be complicated, since they will depend upon the balance between the action of the two hormones. This may vary, so that different populations of the same species may yield contradictory results. Theoretically, the effect of removal should be an acceleration of the onset of proecdysis but a slower completion of this stage, and it could therefore happen that if these two effects were exactly balanced there would be no change in the total speed of moulting, a result which does seem to have been obtained with one population of *Palaemon (Leander) serratus*.

At this point we encounter an aspect of the situation which shows an interesting parallel with the mechanisms involved in the hormonal regulation of the moulting cycle of insects. We shall see in due course how Fukuda in 1940 drew the prothoracic gland into the causal chain in that group, and it was Gabe who in 1953 called attention to the existence in the Malacostraca of an organ which resembled that gland histologically and which he called the Y organ. This, which is innervated from the sub-oesophageal ganglion, lies in either the antennary or second maxillary segment, depending upon the situation of the excretory organ of the species concerned, and it varies somewhat in its form. Its physiological significance, however, seems to be clear-cut, for Echalier has shown that its complete removal from *Carcinus* during the intermoult or early pro-ecdysis will prevent moulting, and will also prevent the removal of the eye-stalks or the injection of eye-stalk extracts from having any effect at all upon the moulting cycle. So far as our present information goes, then, it seems likely that the Y organ is the source of the actual moulting hormone or hormones, in which case the moult-accelerating and moult-inhibiting hormones which we have already discussed must be regarded as tropic hormones acting upon that organ, a point to which we shall return. It follows that proecdysis, on this interpretation, is initiated by the Y organ releasing a hormone in response to a reduction in output of the moult-inhibiting hormone of the ganglionic X organ/sinus gland complex.

Since moulting is merely a special incident in the growth processes of Crustacea, imposed upon them by the nature of their exoskeleton, we might expect that the hormones regulating it would, like the growth hormone of vertebrates, be closely linked with a variety of metabolic processes. At present, however, while hormonal regulation of crustacean metabolism seems to be established, it is impossible to define the nature of the hormones concerned or the pattern of their interaction. We have already noted that swelling as a result of the absorption of water is an important element of the moult, and Carlisle has suggested that this is under the control of a hormone located in the ganglionic X organ/sinus gland complex, but whether this water-balance hormone is distinct from the moult-inhibiting one is not clear, although there is increasing evidence that the complex may secrete a second hormone which is able to influence various aspects of metabolism. Processes for which hormonal control has been suggested include the regulation of the blood-sugar level, calcium and nitrogen metabolism, and oxygen consumption, but the immediate need is to obtain much more evidence relevant to these matters and to the possibility, suggested by Scheer, that the hormones controlling colour change may also themselves be directly involved in the regulation of metabolism.

7. The pericardial organs

One rather isolated example of a presumed endocrine structure which is not directly concerned with moulting is provided by the pericardial organs (Fig. 118). These, which were discovered by Alexandrowicz in

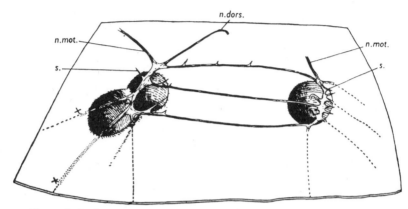

Fig. 118. Pericardial organs of the right side of *Maia squinado*, with part of the lateral pericardium wall showing the three openings of the branchio-cardiac veins. The nerves running from the central nervous system into the pericardial organs are drawn in dotted lines. *n.dors.*, dorsal nerve of the heart; *n.mot.*, nerves running to the muscles; *s.*, strands suspending the trunks.
(From Alexandrowicz, 1953. *J. mar. biol. Assoc. U.K.* **31**, 563–80.)

1952–3, are groups of nerve fibres lying in the pericardial cavity. Their nerve endings have been shown by electron microscopy to contain granules of more than one kind (Plate XIV *A*); these are thought to be neurosecretory in nature, and are perhaps indicative of the production of more than one type of secretion, although the precise function of the organs remains to be discovered. It is known, however, that extracts of them will increase the amplitude of the heart-beat and will also modify its frequency, so that it is possible that regulation of the circulation may be part, at least, of their normal activity. One of the products of the pericardial organs is thought to be closely related to serotonin (5-hydroxytryptamine; 5-HT) (Fig. 119). This substance, a derivative of tryptophan, has an excitatory action upon the crustacean heart closely resembling that of the extracts of the pericardial organs, and occurs in a

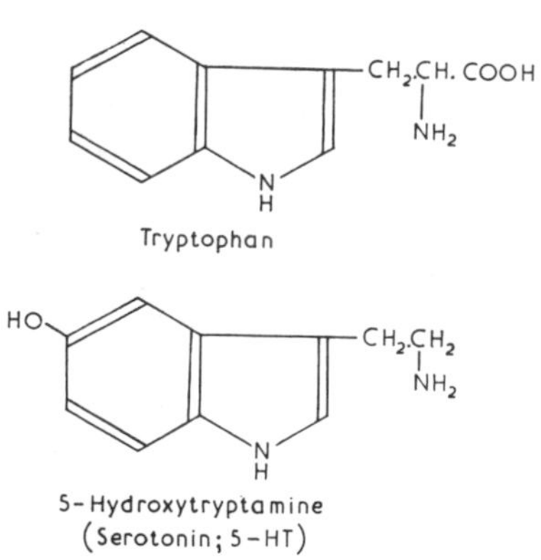

Tryptophan

5-Hydroxytryptamine
(Serotonin; 5-HT)

Fig. 119.

wide range of animal tissue. It is released from mammalian blood platelets at clotting, and has been identified in, for example, the brain of certain mammals and the nervous tissues of some molluscs and crustaceans, so that it has been regarded by some workers as a possible neurohumour or locally acting hormone.

8. Parasitic castration and sex hormones

For many years discussions of the factors controlling sexual differentiation in Crustacea have centred around the phenomenon of parasitic castration, which was first reported in 1881 but which received its name from Giard, who published a series of papers on the subject between 1886 and 1888. It is best known in crustaceans and insects, and, as found in the former group, results from parasitization either by rhizocephalan Cirripedia or by epicaridian Isopoda. Both groups of parasites are very highly specialized. The former develop through larval and endoparasitic stages into sac-like structures which are attached to the exterior of their crustacean host and which feed upon the latter by means of a branching root-like system ramifying inside its body. As for the Epicaridea, one family, the Bopyridae, live either in the gill chamber or attached to the abdomen of a decapod host, while another family, the Entoniscidae, live in the haemo-coele of crabs; unlike the Rhizocephala, they obtain their nutriment by the direct sucking of the blood of the host.

The literature relating to parasitic castration is extensive and complex, and the responses of the host are so variable that it would be impossible to attempt a survey of them here. The essential facts are, however, that the presence of the parasite causes changes in the external sexual characters (Fig. 120), and that these may be associated with a greater or lesser degree of destruction of the gonads. In general, the external changes have been said to involve a feminization of the male, which may develop, for example, the broader abdomen of the female and certain abdominal appendages normally absent in males, while the copulatory appendages characteristic of the latter are reduced. The effects upon the female are very much less and there is certainly no masculinization, although there may be some hyperfeminization shown in the precocious establishment of the female form of abdomen in an immature animal.

Earlier attempts to interpret this phenomenon in terms of hormonal control have been largely based upon hypothetical analogies with verte-brates, and, in particular, upon the supposed production of sex hormones by the crustacean gonads. It has been suggested that the external changes in the host are due to endocrine disturbance resulting from the destruction of organs, but this view has been difficult to sustain, since critical examination shows no close correlation between the degree of external change and the degree of degeneration of the gonads, nor are the time relationships at all well correlated. This has encouraged the development of other suggestions, such as the well-known one that the supposed feminization of *Inachus* by *Sacculina* results from the latter creating in its host a modification in its fat metabolism similar to that resulting in the female from the

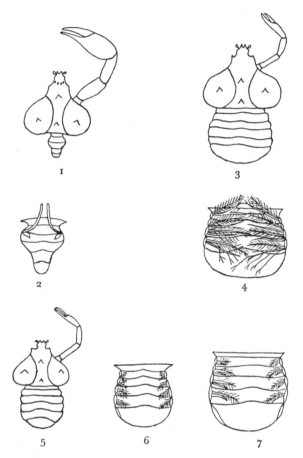

Fig. 120. Parasitic castration of the crab *Inachus*. *1*, normal male; *2*, male abdomen in ventral view; *3*, normal female; *4*, female abdomen in ventral view; *5*, sacculinized male with 'female' characters (small chela and broad abdomen); *6*, abdomen of sacculinized male in ventral view showing 'female' character (pleopods); *7*, abdomen of sacculinized female.

(After Smith, from Hanström, 1939. *Hormones in Invertebrates*. Oxford: Clarendon Press.)

demands created by yolk deposition, but against this is the fact that feminization of structure may begin in the normal life-cycle before the onset of vitellogenesis.

It is now possible to see that these difficulties of interpretation arise from the circumstance that here, as in much other invertebrate endocrinological research, physiological investigations have preceded the morphological identification of the glands concerned, a course of events which has usually been reversed in the development of vertebrate endocrinology. Fortunately evidence has accumulated which clearly shows that the differentiation of sex in Crustacea is under hormonal control. It has shown, too, that the

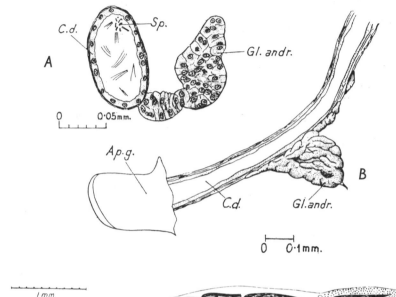

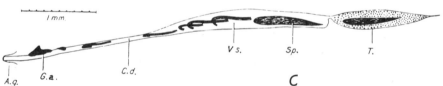

Fig. 121. *A*. Position of the androgenic gland of *Orchestia gammarellus*. *B*. Androgenic gland in a fresh specimen. *C*. Transverse section of gland and vas deferens. *AP.g.*, genital papilla; *C.d.*, vas deferens; *G.a.*, *Gl. andr.*, androgenic gland; *Sp.*, sperm; *T.*, testis; *V.s.*, seminal vesicle.
(From Charniaux-Cotton, 1957. *Ann. Sci. Nat. Zool.* **19**, 413–559.)

pattern of this control does, in fact, bear some resemblance to that characteristic of vertebrates, but yet differs from it in one crucial respect. 'Nature', to quote words used by Ronald Ross in quite another context, 'was more resourceful and astute than all of us.'

It now seems probable that reproduction in the malacostracan Crustacea depends upon hormones originating in several different organs. One of those involved may be the Y organ, for removal of this from juvenile specimens of *Carcinus*, of either sex, has been shown to lead to degeneration of the gonads. On the other hand, if this removal takes place after sexual maturity has been attained it produces no effect at all, so that it remains uncertain whether the influence of this organ results from the production of a specific sex hormone or whether it is due to some more generalized action upon the young animal as a whole.

Far more clear-cut than this is the role of a gland (Fig. 121) called the androgenic gland, discovered by Charniaux-Cotton in 1954. Its function has been particularly studied in the amphipod, *Orchestia gammarellus* (Fig. 121), but it is known to exist in the males of all orders of the Malacostraca except the Isopoda in which, however, the testes seem to act as a substitute for it. This gland, which is distinct from the gonad and is attached to the vas deferens (the duct that leads from the testis to the genital papilla) is essential for the development of the testes and of the male external sexual characters. If it is removed the animal reverts to an indeterminate (i.e. non-sexual) stage at the next moult, and an ovary transplanted into such an animal may be able to mature and thus to evoke the appearance of brooding characters (see below) at a later moult. If the androgenic gland is transplanted into a female, on the other hand, the animal will become masculinized, with male copulatory appendages, and sperm appearing in the ovary; such individuals have been reported to have become the fathers of daughters. In the genetic female the androgenic gland does not develop at all, and it appears that in this sex the gonad develops into a functional ovary without the stimulating action of any hormone, presumably through a process of self-differentiation.

Nevertheless, the ovary does seem to be involved in some degree of hormonal regulation, for it is believed that the development of eggs outside the normal breeding season is prevented by an ovary-inhibiting hormone secreted in the ganglionic X organ/sinus gland complex. The evidence for this includes the facts that removal of the eye-stalk leads in many decapods to precocious ovarian development and oviposition, which can be at least partially prevented by the implanting of sinus glands, and that the normal ovarian development which ushers in the breeding season can be prevented by the injection of eye-stalks, or of the separate parts of the complex. The ovary itself also exerts a positive effect upon sexual differentiation by virtue of a hormone which it secretes when normal ovarian pre-breeding development has begun and, more especially, when yolk deposition has started. This hormone is thought to ensure that the brooding characters, such as the brood pouch and ovigerous hairs, appear at the next moult, the evidence for this resting on the demonstration that after castration of the female these brooding characters do not appear, and that they can be restored by the implantation of ripening ovaries.

As regards parasitic castration, it would appear probable that the effects of the parasite upon the sexual characterization of the male are due to its removal of the androgenic hormone from the blood, and, eventually, to the destruction of the androgenic gland itself, with the result that the host reverts to the non-sexual condition. The belief that the parasitized male is actually feminized is in part a miconception arising from the fact that the external form of the female departs less from the non-sexual condition than does that of the male. The situation is also influenced, however, by the fact that in the absence of the androgenic gland the gonad normally develops into an ovary; because of this an ovary may actually develop in a parasitized male, and if it reaches the stage of maturation it is capable of evoking the apperance of brooding characters as a result of the hormone which it can then secrete. To this extent parasitism may indirectly bring about sex reversal in the host. No doubt other factors may also be involved in the changes effected by parasitic castration, for the parasite may well exert the powerful metabolic and toxic influences that have often been postulated, and it is known, too, that the roots of a rhizocephalan can damage the neurosecretory cells of the thoracic ganglion of the host. There is thus much scope for profound disturbances of the complex hormonal balance of these highly organized animals.

It is interesting, in the light of our earlier discussion of evolutionary relationships (p. 309), to note that the control of sexual organization in Crustacea has much more in common with the pattern found in vertebrates than that found in insects. This applies, as we shall see, to the fundamental importance of sex hormones in the crustaceans and vertebrates, while another, although more superficial, resemblance between the two groups lies in the production by the ovaries of hormones that are concerned with making preparation for the care of the young. There is also said to be some evidence that hormones from the eye-stalk may exert control over the reproductive cycle of the female in a manner that is at least reminiscent of the activities of the pars distalis. The unique feature in the Crustacea, however, and one which convincingly illustrates the danger of looking for too close a degree of resemblance between the plans of organization of unrelated groups, is the androgenic gland, for the production of a sex hormone, capable of determining the primary as well as the accessory characters, by a gland that is entirely separate from the gonad has no parallel within the vertebrates. Indeed, such a situation does not appear to have been described in any other group of the animal kingdom.

XIV. HORMONES IN INSECTA

1. Life-histories

THE study of the endocrinology of insects, in contrast to that of Crustacea, has centred particularly around the analysis of moulting and growth, but there are in other respects some striking parallels to be noted, both in the results themselves and in the ways in which they have been achieved. Here again we encounter the difficulty that the physiological observations have sometimes been in advance of the anatomical ones, so that the full significance of the endocrine pattern has only slowly been unfolded, but the results as they present themselves today are peculiarly satisfying, both in the elegance of the experimental treatment of the problems and in the applicability of their interpretation to species of widely different habits.

The growth of insects, like that of crustaceans, and for the same reason, is marked by a series of moults or ecdyses, at each of which the old cuticle is discarded and a new one laid down, and since this process is so sharply defined in time, and since it determines the size, proportions, and general appearance of the animal, it has been a major focus of endocrinological analysis. We have seen ample evidence in other groups that this kind of response, involving as it does the whole of the body, lends itself particularly well to hormonal control, so that the first questions to be answered are whether such control is operative here and, if so, where the hormones are secreted, what is their nature, and what determines the periodicity of their actions.

In seeking the answers to these questions we shall be referring particularly to two species which have proved exceptionally well suited for experimental treatment, the reduviid bug, *Rhodnius prolixus*, and the giant American silkworm moth, *Hyalophora (Platysamia) cecropia*. The former has a typical hemimetabolous life-history, with five larval (nymphal) instars preceding the adult stage, while the latter is holometabolous, with five larval instars passing into the adult stage through a pupal instar. It has often been held that such life-histories are composed of a sequence of stages of progressive differentiation, with the implication that the future adult begins its life in an imperfect form, but an interpretation found more acceptable at the present time is one that has been argued by Wigglesworth, amongst others. According to this view the insect life-history carries to an extreme the tendency, which is already pronounced in many lower invertebrates, for the larva and adult to undergo independent and increasingly divergent evolution in adaptation to two different modes of life. The caterpillar of *Hyalophora*, for example, is devoted to growth, and with such intense concentration that during early summer it increases its weight 5,000 times; at pupation its accumulated assets are then invested, as Williams puts it, in the construction of an essentially new type of organism, a flying-machine devoted to reproduction.

The life-history, on this interpretation, is regarded as an example of polymorphism, the individual having the capacity for existing in one or other of two alternative forms, with the pupal stage providing the opportunity for the drastic reorganization which is involved in the metamorphosis of the holometabolous type of insect. The larva must therefore be considered to contain, in a latent and unexpressed form, the capacity for adult differentiation, and the reverse could also be true, except in so far as metamorphosis is responsible for irreversible changes which eliminate from the adult tissues the capacity for larval differentiation.

This point is clearly established by Wigglesworth's analysis of the effect of wounds upon the epidermal colour pattern in *Rhodnius*. The larva has black spots on the lateral hind margin of the segments while the adult bug has these on the lateral anterior margin. If a burn is applied between two spots in the larva, the wound is repaired by the migration of cells from the adjacent black areas, and these carry with them the potentiality for producing black pigment in the larva, so that at the next moult these black areas are found to have fused (Fig. 122). The burn has, however, destroyed those cells which possess the particular capacity for producing black spots in the adult, and the migrating cells cannot replace this capacity since they do not possess it; hence, after metamorphosis the corresponding black areas will be absent. Clearly, then, each cell must be thought of as possessing two sets of potentialities, one appropriate to the larva and one appropriate to the adult, and another of our problems is therefore to establish the nature of the switch mechanism determining which particular form shall be realized at any one moult. By analogy with Crustacea we may expect this, too, to be hormonal, for we have seen how in that group the course of a moult may be modified by, for example, the presence of an ovarian hormone capable of evoking the formation of brooding characters.

2. Ecdysone and the prothoracic glands

The first demonstration of a probable hormonal control of an insect life-cycle dates from 1917–22, when Kopeč showed that if larvae of the moth *Porthetria* (*Lymantria*) *dispar* were tied with a thread before a certain critical stage during their last larval instar only the portion of the body anterior to the ligature would pupate, the remainder maintaining its larval form. Since the cutting of the nerve cord had no such effect there was good reason for suspecting that a hormone was concerned, and there was reason also for suspecting an involvement of the brain, for he was able to show that removal of this before the critical stage would prevent pupation, while if the brain were reimplanted pupation would proceed. Here at once we see how the remarkable resistance of insects to drastic manipulation makes it possible to meet some of the classical requirements of vertebrate endocrinology, such as removal and replacement of a suspected gland, by an entirely novel type of experimental procedure.

Much further evidence for the hormonal control of growth and moulting accumulated during the 1930's, more particularly under the stimulus of Wigglesworth's investigations of *Rhodnius*, to which we shall refer below, but the source of the hormone remained in doubt until the demonstration

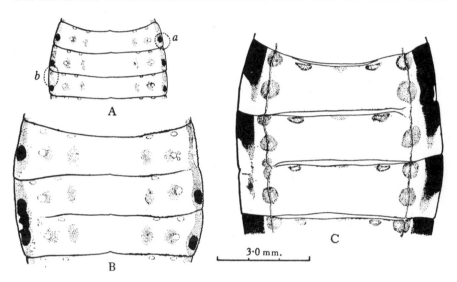

Fig. 122. *A*, third, fourth, and fifth tergites of a normal 3rd instar larva of *Rhodnius*; the broken lines at *a* and *b* show the regions burned. *B*, corresponding segments in the resulting 5th instar. *C*, corresponding segments in the resulting adult.
(From Wigglesworth, 1940. *J. exp. Biol.* **17**, 180–200.)

by Fukuda in 1940 of the significance of the prothoracic gland. This, in Lepidoptera, is a paired and much-branched organ which extends from the head into the prothorax along trunks of the tracheal system. Glands which are thought to correspond with it (Fig. 123) are present in most groups of insects, although their actual homology with the lepidopteran one is usually a matter of assumption. In *Rhodnius*, however, the homology of the relevant organ, there called the thoracic gland, has been justified on embryological grounds, for both it and the prothoracic gland of Lepidoptera have been shown to arise in the same way from the ectoderm of the second maxilla.

The essential importance of Fukuda's work lay in the demonstration that if the larva of the silkworm was ligatured transversely at a level behind this gland, only the anterior portion would pupate, but that the posterior half would also do so if a prothoracic gland were implanted into it. Similar results, obtained either by ligature or by transection, have since been obtained for other species, including *Rhodnius* and *Hyalophora*, and it has been found that isolated posterior regions of pupal stages of the latter may survive for over a year without undergoing any further development; the

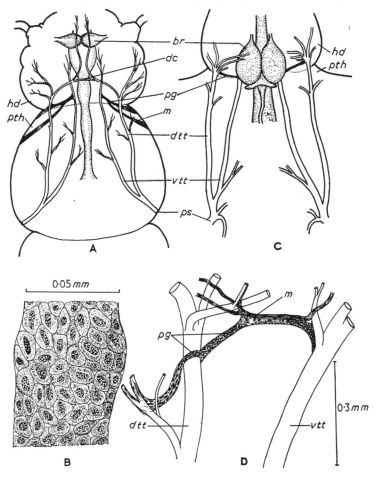

Fig. 123. Prothoracic glands of coleopteran larvae. *A*, *Nebria brevicollis*, in natural position (semidiagrammatic); *B*, *N. brevicollis*, histological appearance; *C*, *Elater rufipennis*, in natural position (semi-diagrammatic); *D*, *E. rufipennis*, gland in relation to dorsal and ventral tracheal trunks. *br*, brain; *dc*, dorsal tracheal commissure; *dtt*, dorsal tracheal trunk; *hd*, head; *m*, muscle; *pg*, prothoracic gland; *ps*, prothoracic spiracle; *pth*, prothorax; *vtt*, ventral tracheal trunk.

(From Srivastava, 1959. *Quart. J. micr. Sci.* **100**, 51–64.)

implantation into them of living prothoracic glands will, however, promptly cause them to resume their development.

It is now accepted, as a result of this and other work, that a growth and moulting hormone, ecdysone, is secreted by the prothoracic gland or its homologue, and useful material for its further study is provided by puparium formation in Diptera, the stage at which the cuticle of the larva

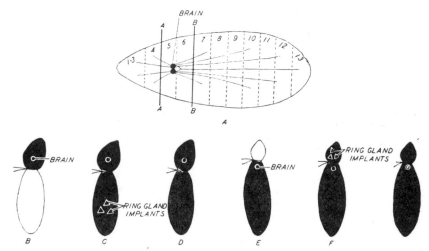

Fig. 124. The puparium reaction in muscid larvae. *A*, Diagram of a larva. Ligatures may be placed in front of the brain and ring gland (at line A—A) or behind them (B—B). *B* to *G*, the regions showing the puparium reaction are indicated in black. *B*, Ligatured behind the brain before the critical period; ecdysone is confined to the anterior region. *C*, As *B*, but with ring glands implanted into the body posterior to the ligature; ecdysone from these evokes a reaction, provided that the larval donors have passed the critical period. *D*, Ligatured behind the brain after the critical period; ecdysone has become distributed throughout the body. *E*, Ligatured in front of the brain before the critical period; ecdysone is confined to the posterior region. *F*, as *E*, but with ring glands implanted into the body anterior to the ligature; ecdysone from these evokes a reaction provided that the larval donors have passed the critical period. *G*, Ligatured in front of the brain after the critical period; ecdysone has become distributed throughout the body.
(From Turner, 1948. *General Endocrinology*. Philadelphia: Saunders.)

hardens by tanning of its proteins immediately before the establishment of the pupal stage, and which is sometimes itself referred to loosely as pupation. In 1935 Fraenkel found that after transverse ligation of mature larvae of the blowfly, *Calliphora*, only the anterior portion would form a puparium provided that the operation was carried out more than sixteen hours before that event (Fig. 124). Since puparium formation could be evoked in the posterior end of such a specimen by injecting into it some blood from an anterior end, he concluded that the reaction was dependent upon a hormone secreted in the anterior region. It is now apparent that this, too, is ecdysone and that after the critical period, at about sixteen hours before puparium formation, this becomes distributed throughout the body so that the whole of it is able to react even though part may be separated by ligature from the initial source of the hormone. This source is the ring gland of Weismann, a compound organ which consists of the corpus allatum (see below) dorsally, the corpus cardiacum (see below) and hypocerebral ganglion ventrally, and the homologue of the prothoracic gland (here called the peritracheal gland) on either side. The functional relationships are exactly as in *Rhodnius* and *Hyalophora*; removal of the peritracheal gland will prevent puparium formation, and this can then be induced by the implantation of peritracheal gland material from third-stage larvae, provided that these have passed beyond the critical stage. Such implants will also induce the reaction in parts of the body which have been separated by ligature from the source of ecdysone (Fig. 124).

The classical requirement of the demonstration of the presence of ecdysone in the blood has been met to a large extent by parabiosis experiments (cf. Figs. 129 & 130) in which, for example, a *Rhodnius* larva decapitated before the critical period, and therefore unable to moult, is joined by capillary tube to one decapitated after the critical period. Both will now moult, the inference being that the former is stimulated to do so because it now shares a common circulation with the latter and receives the hormone from it in the blood stream. Actually, such insects readily become united by regenerating epidermis, so that the possibility of some stimulating agent being distributed through the tissue is not entirely eliminated in these particular experiments, but the results of other ones have completed the proof. For example, the female pupae of certain hybrid moths which do not normally moult into adults can be induced to do so by introducing into them some blood from moulting male pupae.

Biochemical studies by Butenandt and Karlson have led to the isolation of this hormone in crystalline form as α-ecdysone and β-ecdysone, the extent of the effort required being indicated by the yield, which amounted to only 25 mg from 500 kg of the pupae of *Bombyx mori*. The *Calliphora* puparium reaction has provided the basis for a convenient bio-assay procedure for the hormone, the principle of the method being to ligate the larvae transversely in the anterior third of the body and thus to restrict puparium formation to the region anterior to the ligature, the posterior region being, of course, isolated by the ligature from the peritracheal gland. The anterior part of the puparium is then cut off and the test solution injected into the posterior region; the percentage response of the latter, as indicated by puparium formation, is a sensitive measure of the hormone content of the test solution.

Ecdysone appears to be a relatively simple substance, not a steroid, with a molecular weight of 300 and an empirical formula of $C_{18}H_{30}O_4$, and it is probably bound to specific proteins. Its name gives expression to the fact that it evokes ecdysis (shedding of the cuticle), but its more fundamental action is the regulation of mitotic activity and growth processes prior to the actual moult. Thus if the ring gland is removed from the larva of *Calliphora* the imaginal buds cease to grow although the animal continues to feed, while other evidence comes from the detailed histological changes that have been shown by Wigglesworth to result from the injection of ecdysone into *Rhodnius*. The ventral abdominal muscles provide one example of this, for they are fully developed only when the old cuticle is actually being shed, and undergo autolysis directly afterwards so that only the muscle sheath and nuclei remain. Within six hours of injecting the hormone these nuclei and their nucleoli are found to be enlarging, and increasing amounts of nucleic acid become visible. It is for such reasons that ecdysone is referred to as the growth and moulting hormone. Injection of it into *Chironomus* larvae has been shown to be followed by changes in the salivary gland chromosomes (the 'puffing' phenomenon), and this has led Karlson to suggest that the influence of hormones on development may be exerted through a direct action upon the genes.

The availability of the pure hormone has made it possible to show that, like vertebrate hormones, it is not species specific, for it will induce moulting in *Rhodnius* as well as pupation in Lepidoptera and puparium formation in Diptera, nor is its action restricted to any one stage of development, for it will stimulate the development of the imago which follows diapause in Lepidoptera and Hymenoptera (see below). Of particular interest, however, is the question of its possible identity or relationship with the corresponding hormone of Crustacea, for there are clearly some remarkable resemblances in respect of the control of moulting in the two groups. The Y organ is probably under the tropic control of hormones secreted by the brain, and this is certainly true of the prothoracic gland (see below), although there is a difference here in that this control is inhibitory in Crustacea and excitatory in insects. The moulting hormones themselves also seem to function in the same way, for the secretion of the Y organ is required for the initiation of proecdysis, but not for its continuation, and this appears to apply also to ecdysone. Further, the Y organ of *Maia* degenerates after the last moult, while in insects it is common for the prothoracic gland to disappear at that stage.

Such considerations certainly disclose a remarkable similarity of organization between the two groups, and we may add to them the interesting finding that ecdysone is active when injected into shrimps, while extracts of the whole body of *Crangon* contain a fraction that produces a positive response in the puparium reaction. There is, however, no evidence that this fraction is specifically restricted to the Y organ, nor are such responses necessarily good evidence for the presence of a particular hormone. We have seen, for example, that biochemical studies of oestrogens have shown that similarity of response is not necessarily an indication of identity of structure in the active molecules, and it follows that final decisions regarding the identity of hormones or their evolutionary relationships must await the determination of their molecular structure. Nevertheless, it is not surprising to find it suggested that the two glands (Y organ and prothoracic gland) may, in fact, be homologous, but the evidence for this is still incomplete, and the possibility needs to be weighed critically in the light of our earlier dicussion of phylogenetic relationships.

3. Neurosecretion and the prothoracotropic hormone

We must now consider what determines the periodicity of the insect moult. Here it can be said at once that if we are to look in this group for the principles which we have earlier established for the vertebrates we should certainly expect to find that the brain is directly involved in the causal chain. We have seen a suggestion of such an involvement in Kopeč's observations, and it is now an established fact, although since physiological results have tended at times to run ahead of the identification of secretory centres there has been some confusion of interpretation in the earlier literature.

Our understanding of the importance of the brain in this regard derives from Wigglesworth's studies of *Rhodnius*, as a result of which he was able to show in 1934 that the periodicity of its moult was causally related to its feeding habits. The larva takes a large meal of blood on one occasion only during each instar, and it is this which ultimately determines the onset of the moult, although a certain critical period of up to a week or so has to elapse before this determination becomes fully effective. Thus if the animal is decapitated during the first day or two after the meal it will never moult, although it may live for as much as a year, without growing at all during that time. A decapitated larva will, however, moult normally if the removal of its head is delayed until after the lapse of the critical period. A large meal is an essential factor in this response, for an equivalent amount of blood divided into several small meals will not result in the inception of moulting. It can thus be inferred that the stimulus arising from a large meal (actually, it is believed, from the stretching of the gut wall) evokes the secretion of a hormone in the head, that the effect of this has not become fully developed during the first day or two, but that after the critical period it is possible for moulting to proceed normally without any further supply of the hormone being needed, so that decapitation will no longer have any inhibitory effect.

The next step in the analysis required the identification of the precise source of the hormone, and for this we are again indebted to Hanström, who drew attention in 1938 to the presence of large secretory cells, filled with stainable droplets, in the median region (pars intercerebralis) of the protocerebrum. Wigglesworth was able to show that if this region (Fig. 125) was removed from a larva at about the critical period and implanted into one that had been decapitated immediately after feeding, the latter was caused to moult and, since no other part of the brain had this effect, it was clear that these cells were the source of the hormone. For a time it

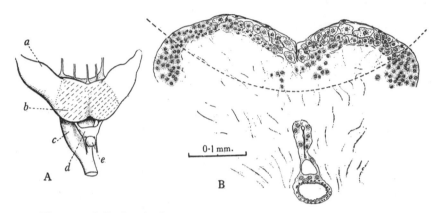

Fig. 125. *A*, Brain of 5th-stage nymph of *Rhodnius*. *a*, optic lobes; *b*, protocerebrum; *c*, suboesophageal ganglion; *d*, sympathetic (oesophageal) ganglion; *e*, corpus allatum. *B*, Vertical section through the posterior part of the protocerebrum; in the central region above are the large cells with fuchsinophil inclusions, while ordinary ganglion cells lie laterally. The shaded area in *A*, and the broken line in *B*, indicate the approximate limits of the region which, when excised and implanted into 4th-stage nymphs decapitated at 24 hours after feeding, will cause these to moult.
(From Wigglesworth, 1940. *J. exp. Biol.* **17**, 201–22.)

seemed possible that this brain hormone might be the growth and moulting hormone itself, but Fukuda's work almost immediately showed that this could not be so, and it is now generally accepted that it is responsible for the activation of the secretion of ecdysone by the prothoracic gland; it may therefore be referred to as the prothoracotropic hormone.

Later, when the significance of neurosecretion in the organization of the endocrine systems of vertebrates and crustaceans had been established, it became apparent that the secretory activity of the pars intercerebralis of insects provided yet another example of this, and it is now recognized that the cells concerned are, in fact, neurosecretory ones. They are usually present as two medial and two lateral groups, and in *Hyalophora* there are known to be twenty-six in all, eight in each of the two medial groups and five in each lateral one. The axons of the former decussate in the middle line and then form a pair of nerves, while the axons of the lateral cells form another pair without decussation. These nerves all join to form an organ called the corpus cardiacum, which is composed in part of cells that may themselves be secretory in function. It seems clear that this organ (which, as we have seen, constitutes part of Weismann's ring in Diptera), is a neurohaemal organ, serving for the storage and release of secretion that has been formed in the pars intercerebralis, but its functions may extend a little further than this, for there is evidence that in *Platysamia* both medial and lateral groups of neurosecretory cells are needed for control to be exercised over the prothoracic gland, and it has been suggested that they may secrete two distinct precursor substances from which the definitive hormone arises after further processing in the corpus cardiacum.

The relationship between this and the pars intercerebralis is clearly similar to that existing between the neural lobe and the hypothalamus in vertebrates, and between the sinus gland and ganglionic X organ in crustaceans, and the nature of the complex has been demonstrated in very similar ways. For example, the characteristic granules of the cells can also be seen in their axons in the medial corpus cardiacum nerves and in the corpus cardiacum itself, while Scharrer has shown that if one of these nerves is cut in *Leucophaea* the secretory material accumulates proximally to the cut and disappears distally (Fig. 126), an experiment and a result precisely comparable with the demonstration of the transport of hypo-thalamic neurosecretion in the vertebrates by sectioning of the pituitary stalk. Further, Thompsen has succeeded in the remarkable feat of ligaturing one of these nerves in the blowfly, *Calliphora erythrocephala*, and has been able to show that this results in an accumulation of secretory material in the axons above the ligature. It seems likely, therefore, that the secretion is normally released through the corpus cardiacum, but since the relevant part of the protocerebrum can certainly evoke the moulting response in *Rhodnius* when it is transplanted by itself the possibility of direct release of the secretion from the brain into the blood is not excluded.

As regards the factors promoting this release, we have seen that the initial stimulus in *Rhodnius* is thought to be the stretching of the wall of the gut by the ingested blood of a large meal, a supposition confirmed by the fact that the effect of the meal can be entirely eliminated, with the prevention of any hormonal discharge from the brain, by cutting the nervous connexions between the latter and the abdomen. This influence of the alimentary canal has been further confirmed by electrophysio-logical methods, for van der Kloot has been able to record the passage of nerve impulses through the corpora cardiaca nerves from the brain. In an unfed larva the impulses are rare, but they are discharged at a rate of about three per second after feeding, and discharge can also be evoked in an unfed animal by stretching the abdomen. Not all the fibres in these nerves are neurosecretory, so that it cannot be assumed that it is this type which are conducting the impulses. It seems likely, however, that they may be doing so, for we know that ordinary nerve cells combine the capacity for conduction with that of secretion (p. 75), and it is not obvious what advantage would be gained if neurosecretory cells had developed the latter at the cost of completely losing control over the release of their own product. Nevertheless we cannot be sure that this is so, and we must leave open the possibility that the release of neurosecretion from nerve endings may be evoked by impulses passing in ordinary fibres lying adjacent to them.

There is also doubt as to the exact course of events which follows this discharge in the corpus cardiacum. According to Wigglesworth, hormone

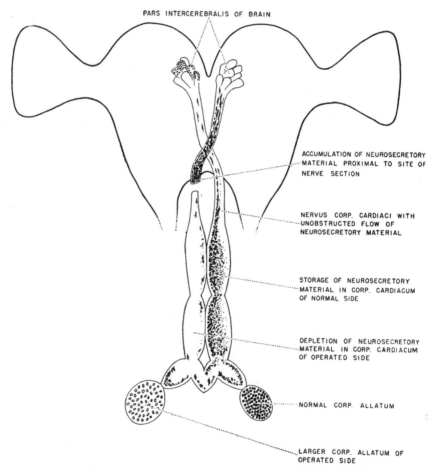

PARS INTERCEREBRALIS OF BRAIN

ACCUMULATION OF NEUROSECRETORY MATERIAL PROXIMAL TO SITE OF NERVE SECTION

NERVUS CORP. CARDIACI WITH UNOBSTRUCTED FLOW OF NEUROSECRETORY MATERIAL

STORAGE OF NEUROSECRETORY MATERIAL IN CORP. CARDIACUM OF NORMAL SIDE

DEPLETION OF NEUROSECRETORY MATERIAL IN CORP. CARDIACUM OF OPERATED SIDE

NORMAL CORP. ALLATUM

LARGER CORP. ALLATUM OF OPERATED SIDE

Fig. 126. Diagram of the dorsal aspect of the pars intercerebralis/corpus cardiacum/corpus allatum complex in the orthopteran *Leucophaea maderae*. Severing of the corpus cardiacum nerve on the left side has resulted in the neurosecretory material being increased proximally and depleted distally, with a consequent decrease in size of the corpus cardiacum and increase of the corpus allatum.
(From Scharrer, 1952. *Biol. Bull.* **102**, 261–72.)

release begins within a few minutes of ingestion, yet it must continue for
several days (to the critical period) if moulting is to result. This suggests
the possibility that some interaction has to develop, perhaps between the
prothoracotropic hormone and the prothoracic gland, or perhaps within
the corpus cardiacum. It is fashionable to say that the one hormone triggers
the release of the other but here, as in other contexts, this is a form of
words which serves for little more than to conceal our ignorance of what
exactly is involved at this crucial stage.

4. Hormones and diapause

An effective illustration of the way in which the general principles
outlined above can be applied to the interpretation of a specialized situation
is provided by Williams's analysis of the endocrinological basis of diapause
in *Hyalophora*. Diapause is a condition of arrested development which
depends upon physiological specialization and is quite distinct from such
temporary inhibition as may be produced solely by the action of adverse
factors in the environment and which may then cease as soon as these
factors disappear. This latter condition can be called quiescence, and the
distinction between this and diapause is of the same order as that between
the simple winter sleep of certain mammals such as the brown bear and the
specialized physiological adaptation called hibernation. Both this and
diapause are essentially ecological adaptations which enable the species
to resist some unfavourable aspect of their environment.

The experimental analysis of diapause has attracted the attention of
many investigators, so much so that a reviewer of the subject writing in
1932 was able to cite 347 titles in his bibliography. It cannot, however,
be said that at that time any clear understanding of the physiology of the
process had emerged, although there was some evidence that pupal
development in Lepidoptera depended upon an active centre in the thorax
(Fig. 127 *B*). This lack must be ascribed in part to the absence of any sound
foundation of endocrinological principles, and also, as Williams points
out, to the unsuitability of much of the experimental material. It is in
this latter respect that *Hyalophora* has proved so useful, for with an adult
weighing up to 8 gm it is amongst the largest of American insects, while
it has a particularly characteristic and well-defined form of diapause
into which the pupae enter at the beginning of the instar. They remain in
it during the winter and if they are kept at ordinary room temperature
while they are in this condition they will never metamorphose, for this
diapause can only be brought to an end after they have been chilled for
one to two months at a temperature of 3° to 5° C.

Williams's analysis of this phenomenon has been based partly upon the
use of isolated abdomens sealed by wax to cover-slips; these lack the prothoracic gland and are consequently unable to moult. If, however, the

glands from post-diapausing (i.e. activated) purpae are implanted into such abdomens these will metamorphose, and may even lay some eggs! The influence of the brain in stimulating the prothoracic glands by releasing the prothoracotropic hormone has been shown by a development of Crampton's method of establishing parabiosis by sealing pupae together with wax (Fig. 127 *A*). If a diapausing pupa from which the brain has been

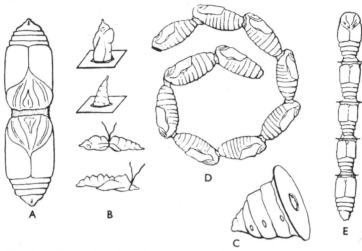

Fig. 127. Examples of methods used in the investigation of growth and moulting in insects. *A*, One of the experiments of Crampton (1899) to show simultaneous development of *Hyalophora* pupae joined with paraffin. *B*, Experiments of Hachlow (1931); pupae of *Aporia* and *Vanessa* are ligatured, or divided and sealed by paraffin to glass slides, and pupal development is shown to be initiated by a centre in the thorax (prothoracic gland). *C–E*, Experiments of Williams (1952) on *Hyalophora* pupae. *C*, Isolated abdomen caused to develop by implantation of prothoracic glands and chilled brain. *D*, Chain of ten brainless diapausing pupae induced to develop by implantation of a chilled brain into the leading pupa. *E*, Four abdomens of diapausing pupae are joined to a chilled pupa with brain and prothoracic gland; only the anterior-most abdomens develop, as only they receive adequate concentrations of ecdysone.

(From Wigglesworth, 1954. *Physiology of Insect Metamorphosis.* Cambridge: University Press.)

removed is grafted to a chilled (activated) and intact pupa it will moult synchronously with the latter as a result of receiving some of its prothoracotropic hormone, while the grafting together of pupae of different species shows that this hormone is neither species nor genus specific. Its capacity for diffusion and stimulation is particularly well shown in experiments in which parabiotic chains of brainless pupae have been constructed (Fig. 127 *D*); if a single chilled (activated) brain is implanted into the most anterior member of the chain its influence will gradually spread so that they will all metamorphose as a result of the successive activation of their prothoracic glands. If, however, one is detached before this activation process has reached it, then it will be unable to metamorphose. Finally, this interaction of brain and prothoracic glands is convincingly shown by experiments in which a previously chilled brain is implanted into the posterior end of a diapausing pupa together with two pairs of diapausing glands; the latter are activated by the brain hormone and will then evoke metamorphosis in the abdomen (Fig. 127 C).

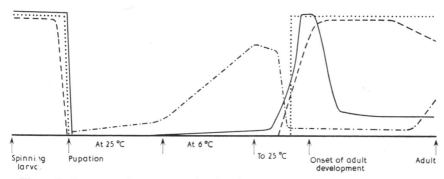

Fig. 128. Sequence of events associated with pupation in *Hyalophora*. ——— release of prothoracotropic hormone; . . . electrical activity of brain; — — — cholinesterase in brain; — · — · acetylcholine-like substance in brain.

Such an analysis suggests that this form of diapause must be initiated in the normal life-cycle by the withdrawal of the prothoracotropic hormone, and van der Kloot has provided some indication of the nature of the physiological adaptations which this involves (Fig. 128). By the insertion of microelectrodes into the brain he has been able to record its electrical activity and to show that after the end of diapause a spontaneous activity can readily be detected, as it can be in the brains of caterpillars. On the other hand, the brain of a pupa during diapause is electrically silent, all trace of activity disappearing suddenly just before pupation, to reappear immediately prior to the resumption of development at the end of diapause, at about the time when the secretion of the brain hormone is thought to begin once again.

This is paralleled exactly by changes in the cholinesterase content, for this enzyme is present in considerable quantities in the brain of the larva, is absent during diapause, and reappears towards the end. During this same period the amount of acetylcholine-like substance in the brain slowly increases until, with the appearance once again of cholinesterase, the content falls and electrical activity can again be detected. Thus the pupal diapause of *Hyalophora* involves what amounts to a complete 'shutting-down' of the brain, a condition which is the more remarkable in that it affects no other part of the central nervous system, for the ganglia of the ventral nerve cord retain their spontaneous activity and their normal content of cholinesterase. We see in this an interesting consequence of the maintenance by the segments of the arthropod body of a considerable degree of independence, a situation which contrasts markedly with the progressive tendency towards unification which overrides much of the initial metamerism of the vertebrates.

As regards the mode of action of ecdysone, already mentioned above (p. 338), there is some suggestion that in *Hyalophora* it may influence the cytochrome system, for this is active in the larva but inactive during diapause, as is shown, for example, by the insensitivity of the diapausing pupa to cyanide. This is associated with an absence of cytochrome *c*, and the synthesis of this is one of the characteristic features of the end of the diapause, but even if this is a direct consequence of the action of ecdysone it could not be of universal significance, for diapause in insects is not always associated with reduced activity in the cytochrome system. Here, as with comparable problems in vertebrate endocrinology, we must await the results of a great deal of further investigation.

5. Metamorphosis and the juvenile hormone

So far we have discussed the regulation of moulting without reference to the closely associated problem of metamorphosis, and it is this which we must examine next. In *Rhodnius* the metamorphic moult occurs at the end of the fifth larval instar and results in the appearance of the full assemblage of adult characters. It is actually an over-simplification to regard this last moult as completely different from the preceding ones, for in fact at each of the larval moults there is a slight change towards the adult characterization; nevertheless it is true that by far the greater part of this change occurs at the last one. We have suggested earlier that this situation is best interpreted as an example of polymorphism, and we have seen that the crucial problem here is to determine the nature of the switch mechanism which evokes the emergence of the adult form.

It is now known, initially from Wigglesworth's studies of *Rhodnius*, that the structures concerned are the corpora allata, glands which develop from the ectoderm and come to be closely associated with the corpora cardiaca (Fig. 126); they are, in fact, innervated from the corpus cardiacum nerves and seem to receive neurosecretory products from them. The function of the corpora allata is the production of a hormone, known as the juvenile hormone (the name neotenin has also been suggested), which appears to exert no effect by itself but which, in association with ecdysone, promotes the development of the larval characters. It is present during the moults of the first four larval instars, but the metamorphosis which results from the moult of the fifth instar is determined by the fact that the juvenile hormone is not being secreted at that stage. At this point, then, the hormonal balance shifts to switch development in favour of the realization of

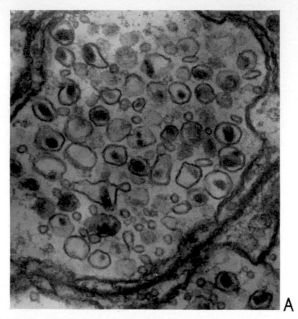

A

B

Plate XIV. *A*. Electron micrographs of nerve endings in the pericardial organ of *Squilla mantis*. Two types of neurosecretory inclusions have been identified in this organ, the one shown here having a crystal-like appearance. (× 76,000.)
(Provided by Sir Francis Knowles.)

B. Parabiosis in the cockroach, *Periplaneta americana*. A last-stage larve (*below*) has been fused with a younger one (*above*); both have moulted synchronously, but the lower one has remained larval instead of metamorphosing.
(From Bodenstein, 1953. *J. exp. Zool.* **123**, 189–232.)

the adult characters, whereas at the previous moults it was favouring the realization of the larval ones.

Amongst the results of experiments which support this concept is the demonstration that a fifth-stage larva of *Rhodnius*, decapitated *before* the critical stage and united in parabiosis with a fourth-stage one that has been decapitated *after* the critical stage, will moult but will not metamorphose, a result of the fact that it is under the combined influence of the juvenile hormone and ecdysone from the fourth-stage larva. A similar result has been obtained with the cockroach (Plate XIV B). Conversely, a first-stage larva, decapitated before the critical stage and then united parabiotically with a moulting fifth-stage larva, will not only moult but will undergo metamorphosis to form a small but reasonably well-formed adult (Fig. 129), for it has lacked the influence of the juvenile hormone which would normally have ensured the development of larval features.

That the corpora allata are actually the source of this hormone has been shown by transplantation experiments. The transference of the glands from any of the first to fourth instars into a fifth-stage larva at one day after it has fed will inhibit metamorphosis to a varying degree; sometimes the animal will moult into a 'sixth-stage larva', but often a mixture of larval and adult characters will be developed, clearly depending upon the degree of balance established in the circulating hormonal system. Corpora allata from fifth-stage larvae will, of course, not have this effect, as they are no longer producing their hormone.

It is accepted that this mechanism for regulating the onset of metamorphosis exists in most other groups of insects, holometabolous as well as hemimetabolous, although with variations in detail which we cannot now discuss. In *Hyalophora*, for example, the moult to the pupal stage is determined by a reduction of the secretion of juvenile hormone below the level characteristic of the earlier moults, while the final metamorphic moult of the pupa is determined by the complete absence of the hormone. Arising out of this, it has been shown that the latter is not genus or order specific. For example, the corpora allata of *Periplaneta* and the ring gland of the larva of *Calliphora* will promote some degree of larval characterization in *Rhodnius*. The other properties of this hormone are still under investigation, but it seems clear that its influence is to be regarded as positive rather than negative; that is to say, it does not simply inhibit the appearance of the adult characters but actually promotes the development of the larval ones. This is well shown by the fact that some reversal of metamorphosis can be induced in an adult *Rhodnius* if it is united parabiotically with fifth-stage larvae after these have passed the critical stage, and if it is supplied at the same time with an adequate number of corpora allata from fourth-stage larvae (Fig. 130). Such an animal will moult, and the new cuticle then formed may show a certain degree of larval characterization in, for example, the distribution of pigmentation pattern, a result that not only demonstrates the positive influence of the juvenile hormone derived from the corpora allata but also further illustrates the persistence throughout life of both larval and adult potentialities.

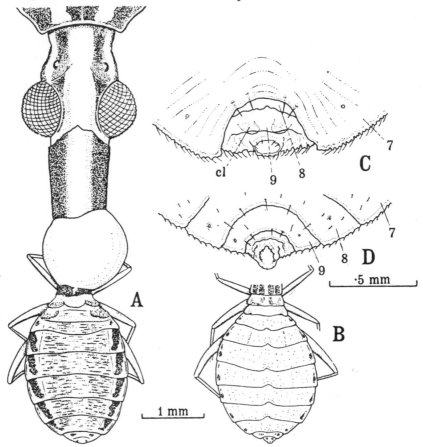

Fig. 129. *A*, Precocious 'adult' *Rhodnius* produced from 1st-stage larva by joining it parabiotically to the head of a moulting 5th-stage larva. *B*, Normal 2nd-stage larva for comparison. *C*, Terminal segments of the precocious 'adult' male. *D*, Terminal segments of a normal 2nd-stage larva. Figures indicate homologous sterna; *cl.* claspers.
(From Wigglesworth, 1934. *Quart. J. micr. Sci.* **77**, 191–222.)

By one of the fortunate chances that sometimes provide an uncovenanted bonus for patient investigators the adult male *Hyalophora* builds up a relatively enormous store of the juvenile hormone in the tissues of its abdomen, as much as 40 per cent. of the wet weight of the latter consisting of ether-extractable lipid as compared with less than 6 per cent. in the female; many other Lepidoptera do this also, but to nothing like the same extent. With material from this source it has been possible to study some of the properties of the hormone, and to show that it is probably a lipid, possibly a steroid, and certainly very stable, for it has been recovered from dried museum specimens. As with other hormones, a sensitive qualitative test is an essential prerequisite for its further study, and one that has recently been introduced depends upon the fact that regenerating epidermis is particularly responsive to the hormone. A small piece of the integument of a pupa of a suitable species is removed, the test substance inserted into the animal, and the wound plugged; the presence of the

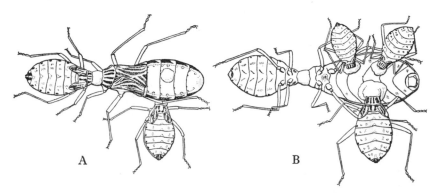

Fig. 130. A, Adult Rhodnius, with wings cut short and corpora allata of 4th-stage larvae implanted in abdomen and joined to two 5th-stage larvae. B, Adult Rhodnius, decapitated and joined to two 5th-stage larvae and two 4th-stage larvae. Adults can be caused to moult by either of these procedures and their cuticle may become partially larval in character.
(From Wigglesworth, 1940. J. exp. Biol. 17, 201-22.)

hormone in the introduced material will be revealed at metamorphosis, for the adult will show a small patch of pupal cuticle at the point of injury.

Using this method, in addition to ordinary injection procedures, Schneiderman and Gilbert have found juvenile hormone activity in beetles, in *Uca*, and in the eye-stalks of *Homarus*, but have obtained negative results with *Palaemonetes vulgaris*, *Carcinus maenas*, and the crayfish *Orconectes immunis*. We have seen that there is some evidence for the presence of an ecdysone-like substance in crustaceans and it would not be altogether surprising, therefore, if a substance resembling another insect hormone were also present. As we have already emphasized, however, it would be unwise to assume that these active substances really are identical until we know something of their molecular structure, and the need for such caution is increased by the discovery that similar activity is also present in ether extracts of a wide range of invertebrates, including Hydrozoa, Polychaeta, Oligochaeta, a holothurian, and the protochordate *Saccoglossus*, and that it is also present in extracts of the adrenocortical tissue of cattle. We are in no position yet to assess these observations, which do not necessarily indicate the presence of identical molecules, but they should be borne in mind against the background of, for example, the wide distribution of biologically active steroids. No doubt the evolution of hormones, like that of the glands that secrete them, has followed many paths, but such facts as these suggest that one of the paths may have involved the utilization of molecules that were abundant but of little biological significance until certain groups of animals became increasingly dependent upon them as a result of incorporating them into some biochemical mechanism. Whether the juvenile hormone has arisen in such a way is, however, a question that future research will have to answer.

6. Hormones in the adult

With the completion of the metamorphic moult there comes a change in the endocrine balance of the animal, for the prothoracic gland and its homologues now disappear; as a result of this, no more moults can occur, the only known exception to this situation being in the Thysanura, which continue to moult throughout life and in which the relevant glands (ventral glands) are consequently retained. The corpora allata, however, do resume activity, and in some insects their presence in the adult is necessary for the maintenance of normal ovarian function. This is the more notable because of the fact that in insects the sex-determining chromosome mechanism retains its primacy throughout development and can determine the sexual organization of all regions of the body without being overridden by the unifying action of endocrine secretions; in this absence of a well-defined system of sex hormones the insects, as we have already emphasized, differ fundamentally from both crustaceans and vertebrates.

In *Rhodnius* resumption of activity in the corpora allata takes place very soon after the adult has fed, and it has been shown that if feeding is prevented, or if the corpora allata are removed by decapitating the animal, the oocytes begin to degenerate immediately prior to the stage at which yolk deposition should be taking place, while in the male the accessory glands do not secrete properly. The normal development of the eggs can be restored in a female that has been so treated by joining it parabiotically with a normal adult, either male or female, which contains intact corpora allata. Moreover, corpora allata from a larva will also produce this alleviation, which suggests that the ovary-regulating hormone of the adult is the same as the juvenile hormone, a conclusion strengthened by the observation that the gland of the adult will inhibit metamorphosis if it is transplanted into a fifth-stage larva.

In other insects, however, the situation is less clear. Normal egg development can certainly take place in some lepidopteran species, for example, in the absence of the corpora allata, although this may merely mean that in these forms some other secretory centre is concerned. Certain results obtained with *Calliphora* provide some support for such a suggestion, for it has been found that in that animal not only the corpora allata but also the neurosecretory cells of the brain, together with the corpus cardiacum, can influence the maintenance of ovarian function.

Finally, we may note that there is some evidence that in insects, as in crustaceans and vertebrates, the hormonal control of growth and moulting is closely interlinked with metabolic effects. The evidence again centres around the corpora allata, which have been said to influence such processes as digestive activity, protein anabolism, oxygen consumption, and the maintenance of normal tissue growth. It is well recognized, however, that it is impossible as yet to say whether such effects are specific ones or are merely the consequences of some generalized influence upon metabolism. Indeed, it has been suggested that the effect of this gland upon the ovary may also be a result of the latter possibility rather than a specific gonadotropic action.

7. Colour change

The pigmentation of insects is a familiar enough sight, but colour change, in the sense in which we have considered it in the vertebrates and crustaceans, does not play an important part in their lives, and responses are usually morphological rather than physiological. As with vertebrates, however, hormonal control plays a part in such changes. The larva of *Acrida turrita*, for example, becomes green in a green and wet meadow, and brown in a dry and yellow one, a morphological colour change that has been shown by implantation experiments to be controlled by the corpora allata. These organs also control the morphological colour change of *Locusta migratoria*, a phenomenon that is associated with phase-polymorphism, implantation of corpora allata into brown *gregaria* larvae producing the green colour of the *solitaria* phase. The stick-insect *Carausius* (*Dixippus*) *morosus*, however, is unusual in showing not only a morphological range of colour from green to brown but also physiological changes within this range. These latter changes are not, however, effected by typical chromatophores, as we have already noted, but by the movement of pigment granules within the epidermal cells (Fig. 131), the dark condition resulting from their migration towards the outer surface of the cells and the light position from their concentration in the deeper regions.

The colour change of this animal is fundamentally an expression of a diurnal rhythm, giving a light colour by day and a dark one by night, but the extent of the reaction depends upon the individual's basic colour. This is determined by the proportions in which the green, orange, and dark brown pigments are present, and the last of these makes the greatest contribution. It is well established that these colour changes are determined by environmental stimuli through the eyes, for if the latter are removed the responses are lost and the rhythm does not develop in insects that are kept in the dark from the time of hatching.

In addition to showing this diurnal rhythm, however, the animal, like amphibians, shows a humidity response, tending to be dark in damp conditions and pale in dry ones, and it has been possible to show that nervous and endocrine factors cooperate in bringing about this reaction. For example, if the abdomen is placed in a moist chamber, but the head and thorax left outside in a dry environment, darkening will normally

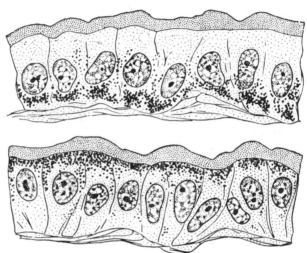

Fig. 131. Intracellular migration of pigment in the hypodermal cells of *Carausius morosus*. *1*, light colour during the day (*above*); *2*, dark colour during the night (*below*).
(From Dupont-Raabe, 1957. *Arch. Zool. exp. gén.* **94,** 61–291.)

begin in the head region and spread over the whole body, but this can be prevented in two ways, either by ligation of the thorax or by section of the central nervous system between the suboesophageal and thoracic ganglia. The first of these operations will result in the backward spread of darkening being arrested at the ligature, presumably because this is preventing the further diffusion of a hormone. The second operation will result in the whole of the anterior region remaining pale, presumably because the normal reaction is mediated by the passage to the brain of nerve impulses arising from receptors in the abdomen. That the capacity for reacting is still present is shown by placing the head end of such an animal into the moist chamber; there is now no barrier to the transmission of nerve impulses from receptors to the brain, and darkening of the head region is immediately initiated.

The hormonal basis of the regulation of colour change in *Carausius* has been studied by Dupont-Raabe, who has obtained evidence from ablation and injection experiments that two hormones may be involved, one located particularly in the tritocerebral region of the brain, where there is cytological evidence for neurosecretory activity, and the other in the corpora cardiaca. The two supposed hormones are not identical in their effects, and this raises the question of the relationship between the corpora cardiaca and the brain, which so far we have interpreted on the basis of the former acting as a release centre for neurosecretion produced in the pars intercerebralis of the latter. That a similar possibility exists also in the present case is shown by Dupont-Raabe's discovery of a third pair of corpora cardiaca nerves, running in this instance from the tritocerebrum, but if these do, in fact, convey a secretory product to the corpora cardiaca it must undergo some further processing there to account for the change in its properties. On the other hand, there appear to be secretory cells in the corpora cardiaca, so that the possibility of them producing their own independent secretion is a very real one.

An additional complication in the interpretation is that the corpora cardiaca do not seem to have any function in determining the normal diurnal colour change. It is clearly established that removal of the deutotritocerebral region of the brain eliminates this response, the animal then taking on a pale grey colour owing to the inward migration of the brown granules, but removal of the pars intercerebralis, or of this together with the corpora cardiaca, has no effect at all. It may be, then, that a secretion of the latter organ is concerned, as Dupont-Raabe has suggested, with the maintenance of an intermediate coloration, or it may have quite other functions, its influence upon colour being an unimportant by-product of these.

The activity associated with the tritocerebral secretion can be detected in other parts of the central nervous system also, more particularly in the suboesophageal ganglion, and it seems possible that this is a result of diffusion or transport of a secretion through the circumoesophageal connectives. It is not clear whether the secretion is released directly from its point of origin in the brain or from other points elsewhere in the nervous system, but it is clear that there is no specialized release centre comparable with those of the crustaceans. The corpora cardiaca would have been expected to fulfil this function, but in this instance their precise role is difficult to interpret.

Although the colour responses of *Carausius* constitute a behaviour pattern unusual amongst insects it would be of the greatest interest to determine how far its hormonal basis shares common features with the Crustacea, and this problem has been investigated by Dupont-Raabe in association with Knowles and Carlisle, who have used for this purpose the techniques of differential extraction and separation to which we have already referred. The results have shown that the corpora cardiaca of *Carausius* contain an A-substance similar to that present in extracts of the sinus gland and post-commissure organs of *Palaemon* (*Leander*) in that it causes contraction of the red pigments of the latter animal. The B-substance of *Palaemon* is not represented in the *Carausius* extracts, but the brain extracts of the latter animal contain a C-substance that is not present in *Palaemon*; it has no effect upon the pigment of that animal, but produces darkening in *Carausius* itself, as would be expected, and concentrates the dark pigments of *Crangon*.

It would seem that the pigment effector systems of these animals may eventually prove to have something in common, but it is again impossible as yet to judge the physiological significance of either the resemblances or the differences in the absence of precise chemical information. It needs to be remembered that the effector cells themselves are quite different in the two groups and having regard to this, and to the early separation of their evolutionary paths which we have commented on earlier, such resemblances as exist between them need cautious evaluation before they can be ascribed to homology.

8. Ectohormones (pheromones)

An aspect of chemical co-ordination in insects which has attracted increasing attention in recent years is the regulation of the responses of individuals by means of secretions which are discharged externally and distributed amongst them. Some writers have referred to these substances as ectohormones, a term which would be acceptable if the term hormone could be understood to carry only the strict meaning of its Greek root (see below, and p. 17). If it is to be understood to imply internal secretion the term ectohormone becomes self-contradictory, and to meet this difficulty the new term pheromone has been introduced as a designation of substances which are excreted to the outside in minute amounts by one individual and received by a second individual of the same species in which they then release a specific reaction. This term was intended to be derived from the two Greek roots, *pherein* (to bear) and *hormaein* (to excite), but the mutilation of the second root unfortunately destroys this derivation, so that the word is somewhat uncomfortable to use.

Following Karlson and Butenandt, we may distinguish between ectohormones which act upon the olfactory receptors of the recipient and those which act through the mouth. The best-known examples in the former category are the sex attractants of Lepidoptera, such as that produced by the female of the silkworm moth, *Bombyx mori*. This substance is secreted by certain abdominal glands, and extracts of these, when presented to the males, will induce in them signs of great excitement, accompanied by erratic dancing and attempts to copulate with the test object.

An example of the second category is the queen substance of the honey-bee, a secretion of the mandibular glands of the queen which is taken up by the workers when they lick her body and which becomes distributed by them through the colony, possibly in the food that they pass from one to another. Its effect is to influence the behaviour of the workers by pre-venting them from constructing queen-cells, while it also inhibits the development of their ovaries; because of this the removal of the queen from the colony results in the initiation of queen-rearing within a few hours, and the inhibition of this reaction has been used by Butler in his studies of this substance as a basis for its quantitative assay. It has now been extracted as a crystalline material, and Callow and Johnston have confirmed by synthesis that it is 9-oxodec-2-enoic acid ($CH_3.CO.[CH_2]_5.CH:CH.COOH$), closely related chemically to the 10-hydroxydec-2-enoic acid which is present in the royal jelly secreted by the mandibular glands of worker bees. It would appear, therefore, that we have here another example of the evolution of substances of different properties from some common molecular pattern. It will not escape notice, either, that there is a certain degree of analogy between the fabrication of orally administered contraceptives by man (p. 126) and the mechanism of sexual regulation practised in the beehive.

At the present time we know too little of any of these substances to be able to judge whether or not they should be included within the general concept of hormones, but it would seem prudent for students of compara-tive endocrinology to keep them within their fields of view. Not only are there many other examples of them amongst insects, such as the marking scents of bees and ants, the queen substance of ants, and the sex-inhibit-ing substances of termites, but the principle of influencing other indi-viduals of a species by the use of secretions is also known in other groups, one suggestive example being provided by the common prawn, *Palaemon* (*Leander*) *serratus*, in which species mating occurs when a female with a ripe ovary possesses a soft cuticle resulting from a recent moult. Males are immediately attracted to such an individual when their antennae have touched her body surface, a result that it is thought may be due to a chemical stimulus emanating from the latter.

We remark elsewhere upon the possible evolutionary significance of reactions to externally transmitted substances, and in this connexion it is worth noting that injection of the queen substance of the honey-bee into prawns has been claimed to inhibit the growth of their ovaries, and extracts of the X organ/sinus gland complex of the latter animals to inhibit ovarian development in bees. This cross-relationship, like others mentioned earlier, needs further investigation, but it is evident that if it could eventually be shown that identical or similar secretions act by internal transmission in one species and by external transmission in another, we should have an effective demonstration of the essential unity of principle underlying the production and evolution of these chemical regulators.

XV. SOME EVOLUTIONARY ASPECTS OF ENDOCRINE SYSTEMS

1. The evolution of hormones

WE are now in a position to judge how fruitful the comparative method has been in yielding up the general principles which we hoped might emerge from its application. One set of problems to which we have made repeated reference revolves around the origin and evolutionary history of hormones, and in this connexion comparisons are often drawn with vitamins, for the two groups of substances resemble each other in being required only in very minute quantities and in influencing the activities of the body without providing energy for them. The obvious difference between them is that in general the hormones can be synthesized from the raw materials provided in the food, whereas vitamins must be made available from external sources, and from this point of view the latter substances have sometimes been referred to as exogenous hormones. This, however, is a simplification which obscures some important considerations.

If we look at this matter with particular reference to the B vitamins, we find these to be a group of substances which are essential at all levels of plant and animal life. This is because they are obligatory components of fundamental biochemical mechanisms which must be almost, if not quite, as old as life itself, and we are able to define their function with some precision because we are able to analyse those mechanisms. The B vitamins can be synthesized by the autotrophic plants, and it has been plausibly suggested that the inability of animals to do so is a consequence of the loss of synthetic capacity during the course of evolution. The dependence of animals upon their hormones, however, seems to be of a character quite different from this, although the distinction is obscured by the fact that while the green plant as a whole can synthesize its requirements of B vitamins, this capacity is not shared equally by all the parts of it. For example, roots are in general unable to synthesize thiamine, and so we find that this substance has to be formed in the leaves and transported down to the roots, where it then exerts a specific physiological effect upon their growth. Thereby it clearly satisfies our formal definition of a hormone.

In so far as we understand the mode of functioning of the hormones of animals, however, these differ fundamentally from the B vitamins in that they do not appear to be essential components of biochemical machinery, for life can often proceed in their absence, even if with reduced efficiency. They seem rather to have been evolved *pari passu* with the development of the increasing complexity of animal organization, and probably with a great deal of independent evolution, at least in the major phyla, although we do not yet know enough to feel sure of this. Their function appears to be to serve as the regulators of specialized reactions rather than as primary components of these, and the difficulties that we encounter in trying to define their individual modes of action are surely a consequence of their relatively late introduction into these complex relationships. There seems here to be some resemblance to the fat-soluble vitamins, which are a characteristic requirement of the vertebrates, and the history of which must therefore have differed from that of the B vitamins. Vitamin A, in fact, offers an interesting parallel with the catechol hormones for, like those substances, it is present in certain invertebrates although its physiological significance in them remains obscure. As regards vitamin D_2, it is of particular interest to find that its molecular structure is based upon the steroid nucleus which has been turned to such profitable use by vertebrates in their endocrine systems. In fact, it is difficult to see why they should be able to synthesize a variety of steroid hormones and yet have to rely upon ultra-violet irradiation for the transformation of 7-dehydro-cholesterol into calciferol. It is possible that this reflects some biochemical limitation in the higher forms, for the accumulation of the vitamin in certain fish shows no obvious correlation with their diet or with their exposure to sunlight, and there is some slight evidence that complete synthesis may occur in this group.

We may consider animal hormones, then, as products of biological progress, a term which we use in the broad sense of an increasing improvement of adaptation leading to an increasing mastery of the environments which have been available for exploitation by animal life. In this connexion we have seen reason to suppose that the evolution of endocrine systems may sometimes have depended on animals making use of molecules which happened, as it were, to be available, either in the external medium or as a result of their own metabolism. The wide distribution of iodine binding, the appearance of which clearly antedated the origin of vertebrates, is one illustration of this possibility, and another suggestive fact is the presence of acetylcholine and adrenaline in *Paramecium*. Even more significant is the wide distribution of the steroid ring system, for its presence in yeasts and in green plants suggests that the wide-ranging possibilities implicit in steroid synthesis had been well sifted before the vertebrates began to exploit them. Indeed, this would seem to follow from the universal distribution of steroids throughout the animal kingdom, and from the fact that a greater variety of them is synthesized in the lower forms than in the higher ones.

Such modes of origin, however, can hardly be applicable to all hormones, for the complex protein secretions of the adenohypophysis seem to be largely peculiar to it, and we have found reason to suspect an entirely different course of events here. It is possible to conceive that this particular organ began as an externally secreting gland, concerned, perhaps, in the type of ecological inter-relationship which we discussed earlier (p. 2), and that its diverse secretions might have arisen by molecular evolution of a protein product that was already complex in character. Insulin, too, and the other hormones of the gastro-intestinal tract might similarly have evolved out of the secretory activity of a primarily digestive epithelium, while thyroglobulin, essential for the biosynthesis of the thyroid hormones, may have evolved out of the secretions of the endostyle.

We can thus see that to ask whether the establishment of endocrine systems has involved the evolution of hormones or merely the evolution of their effects is to raise a question which permits of no simple answer. Hormones are parts of evolving systems and in some instances, as with the thyroid hormones, they seem to have retained a fixed molecular structure while natural selection has modified their relationships with their so-called target organs. In other instances, as notably with the hypothalamic polypeptides, there has equally clearly been an evolution of molecular pattern although we have seen that here, too, the modification of the effects of the hormones must have been an important element in adaptive evolution. In other instances again, as where we find the corticotropins and the melanocyte-stimulating hormones sharing a common sequence of amino acids, we may suspect that hormones have evolved by divergence from some common ancestral pattern of biosynthesis, almost the equivalent at the molecular level of the principle of adaptive radiation. Certainly the potential variability of the structure of the more complex protein hormones provides a basis for natural selection to achieve a close adaptive relationship between the secretion and the effectors that it regulates, and we may look to physico-chemical studies to reveal here an evolutionary picture no less absorbing than that with which we are already familiar at the organismal level (cf. p. 91).

2. The origin of neurohormonal systems

If we turn now to consider the principles that underlie the integration of endocrine systems, we cannot fail to be struck by the important part played by neurosecretory cells in the crustaceans, insects, and vertebrates, the dominant position of these in the two invertebrate classes being such that we must suspect them to be a fundamental and primitive feature of animal organization. This conclusion is not a surprising one, having regard to our present-day knowledge of the functioning of nerve cells, for it is well established that their secretory capacity is as fundamental to them as is their capacity for conducting nerve impulses. This is most easily seen in their production of neurohumours as chemical transmitter substances, but the same principle is probably shown by the way in which certain tissues may be dependent upon their innervation for their development and maintenance. Such, for example, are the muscles of the silkworm moth, which do not develop at all if the pupae are denervated, a result that may very well be due to the lack of some chemical factor normally supplied by the nerve endings.

With such cell relationships as a starting point it is not difficult to visualize the nervous system coming to extend its powers of chemical regulation, and that this may have happened early in evolution is suggested by the fact that cells looking like neurosecretory ones are widespread in the central nervous systems of the lower invertebrates, and particularly in the three major groups of annelid worms. Groups of such cells have been described as occurring in the cerebral ganglia of *Nereis* and *Aphrodite*, and are so abundant in the latter that they are said to occupy almost one-half of those ganglia. They occur also in the cerebral ganglia (Plate xv) of the earthworm (*Lumbricus terrestris*) and molluscs, and in the brain and ventral nerve cord of leeches (Plate xvi). The use of various staining methods, such as the aldehyde-fuchsin, Azan, and periodic acid/Schiff procedures, makes it possible to classify these cells into different categories, but as stainable inclusions can be identified in most of the cells of the brain in some of these annelids it would be unwise to assume that everything which stains in them is necessarily a neurohormonal product.

The evidence does not depend solely, however, on staining reactions. Tracts of neurosecretory fibres can be seen in the ventral nerve cord of the leech (cf. Plate xvi), and section of this results in the accumulation of presumed neurosecretory material at the posterior side of the cut. This implies that there is a movement of this substance forwards from its cells of origin towards the brain, an effect similar to that which has been demonstrated in the neurosecretory systems of arthropods and vertebrates, although there the movement seems normally to be in the opposite direction. We have seen that neurohaemal organs are a characteristic feature of these systems, and what may be a primitive form of such an organ has been described in the polychaete *Nephtys*. In this animal a tract of nerve fibres runs to the base of the supra-oesophageal ganglion (brain) where they are separated from the dorsal blood vessel only by the modified connective tissue sheath and pericapsular membrane (Fig. 132). Although the evidence is still very incomplete, there is some reason for believing that this cerebro-vascular complex, as it has been called, is a site at which neurosecretion is transferred from certain of the nerve fibres into the blood stream.

The evidence is meagre compared with that available for higher groups, but we can feel that there is some justification for suspecting the existence of neurohormonal mechanisms in annelids, although we have only a few

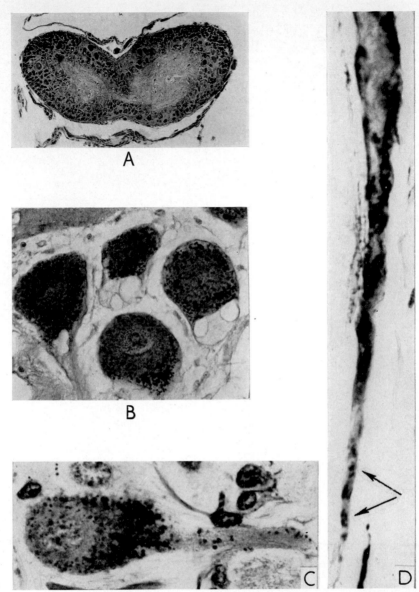

Plate XV. *A*. Section through the cerebral ganglion of the earthworm, *Lumbricus terrestris*. The numerous neurosecretory cells are conspicuous by their darker coloration. (Zenker-formol, chrome-alum-haematoxylin, and phloxine.ʻ ×66.)

B. Neurosecretory cells from the cerebral ganglion of the opisthobranch snail, *Aplysia limacina*. Note dark-staining secretory granules in the characteristic large nucleolus. (Bouin, C.A.H., and phloxine. ×580.)

C. Neurosecretory cell from the suboesophageal ganglion of the insect, *Leucophaea maderae*. Numerous granules are seen in the cell body and extend into the axon. (Zenker-formol, C.A.H., and phloxine. ×725.)
(From Scharrer & Scharrer, 1954. *Rec. Prog. Horm. Res.* **10**, 183–240.)

D. An axon associated with the urohypophysis (urophysis spinalis) of the eel, *Anguilla rostrata*. Neurosecretory materials are present, forming both clusters and granules (arrows). (Bouin, Heidenhain's haematoxylin. ×225.)
(From Holmgren, 1959. *Anat. Rec.* **135**, 51–60.)

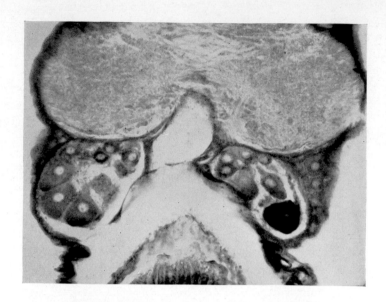

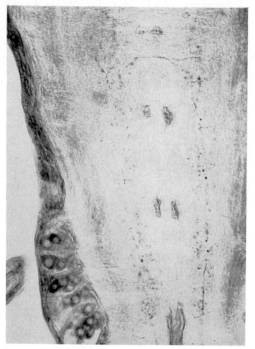

Plate XVI. *A*. Frontal section through the supra-oesophageal ganglion of the leech, *Theromyzon rude*. The dorsal commissure is at the top, partly surrounding the sub-commissural blood vessel, at the sides of which are seen two of the 36 compartments of cells which make up the supra-oesophageal and suboesophageal ganglia. The neurosecretory cell at the extreme right has contents which are intensely stained with aldehyde-fuchsin and which extend into the axon. (× 324.)

B. Frontal section through the suboesophageal ganglion of the same species. Axons containing neurosecretory material which stains with aldehyde-fuchsin form two well-defined tracts of fibres, one on each side of the mid-line. (× 276.)

(From Hagadorn, 1958. *J. Morph.* **102**, 55–90.)

clues to their possible functions. Of particular interest, bearing in mind
what we have seen above regarding the organization of the annelid brain,
is evidence that this organ influences sexual maturation in the polychaete
Perinereis. It is said that removal of the brain in this animal results in the
transformation of the individual into the sexually mature heteronereid
stage, regardless of its previous state of development, while reimplantation
of the brain into such individuals results in many of them remaining
sexually immature. These observations have been interpreted as evidence
for the production of an inhibitory hormone by the neurosecretory cells

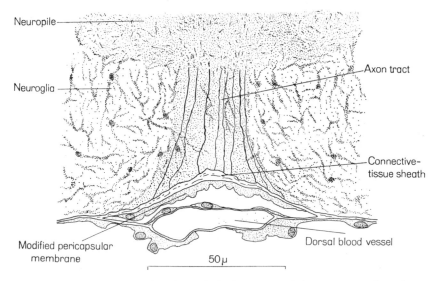

Fig. 132. Transverse section through the lower part of the supra-oesophageal
ganglion of *Nephtys caeca*, showing the cerebro-vascular complex.
(From Clark, 1959. *Zool. Jahrb. At. Allg. Zool. Physiol.* **68**, 395–424.)

of the brain, and it is claimed also that certain cells are responsible at the
onset of sexual maturity for transmitting some product to the surface of
the body where, it is suggested, it may act as an ectohormone, serving
the function of sexual attraction.

There is also evidence that such brain cells may influence the regeneration of posterior segments after the amputation of the hind end of the
animal, for it has been found that such caudal regeneration is totally
inhibited in earthworms if the supra-oesophageal ganglion is removed at
the time of the amputation. A similar situation exists in *Nereis diversicolor*,
for removal of this ganglion before amputation of the posterior segments
inhibits the regeneration of new ones so that at most only a new pygidium
is formed. If the ganglion is removed three days after the amputation there
results a retardation of regeneration, although the formation of new

segments is not now entirely inhibited (Fig. 133). Confirmatory evidence that the supra-oesophageal ganglion has an important role to play in regeneration, at least in the early stages of this process, can be seen in the

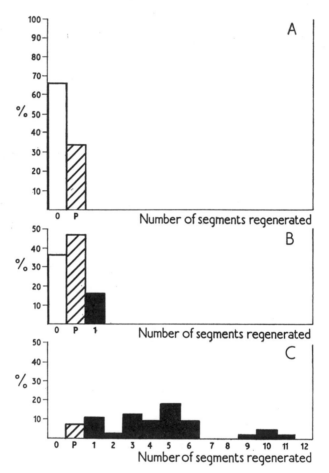

Fig. 133. Number of segments regenerated by *Nereis diversicolor* during thirty days after amputation of posterior segments. *A*, Supra-oesophageal ganglion removed one day before amputation. *B*, Ganglion removed three days after amputation. *C*, Ganglion intact. *O*, no regeneration; *P*, pygidium only regenerated.
(From Clark & Bonney, 1960. *J. Embryol. exp. Morph.* **8**, 112–18.)

fact that amputation of posterior segments from an otherwise intact *Nereis* is followed after about twelve hours by an increase in the amount of neurosecretion in certain of the ganglion cells. It is said, too, that the passage of neurosecretion through the cerebro-vascular complex of *Nephtys* into the blood stream is particularly evident when such regeneration is in progress.

It may well be that further exploration of such situations would shed a good deal of light on the early evolution of neurohormonal systems such as we find so well established in crustaceans, insects, and vertebrates. These must have evolved independently, as least as far as the arthropods and vertebrates are concerned, and quite possibly within the arthropods themselves. Indeed, the situation in the central nervous system of fish shows how such a pattern can develop independently in different parts of

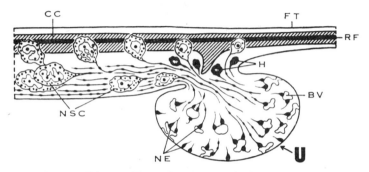

Fig. 134. Diagram illustrating the organization of the caudal neurosecretory system (urohypophysis, or urophysis spinalis, *U*) of a teleost fish. *BV*, blood vessel; *CC*, central canal of spinal cord; *FT*, filum terminale; *H*, Herring body; *NE*, nerve ending; *NSC*, neurosecretory cells; *RF*, Reissner's fibre.
(From Enami, 1959. *Comparative Endocrinology*, ed. Gorbman. Wiley.)

the same body. The existence of large cells of neurosecretory type in the spinal cord of these animals has long been known, and it is now apparent that there are accumulations of these at the hind end where they give rise in teleosts to a system that is called the urohypophysis, or urophysis spinalis (Fig. 134), and that is thought possibly to be involved in osmoregulation. The neurosecretion is discharged down axons (Plate XV) into storage centres that form conspicuous ventral swellings of the cord, and the parallelism of organization, both structural and ultra-structural, with that of the cephalic neurohypophyseal system is a very striking one.

In our search for common principles underlying the evolution of the major neurosecretory systems we may take note of evidence that they have been associated with the body surface and with a receptor organ. This certainly seems to apply to the sensory pore X organ of crustaceans, which, as argued by Hanström, appears to represent the transformed receptor cells of a sensory pore or papilla. The same may be true of the secretory cells of the pars intercerebralis of insects, for in the Apterygota these are said to be represented by a group of cells lying dorsal to the brain and separate from it, and corresponding in position with the lateral frontal organs of the lower crustaceans; from these cells, which have contents staining with chrome-alum-haematoxylin, arise axons that pass through the brain to enter the corpora cardiaca.

A closely comparable situation appears to exist in the gephyrean *Sipunculus nudus*; presumed neurosecretory cells in the brain of this animal give off axons that run to the unpaired sensory organ, a hollow structure which opens to the outside in the proboscis region by a ciliated canal. Here the axons make loops amongst the sensory cells, and then end in close relation to blood vessels in a manner which Carlisle describes as typical of neurohaemal nerve endings.

Lastly, of course, we have seen evidence that the pituitary gland must almost certainly have evolved out of a sensory pit, which seems to be a fundamental characteristic of the earliest chordates, but it should be noted that here the presumed sensory component (the future adenohypophysis) remains functionally distinct from the source of the neurosecretion (hypothalamus), in a manner more akin to the situation in *Sipunculus* than that in crustaceans and insects.

It is not yet possible to bring these facts together into a single pattern, if, indeed, such a pattern exists. Some believe that neurosecretory cells have evolved within the nervous system out of the inherent secretory capacity of the neuron. Others would argue that they have evolved independently from secretory cells in the ependyma, or even in the ectoderm, from which, of course, the nervous system itself is derived, and from which, perhaps, it has inherited its own secretory capacity. However this may be, Carlisle has suggested that some general principle dictates the development of a major endocrine centre around a receptor organ that is associated with the brain, and we have touched earlier on the possibility that such a receptor organ might have been responsible, perhaps by means of its own secretions, for evoking responses to ectohormones or other exogenous stimuli. Thereafter, it might conceivably have become sensitive to endogenous stimuli, and so have evolved into an organ that was purely internal and endocrine in its functional relationships.

3. The activity cycle of *Periplaneta*

An elegant demonstration of the subtlety of the relationships which can exist between a receptor system and a neurosecretory centre has emerged from Harker's studies of the activity cycle of the cockroach, *Periplaneta americana*. In an environment in which there is a regular twelve-hour alternation of light and darkness it is possible to distinguish in this cycle six stages (Fig. 135), the significant one from our present point of view being the period of high activity which sets in shortly after the beginning of darkness, and which lasts for two to three hours. This rhythm is reversed if the alternation of light and darkness is reversed, while it is disturbed or abolished if the animal is exposed to continuous

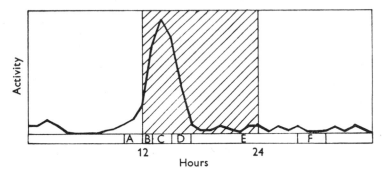

Fig. 135. The six stages of the locomotor activity rhythm of *Periplaneta americana* in alternating light and darkness. Hatched area represents dark period.
(From Harker, 1960. *J. exp. Biol.* **37**, 154–63.)

light or darkness, the receptors concerned being probably the ocelli. The rhythm is also lost after decapitation, although the animal may remain active for ten days in this condition; if, however, suboesophageal ganglia are implanted into decapitated individuals the latter will develop a rhythm similar to that of the donors. Neurosecretory cells are present in those ganglia (cf. Plate xv C), and it is believed that the activity cycle is regulated by the rhythmic discharge from these of a hormone. Amongst confirmatory evidence for this may be mentioned experiments in which an animal that had lost its rhythm through being exposed to continuous light was united parabiotically with a normal one in such a way that it carried the latter on its back (cf. Plate xiv B); it then displayed an activity rhythm corresponding with that of the normal animal (Fig. 136), a result that was presumed to be due to a hormonal factor distributed through the body fluids or, conceivably, through the tissues.

This, however, is not the whole story, as is shown by the following observations, which start from the fact that cockroaches that have been made arrhythmic by exposure to continuous light or darkness can be made rhythmic again by the implantation of suboesophageal ganglia from normally rhythmic animals. Harker developed a technique which made it possible to lower the temperature of the suboesophageal ganglia to 3°C without affecting the temperature of the rest of the body. If this cooling is maintained for four hours and the ganglia are then removed and implanted into arrhythmic animals it is found that the latter develop a rhythm that is delayed for four hours by comparison with that of unchilled animals (Fig. 137); that is to say, the maximum activity occurs at about six hours after the onset of darkness instead of at the usual two hours. If, however, the chilled ganglia are returned to normal temperature after four hours, but are left in their normal position in the animal to which they belong, it is found that the activity rhythm of the latter does not show this delay. The suggested explanation of these results, and of other relevant data, is that the phases of the neurosecretory cycle are delayed by chilling, but that the phases of a second cycle, in which the nervous system is in some way involved, are immediately reset by the change from light to darkness. This

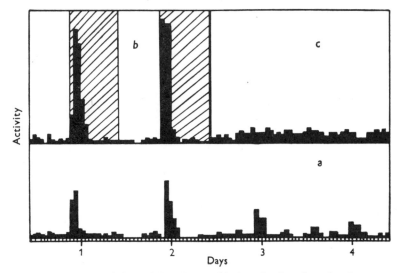

Fig. 136. The activity of a parabiotic pair of cockroaches in continuous light. The lower (mobile) cockroach had previously been in continuous light and had shown the arrhythmic activity recorded in (c), the upper cockroach had previously been in alternating light and darkness and had shown the rhythm of activity recorded in (b). Dark periods hatched.
(From Harker, 1956. *J. exp. Biol.* **33**, 224–34.)

neutralizes the effect of the chilling in the intact animal in the second of the above two experiments, but is unable to do so in the first type of experiment because the ganglia are removed before they can come under the influence of this second cycle.

A further subtlety is that the second cycle can only influence the neuro-secretory one at a time within three or four hours of the time of the previous onset of darkness; at all other times the neurosecretory cells are un-responsive. Harker points out that the practical advantage of this to the animal is that the second cycle can serve to reset the activity cycle rhythm in relation to changes in the length of the day but will not be free to disturb the rhythm by allowing it to be influenced by abnormal illumination during the night. For example, a change from light to darkness on, say, a bright moonlight night could quite conceivably reset the second rhythm; if this rhythm were then able to reset the activity rhythm the latter would be in danger of becoming completely out of phase with the normal sequence of day and night. This, however, is prevented from happening because the period during which the activity rhythm can be so reset is strictly limited.

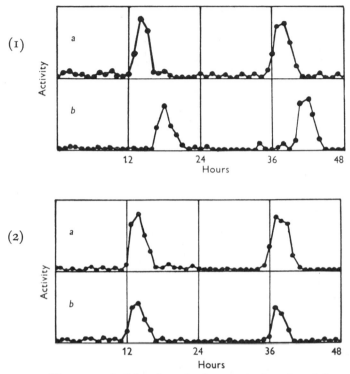

Fig. 137. 1. Activity of previously arrhythmic cockroach into which had been implanted suboesophageal ganglia taken from (a) normally rhythmic cockroaches, (b) cockroaches in which the ganglion had been chilled for 4 hours. 2. (a) Activity of cockroaches in which suboesophageal ganglia had been chilled for 4 hours. (b) Activity of previously arrhythmic cockroaches into which the suboesophageal ganglia taken from (a) were implanted 24 hours after chilling.
(From Harker, 1960. *J. exp. Biol.* **37**, 164–70.)

There could hardly be a better example of the interplay of exogenous and endogenous factors in the regulation of short-term rhythms; the principles involved, which are closely analogous with those which we have discussed in connexion with the long-term sexual rhythms of vertebrates, demonstrate clearly the close interdependence of neural and endocrine regulation, and the particular value of neurosecretory systems presumably lies in the way in which they facilitate this.

TABLE 6

Examples of different types of interrelationship in endocrine systems (partly after B. Scharrer).

Source	First order effects on:	Second order effects on:	Third order effects on:
X organ/sinus gland ⟶	Chromatophore activation		
hypothalamus/neuro-hypophysis ⟶	milk ejection; ⟶ anti-diuresis		
X organ/sinus gland ⟶	inhibition of Y organ	initiation of moult after removal of inhibition of Y organ	
pars intercerebralis/ corpora cardiaca →	activation of prothoracic gland ⟶	initiation of moult	
hypothalamus/neuro-hypophysis ⟶	pars intermedia →	chromatophore activation	
hypothalamus ⟶	pars distalis →	adrenocortical tissue ⟶	water; salt-electro-lytes: etc.
hypothalamus ⟶	pars distalis →	thyroid gland ⟶	metabolism, etc.
hypothalamus ⟶	pars distalis →	gonads (endocrine cells) ⟶	sex characters, etc.

4. Interrelationships of endocrine systems

It will be appreciated that such comparisons and speculations as these are difficult to formulate in detail in the imperfect state of our present knowledge, and that their chief value at this stage lies in the stimulus that they can give to the planning of further investigations. We may conclude, however, by examining briefly the types of functional relationships in which these neurohormonal systems are involved. Examples of these, some better established than others, are illustrated in Table 6, from which it may be seen that they comprise causal chains of varying lengths, corresponding to what Scharrer has described as systems of the first order, second order, and third order.

First order systems are those in which the secretory and release components of the neurosecretory complex discharge a hormone that acts directly upon its target tissues, and examples are the chromatophore responses evoked by the X organ/sinus gland complex and the milk ejection response evoked by the hypothalamus/neurohypophysis complex.

Second order systems are those in which the complex discharges a hormone that acts upon another endocrine gland, this then evoking a response in its target tissue. Examples are the moult-initiation action of the pars intercerebralis/corpora cardiaca complex, mediated through the prothoracic gland, and the chromatophore responses evoked by the pars intermedia, assuming that the latter is regulated by the hypothalamus/neurohypophysis complex, although this has yet to be clarified. Thus we see that colour change may be regulated in the vertebrates through a second order system while in the crustaceans it is regulated through a first order one. We see too, that the second order system which controls the initiating of the moult in insects is a stimulating (or positive) one, while in crustaceans the corresponding system, although also a second order one, exerts an inhibiting (or negative) action. Such comparisons could usefully be extended to all the systems that we have studied, but it will suffice now to note only one further example, that of the pars distalis, the tropic effects of which differ from those that we have so far enumerated in constituting a third order system.

The significance of such differences, like that of the ones previously discussed, is that they present a warning against allowing these fascinating similarities of pattern to blind us to differences that may be of the greatest importance in the final analysis of function. In this connexion it is particularly instructive to examine an illustration provided by work on the molluscs, a group which stands closer to the arthropods than to the vertebrates but which is remote from both. We now know from the work of M. J. Wells that the maturation of the gonads in *Octopus* is regulated by the optic glands, paired structures lying on the optic stalks on either side of the brain (Fig. 138). Prior to sexual maturity the secretory activity of these glands is inhibited by a controlling system which is neural rather than neurosecretory, as is shown by its localized action, for if the optic nerve is cut on one side there results an enlargement of the gland on that side, while the gland on the other side is unaffected. The eventual onset of sexual maturity, whether this be normal or induced by experimental treatment, is preceded by an enlargement of the optic glands resulting from a release of this inhibition; they then discharge a gonadotropic secretion which influences the gonads after transmission through the blood stream.

Transection experiments in these animals have shown that the inhibitory nerve supply originates in the subpedunculate lobes (Fig. 138) situated in the supra-oesophageal region of the brain mass, for a central lesion involving these lobes results in an increase in the secretory activity of the optic glands and a rapid enlargement of the ovary (Fig. 139). Here, then, as in the other groups that we have just considered, sexual maturation is under the control of the higher nerve centres, but the interesting difference is that there is no indication that neurosecretory nerves are concerned in *Octopus*. Evidently, therefore, nature does not always work through similar sets of blueprints, and it is prudent not to assume too confidently the existence of a particular type of design until this has actually been proved to exist.

This is not, of course, an argument against the comparative method as such, but merely a warning to show the caution with which it should be used. Indeed, it must be hoped that its value has by now been sufficiently demonstrated to justify us in ending our argument, as we began, with William Harvey, who once remarked that if only anatomists 'had been

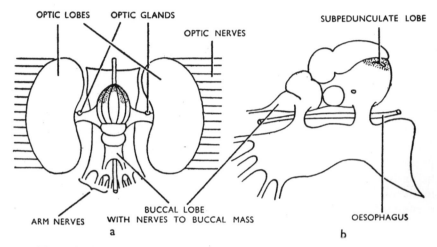

Fig. 138. Anatomy of the brain of *Octopus*. (*a*) As it would be seen from above after removal of the cartilage surrounding the central mass, and (*b*) in vertical longitudinal section. In an animal of 500 g the supra-oesophageal part of the brain would be about 4 mm long. The subpedunculate lobe is stippled in both diagrams.

(From Wells, 1960. *Symp. Zool. Soc. Lond.* **2,** 87–107.)

as conversant with the dissection of the lower animals as they are with that of the human body, many matters that have hitherto kept them in a perplexity of doubt would, in my opinion, have met them freed from every kind of difficulty'. Biologists will not doubt the fundamental truth of this, even when they find difficulties to be more in evidence than the prospect of overcoming them, as may sometimes seem to be true of comparative endocrinology at the present time. Such difficulties are not, however, to be regretted; rather should they be readily accepted as an indication that the subject is growing up, and welcomed as a tribute to the range and penetration of the investigations that are contributing to its maturation. Perhaps, too, they are not ill-suited to a period in which, according to one contemporary observer, 'a worried frown has replaced the lifted eyebrow as the proper expression for pundits'.

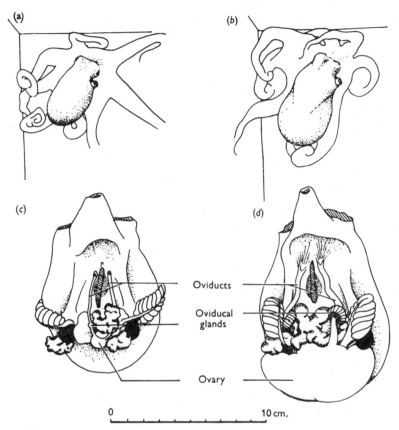

Oviducts

Oviducal
glands

Ovary

0   10 cm.

Fig. 139. Experimental modification of the condition of the ovary in *Octopus*.
(*a*) Unoperated female, and (*c*) the same dissected to show the contents of the
mantle cavity. (*b*) animal in which a central brain lesion including the subpedunculate lobe had been made, and (*d*) the same dissected; note the enlargement of the ovary and oviducts.
(From Wells and Wells, 1959. *J. exp. Biol.* **36,** 1–33.)

SUGGESTIONS FOR FURTHER READING

THESE suggestions are intended to provide paths of entry into the more specialist literature and are therefore restricted mainly to books, reviews, and reports of symposia, all of which contain extensive bibliographies. Many of them are relevant to several chapters but is has seemed unnecessary to mention them more than once.

References are occasionally given to individual research papers, either because the work with which they are concerned is particularly prominent in the text or because they are too recent to have found their way yet into reviews. Many such references will also be found in the legends to text figures and plate figures, and it should be noted that these are not usually repeated in the separate reading lists; they therefore constitute what is, in effect, an additional bibliography.

References to individual articles and chapters in such comprehensive works as *Marshall's Physiology of Reproduction* and the *Memoirs of the Society of Endocrinology* are not exhaustive. Much of the contents of these and other volumes of similar scope are relevant to the problems discussed in this book, and it is hoped that the reader will regard mention of them as an invitation to personal exploration.

General

BALDWIN, E. 1952. *Dynamic Aspects of Biochemistry*. Cambridge: University Press.

BELL, G. H. *et al.* 1961. *Textbook of Physiology and Biochemistry*, 5th edn. London: Livingstone.

BUDDENBROCK, W. VON. 1950. *Vergleichende Physiologie*. Bd. IV: *Hormone*. Birkhäuser Verlag.

DALE, H. H. 1953. *Adventures in Physiology*. London: Pergamon.

—— 1954. *An Autumn Gleaning*. London: Pergamon.

DODDS, C. 1957. *Biochemical Contributions to Endocrinology*. Stanford: University Press.

GARDINER-HILL, H. (ed.) 1958. *Modern Trends in Endocrinology*. London: Butterworths.

GORBMAN, A. (ed.) 1959. *Comparative Endocrinology*. New York: Wiley.

GREEP, R. O. 1954. *Histology*. London: Churchill.

HANSTRÖM, B. 1939. *Hormones in Invertebrates*. Oxford: Clarendon Press.

HARINGTON, C. R. 1946. 'The scientific foundations of endocrinology'. *J. Endocrin.* **5**, Proc., ii-xi.

HARRIS, G. W. 1955. *Neural Control of the Pituitary Gland*. London: Arnold.

HECHTER, O. 1955. 'Concerning possible mechanisms of hormone action.' *Vitamins & Hormones* **13**, 293–346.

KLYNE, W. 1957. *The Chemistry of Steroids*. London: Methuen.

PEARSE, A. G. E. 1960. *Histochemistry: Theoretical and Applied*. London: Churchill.

PICKFORD, G. E. & ATZ, J. W. 1957. *The Physiology of the Pituitary Gland of Fishes*. New York: Zoological Society.

PINCUS, G. & THIMANN, K. (eds.) 1948–55. *The Hormones*. Vols. 1–3. New York: Academic Press.

TAKEWAKI, K. (ed.) 1962. *Progress in Comparative Endocrinology. Gen. comp. Endocrin. Supplement I.*

WILLIAMS, P. C. & AUSTIN, C. R. (eds.) *Cell Mechanisms in Hormone Production and Action. Mem. Soc. Endocrin.* **11.**

Chapter I

GIESE, A. A. 1959. 'Annual reproductive cycle of marine invertebrates.' *Ann. Rev. Physiol.* **21**, 547–76.

GLINOS, A. D. 1958. 'The mechanism of liver growth and regeneration.' In *The Chemical Basis of Development*, ed. McElroy, W. D. & Glass, Bentley. Baltimore: Johns Hopkins Press.

LOOMIS, W. L. 1959. 'Feedback control of growth and differentiation by carbon dioxide tension and related metabolic variables.' In *Cell, Organism and Milieu*, ed. Rudnick, D. New York: Ronald Press Company.

LUCAS, C. E. 1949. 'External metabolites and ecological adaptation.' *Symp. Soc. Exp. Biol.* **3**, 336–56.

—— 1955. 'External metabolites in the sea.' In *Papers in Marine Biology and Oceanography* (*Deep Sea Research* **3**, suppl.)

PANTIN, C. F. A. 1950. In 'Discussion on morphology and fine structure. *Proc. Linn. Soc. Lond.* **162**, 65–67.

PANTIN, C. F. A. 1951. 'Organic design.' *Adv. Sci.* **8**, 138–50.

POWELL, A. (ed.) 1949. *John Aubrey's Brief Lives and other selected Writings*. London: Cresset Press.

WEST, L. B. 1960. 'The nature of growth-inhibiting material from crowded *Rana pipiens* tadpoles.' *Physiol. Zool.* **33**, 232–39.

WILLIS, R. 1847. *The Works of William Harvey* (transl.). London: Sydenham Society.

Chapter II

BABKIN, B. P. 1950. *Secretory Mechanism of the Digestive Glands*, 2nd edn. New York: Hoeber.

BARRINGTON, E. J. W. 1957. 'The alimentary canal and digestion.' In *The Physiology of Fishes*, ed. Brown, M. E. New York: Academic Press.

BROCKLEHURST, R. J. 1950. 'Hormones of the digestive tract.' *Adv. Sci.* **9**, 197–206.

BROWN, L. 1957. 'Chemical transmission at nerve endings.' *Adv. Sci.* **14**, 103–8.

GROSSMAN, M. I. 1950. 'Gastrointestinal hormones.' *Physiol. Rev.* **30**, 33–90.

—— 1958. 'The physiology of secretin.' *Vitamins & Hormones.* **16**, 179–203.

HOYLE, G. 1957. *Comparative Physiology of the Nervous Control of Muscular Contraction.* Cambridge: University Press.

NICOL, J. A. C. 1952. 'Autonomic nervous systems in lower chordates.' *Biol. Rev.* **27**, 1–49.

PAVLOV, I. P. 1910. *The Work of the Digestive Glands* (transl. W. H. Thompson), 2nd English edn. London: Griffith & Co.

THOMAS, J. E. 1950. *The External Secretion of the Pancreas.* Springfield, Illinois: C. C. Thomas.

WOODWARD, E. R. & DRAGSTEDT, L. R. 1960. 'Role of the pyloric antrum in regulation of gastric secretion.' *Physiol. Rev.* **40**, 490–504.

Chapter III

ANFINSEN, B. 1959. *The Molecular Basis of Evolution.* New York: Wiley.

BEHRENS, O. K. & BROMER, W. W. 1958. 'Glucagon.' *Vitamins & Hormones.* **16**, 264–301.

BENSLEY, R. R. 1911. 'Studies on the pancreas of the guinea-pig.' *Amer. J. Anat.* **12**, 297–388.

BEST, C. H. 1959. 'A Canadian trail of medical research'. *J. Endocrin.* **19**, *Proc.* i–xvii.

GOMORI, G. 1943. 'Pathology of the pancreatic islets.' *Arch. Path.* **36**, 217–32.

HOUSSAY, B. A. 1959. 'Comparative physiology of the endocrine pancreas.' In *Comparative Endocrinology*, ed. Gorbman, A. New York: Wiley.

LANGERHANS, P. 1869. 'Beiträge zur mikroskopischen Anatomie der Bauchspeicheldrüse.' Reprinted in *Bull. Inst. Hist. Med.* **5**, 259.

LI, C. H. 1956. 'Pituitary growth hormone as a metabolic hormone.' *Science.* **123**, 617–19.

MILLER, M. R. & WURSTER, D. H. 1958. 'The morphology and physiology of the pancreatic islets in urodele amphibians and lizards.' In *Comparative Endocrinology*, ed. Gorbman, A. New York: Wiley.

STEVENSON, LLOYD. 1947. *Sir Frederick Banting*, 2nd edn. London: Heinemann.

VARIOUS AUTHORS. 1956. *Internal Secretions of the Pancreas. Ciba Foundation Colloquia in Endocrinology.* **9.**

YOUNG, F. G. (ed.) 1960. *Insulin. Brit. Med. Bull.* **16,** 175–259.

Chapter IV

BARGMANN, W. 1960. 'The neurosecretory system of the diencephalon.' *Endeavour,* **19,** 125–33.

FOLLEY, S. J. 1952. 'Aspects of pituitary-mammary gland relationships.' *Rec. Prog. Horm. Res.* **7,** 107, 137.

—— 1956. *The Physiology and Biochemistry of Lactation.* Edinburgh: Oliver & Boyd.

FOTHERLEY, K. *et al.* (eds.) 1960. *Progress in Endocrinology. Part I: Neuroendocrinology and Endocrinology of the Thyroid and Parathyroid Glands. Mem. Soc. Endocrin.* **9.**

HELLER, H. 1945. 'The effect of neurohypophysial extracts on the water balance of lower vertebrates.' *Biol. Rev.* **20,** 147–58.

—— (ed.) 1957. *The Neurohypophysis.* London: Butterworths.

O'CONNOR, W. J. 1947. 'The control of urine secretion in mammals by the pars nervosa of the pituitary.' *Biol. Rev.* **22,** 30–53.

ROBERTSON, J. D. 1957. 'The habitat of the early vertebrates.' *Biol. Rev.* **32,** 156–87.

SAWYER, W. H. 1961. 'Neurohypophysial hormones.' *Pharmacol. Rev.* **13,** 225–77.

—— 1961. 'Comparative physiology and pharmacology of the neurohypophysis.' *Rec. Prog. Horm. Res.* **17,** 437–65.

SCHARRER, E. & SCHARRER, B. 1945. 'Neurosecretion.' *Physiol Rev.* **25,** 171–81.

SLOPER, J. C. 1958. 'Hypothalamo-neurohypophysial neurosecretion.' *Int. Rev. Cyt.* **7,** 337–89.

VARIOUS AUTHORS. 1958. 'A discussion on the physiology and biochemistry of lactation.' *Proc. Roy. Soc.* B **149,** 301–424.

WELSH, J. H. 1959. 'Neuroendocrine substances.' In *Comparative Endocrinology,* ed. Gorbman, A. New York: Wiley.

Chapter V

ALLEN, E. (ed.) 1939. *Sex and Internal Secretions.* London: Baillière, Tindall & Cox.

ASDELL, S. A. 1946. *Patterns of Mammalian Reproduction.* New York: Comstock.

BULLOUGH, W. S. 1951. *Vertebrate Sexual Cycles.* London: Methuen.

COLE, H. H. & CUPPS, P. T. 1959. *Reproduction in Domestic Animals.* Vols. 1 & 2. New York: Academic Press.

ENGLE, L. L. 1959. 'Mechanism of action of estrogens.' *Vitamins & Hormones.* **17**, 205–22.

GASSNER, F. X. *et al.* 1958. 'Effect of hormones on growth, fattening, and meat production potential of livestock.' *Rec. Prog. Horm. Res.* **14**, 183–219.

HALL, K. 1960. 'Relaxin.' *J. Reproduc. Fert.*, **1**, 368–84.

HEDIGER, H. 1950. *Wild Animals in Captivity.* London: Butterworths.

LLOYD, C. W. (ed.) 1959. *Recent Progress in the Endocrinology of Reproduction.* New York: Academic Press.

LYONS, W. R. *et al.* 1958. 'The hormonal control of mammary growth and lactation.' *Rec. Prog. Horm. Res.* **14**, 219–54.

PARKES, A. S. (ed.) 1952-60. *Marshall's Physiology of Reproduction.* Vol. 1, parts 1 & 2; Vol. 2. London: Longmans.

PINCUS, G. 1959. 'Progestational agents and the control of fertility.' *Vitamins & Hormones* **17**, 307–24.

Chapter VI

AMOROSO, E. C. 1955. 'Endocrinology of pregnancy.' *Brit. Med. Bull.* **11**, 117–25.

AUSTIN, C. E. (ed.) 1960. *Sex Differentiation and Development. Mem. Soc. Endocrin.* **7**.

BEACH, F. A. 1948. *Hormones and Behaviour.* New York: Hoeber.

CHESTER JONES, I. & ECKSTEIN, P. (eds.) 1955. *Comparative Physiology of Reproduction. Mem. Soc. Endocrin.* **4**.

DODD, J. M. *et al.* 1960. 'Reproductive endocrinology in cyclostomes and elasmobranchs.' *Symp. Zool. Soc. Lond.* **1**, 77–103.

EISNER, ERICA. 1960. 'The relationship of hormones to the reproductive behaviour of birds, referring especially to parental behaviour: a review.' *Animal Behaviour,* **8**, 155–79.

GRUMBACH, M. M. & Barr, M. L. 1958. 'Cytological tests of chromosomal sex in relation to sexual anomalies in man.' *Rec. Prog. Horm. Res.* **14**, 255–334.

HISAW, F. L. 1959. 'Endocrine adaptations of the mammalian estrous cycle and gestation.' In *Comparative Endocrinology*, ed. Gorbman, A. New York: Wiley.

MARSHALL, A. J. 1960. 'The environment, cyclical reproductive activity and behaviour in birds.' *Symp. Zool. Soc. Lond.* **2**, 53–67.

VAN OORDT, P. G. W. J. 1960. 'The influence of internal and external factors in the regulation of the spermatogenetic cycle in amphibia.' *ibid.*, 29–52.

WADDINGTON, C. H. 1960. *The Ethical Animal.* London: Allen & Unwin.

WATTERSON, R. L. (ed.) 1959. *Endocrines in Development*. Chicago: University of Chicago.

WITHROW, R. B. (ed.) 1959. *Photoperiodism*. Washington, D.C.

WOLFSON, A. 1959. 'Ecological and physiological factors in the regulation of spring migration and reproductive cycles in birds.' In *Comparative Endocrinology*, ed. Gorbman, A. New York: Wiley.

Chapter VII

BARRINGTON, E. J. W. 1959. 'Some endocrinological aspects of the Protochordata.' In *Comparative Endocrinology*, ed. Gorbman, A. New York: Wiley.

BERRILL, N. J. 1953. *The Origin of Vertebrates*. Oxford: Clarendon Press.

BROWN-GRANT, K. *et al.* 1954. 'The measurement and experimental modification of thyroid activity in the rabbit.' *J. Physiol.* **126**, 1–28.

FOTHERLEY, K. *et al.* (eds.) 1960. *Progress in Endocrinology. Part I. Neuroendocrinology and Endocrinology of the Thyroid and Parathyroid Glands. Mem. Soc. Endocrin.* **9**.

GROSS, J. 1957. 'The dynamic cytology of the thyroid gland.' *Int. Rev. Cyt.* **6**, 265–88.

HARINGTON, C. R. 1933. *The Thyroid Gland, its Chemistry and Physiology*. London: Oxford University Press.

—— 1946. 'The scientific foundations of endocrinology.' *J. Endocrin.* **5**, *Proc.* ii–xi.

HOFFERT, J. R. & FROMM, P. O. 1959. 'Estimation of thyroid secretion rate of rainbow trout using radioactive iodine.' *J. cell. comp. Physiol.* **54**, 163–69.

LELOUP, J. & FONTAINE, M. 1960. 'Iodine metabolism in lower vertebrates.' In 'Modern concepts of thyroid physiology'. *Ann. N.Y. Acad. Sci.* **86**, 316–53.

MYANT, N. B. (ed.) 1960. *The Thyroid Gland. Brit. Med. Bull.* **16**, 89–169.

PITT-RIVERS, R. & TATA, J. R. 1959. *The Thyroid Hormones*. London: Pergamon.

ROCHE, J. 1959. 'On some aspects of iodine biochemistry in marine animals.' *Pubbl. Staz. Zool Napoli* **31**, Suppl. 176–89.

ROCHE, J., SALVATORE, G. & COVELLI, I. 1961. 'Métabolisme de ^{131}I et fonction thyroïdienne chez la larve (ammocoete) d'un cyclostome, *Petromyzon planeri* Bl.' *Comp. Biochem. Physiol.* **2**, 90-99.

SOLOMON, D. H. & DOWLING, J. T. 1960. 'The thyroid.' *Ann. Rev. Physiol.* **22**, 615–50.

VARIOUS AUTHORS. 1957. *Regulation and Mode of Action of Thyroid Hormones. Ciba Foundation Colloquia in Endocrinology.* **10**.

RASMUSSEN, H. 1961. 'The parathyroid hormone.' *Scientific American* **204**, 56–63.

Chapter VIII

ADAMS, A. E. 1946. 'Variations in the potency of thyrotropic hormone in animals.' *Quart. Rev. Biol.* **21,** 1–32.

BAGGERMAN, B. 1960. 'Factors in the diadromous migrations of fish.' *Symp. Zool. Soc. Lond.* **1,** 33–60.

—— 1960. 'Salinity preference, thyroid activity and the seaward migration of four species of Pacific salmon (*Oncorhynchus*).' *J. Fish. Res. Bd. Canada* **17,** 295–322.

BARRINGTON, E. J. W. 1961. 'Metamorphic processes in fishes and lampreys.' *Amer. Zool.* **1,** 97–106.

CHARIPPER, H. A. & GORDON, A. S. 1947. 'The biology of anti-thyroid agents.' *Vitamins & Hormones* **5,** 274–316.

FLEISCHMANN, W. 1947. 'Comparative physiology of the thyroid hormone.' *Quart. Rev. Biol.* **22,** 119–40.

FONTAINE, M. 1954. 'Du déterminisme physiologique des migrations.' *Biol. Rev.* **29,** 390–418.

GORBMAN, A. 1959. 'Problems in the comparative morphology and physiology of the vertebrate thyroid gland.' In *Comparative Endocrinology*, ed. Gorbman, A. New York: Wiley.

HARRIS, G. W. & WOODS, J. W. 1958. 'The effect of electrical stimulation of the hypothalamus or pituitary gland on thyroid activity.' *J. Physiol.* **143,** 246–74.

HOAR, W. S. 1953. 'Control and timing of fish migration.' *Biol. Rev.* **28,** 437–52.

LYNN, W. G. & WACHOWSKI, H. E. 1951. 'The thyroid gland and its functions in cold-blooded vertebrates.' *Quart. Rev. Biol.* **26,** 123–68.

MATTY, A. J. 1960. 'Thyroid cycles in fish.' *Symp. Zool. Soc. Lond.* **2,** 1–15.

SONNENBERG, M. 1958. 'Chemistry and physiology of the thyroid-stimulating hormone.' *Vitamins & Hormones* **16,** 206–41.

VANDERLAAN, W. P. & STORRIE, V. M. 1955. 'A survey of the factors controlling thyroid function, with especial reference to newer views on antithyroid substances.' *Pharmacol. Rev.* **7,** 301–34.

Chapter IX

AUGUSTINSSON, K.-B. *et al.* 1955. 'Histological, physiological and bio-chemical studies on the heart of two cyclostomes, hagfish (*Myxine*) and lamprey (*Lampetra*).' *J. Physiol.* **131,** 257–76.

BOURNE, G. H. 1949. *The Mammalian Adrenal Gland.* Oxford: Clarendon Press.

FÄNGE, R. & ÖSTLUND, E. 1954. 'The effects of adrenaline, noradrenaline, tyramine and other drugs on the isolated heart from marine invertebrates and a cephalopod (*Eledone cirrosa*).' *Acta Zool.* **35,** 289–305.

HAGEN, P. & WELCH, A. D. 1956. 'The adrenal medulla and the biosynthesis of pressor amines.' *Rec. Prog. Horm. Res.* **12,** 27–44.

HARTMAN, F. A. & BROWNELL, K. A. 1949. *The Adrenal Gland.* Philadelphia: Lea & Febiger.

ÖSTLUND, E. 1954. 'The distribution of catechol amines in lower animals and their effect on the heart.' *Acta Physiol. Scand.* **31,** Suppl. 112, 1–67.

VON EULER, U. S. 1958. 'Distribution and metabolism of catechol hormones in tissues and axones.' *Rec. Prog. Horm. Res.* **14,** 483–512.

WEST, G. B. 1955. 'The comparative pharmacology of the suprarenal medulla.' *Quart. Rev. Biol.* **30,** 116–37.

Chapter X

CHESTER JONES, I. 1957. *The Adrenal Cortex.* Cambridge: University Press.

—— & ECKSTEIN, P. (eds.) 1956. '*The Hormonal Control of Water and Salt-Electrolyte Metabolism. Mem. Soc. Endocrin.* **5.**

—— & PHILLIPS, J. G. 1960. 'Adrenocorticosteroids in fish.' *Symp. Zool. Soc. Lond.* **1,** 17–32.

DEANE, H. W. & SELIGMAN, A. M. 1953. 'Evaluation of procedures for the cytological localization of ketosteroids.' *Vitamins & Hormones* **11,** 173–204.

GANONG, W. F. & FORSHAM, P. H. 1960. 'Adenohypophysis and adrenal cortex.' *Ann. Rev. Physiol.* **22,** 579–614.

HOLMES, W. N., Phillips, J. G. & Butler, D. G. 1961. 'The effect of adrenocortical steroids on the renal and extra-renal responses of the domestic duck (*Anas platyrhynchus*) after hypertonic saline loading.' *Endocrinology,* **69,** 483–495.

PRUNTY, F. T. G. 1962. *The adrenal cortex. Brit. Med. Bull.* **18,** 89–175.

SELYE, H. 1957. *The Stress of Life.* London: Longmans.

WILLMER, E. N. 1960. *Cytology and Evolution.* London: Academic Press.

Chapter XI

BILLINGHAM, R. E. & SILVERS, W. K. 1960. 'The melanocytes of mammals.' *Quart. Rev. Biol.* **35,** 1–40.

ENAMI, M. 1955. 'Melanophore-contracting hormone (MCH) of possible hypothalamic origin in the catfish, *Parasilurus.*' *Science* **121,** 36–37.

FINGERMAN, M. 1959. 'The physiology of chromatophores.' *Int. Rev. Cyt.* **8,** 175–210.

GESCHWIND, I. I. 1959. 'Species variation in protein and polypeptide hormones.' In *Comparative Endocrinology,* ed. Gorbman, A. New York: Wiley.

GORDON, M. (ed.) 1959. *Pigment Cell Biology.* New York: Academic Press.

HEALEY, E. G. 1957. 'The nervous system'. In *The Physiology of Fishes*, ed. Brown, M. Vol. 2. New York: Academic Press.

HOGBEN, L. 1942. 'Chromatic behaviour.' *Proc. Roy. Soc.* B **131**, 111–36.

KENT, A. K. 1959. 'Significance of the time relations of humorally co-ordinated chromatic responses. *Nature* **184**, 2027.

LERNER, A. B. & TAKAHASHI, Y. 1956. 'Hormonal control of melanin pigmentation.' *Rec. Prog. Horm. Res.* **12**, 303–20.

MORI, W. & LERNER, A. B. 1960. 'A microscopic bioassay for melatonin.' *Endocrinology* **67**, 443–50.

PAGE, I. H. 1958. 'Serotonin (5-hydroxytryptamine); the last four years.' *Physiol. Rev.* **38**, 277–335.

PARKER, G. H. 1948. *Animal Colour Changes and their Neurohumours.* Cambridge: University Press.

UDENFRIEND, S. 1959. 'Biochemistry of serotonin and other indolamines.' *Vitamins & Hormones* **17**, 133–54.

WARING, H. 1942. 'The co-ordination of vertebrate melanophore responses.' *Biol. Rev.* **17**, 120–50.

Chapter XII

BARRINGTON, E. J. W. 1960. 'Some problems of adenohypophysial relationships in cyclostomes and fish.' *Symp. Zool. Soc. Lond.* **2**, 69–85.

GORBMAN, A. 1941. 'Comparative anatomy and physiology of the anterior pituitary.' *Quart. Rev. Biol.* **16**, 294–310.

GREEN, J. D. 1951. 'The comparative anatomy of the hypophysis, with special reference to its blood supply and innervation.' *Amer. J. Anat.* **88**, 225–312.

HOUSSAY, B. A. 1949. 'Hypophyseal functions in the toad, *Bufo arenarum* Hensel.' *Quart. Rev. Biol.* **24**, 1–27.

JØRGENSEN, C. BARKER & LARSEN, L. O. 1960. 'Comparative aspects of hypothalamic-hypophyseal relationships.' *Ergeb. Biol.* **22**, 1–29.

OLIVERAU, M. 1954. 'Hypophyse et glande thyroïde chez les poissons.' *Ann. Inst. Océanog.* **29**, 95–296.

VARIOUS AUTHORS. 1952. *Anterior Pituitary Secretion. Ciba Foundation Colloquia in Endocrinology* **4**.

WINGSTRAND, K. G. 1951. *The Structure and Development of the Avian Pituitary.* Lund.

Chapter XII

BROWN, F. A. 1944. 'Hormones in the Crustacea.' *Quart. Rev. Biol.* **19**, 32–46, 118–43.

CARLISLE, D. B. 1960. 'Moulting cycles in Crustacea.' *Symp. Zool. Soc. Lond.* **2**, 109–20.

—— & KNOWLES, F. 1959. *Endocrine Control in Crustaceans.* Cambridge: University Press.

CHARNIAUX-COTTON, H. 1960. 'Sex determination.' In *The Physiology of Crustacea*, ed. Waterman, T. H. Vol. 1. New York: Academic Press.

GABE, M. 1954. 'La neuro-sécrétion chez les invertébrés.' *Ann. Biol.* **30**, 5–62.

KLEINHOLZ, L. H. 1942. 'Hormones in Crustacea.' *Biol. Rev.* **17**, 91–119.

—— 1961. 'Pigmentary effectors.' In *The Physiology of Crustacea*, ed. Waterman, T. H. Vol. 2. New York: Academic Press.

KNOWLES, F. 1955. 'Crustacean colour change and neurosecretion.' *Endeavour* **14**, 95–104.

—— & CARLISLE, D. B. 1956. 'Endocrine control in the Crustacea.' *Biol. Rev.* **31**, 396–473.

PASSANO, L. M. 1960. 'Molting and its control.' In *The Physiology of Crustacea*, ed. Waterman, T. H. New York: Academic Press.

REINHARD, E. G. 1956. 'Parasitic castration of Crustacea.' *Exp. Parasit.* **5**, 79–107.

SCHEER, B. T. 1960. 'The neuroendocrine system of arthropods. *Vitamins & Hormones* **18**, 141–204.

TIEGS, O. W. & MANTON, S. M. 1958. 'The evolution of the Arthropoda.' *Biol. Rev.* **33**, 255–337.

WELSH, J. H. 1961. 'Neurohumors and Neurosecretion.' In *The Physiology of Crustacea*, ed. Waterman, T. H. Vol. 2. New York: Academic Press.

Chapter XIV

BODENSTEIN, D. 1954. 'Endocrine mechanisms in the life of insects.' *Rec. Prog. Horm. Res.* **10**, 157–82.

BUTLER, C. G. 1959. 'Queen substance.' *Bee World* **40**, 269–75.

CALLOW, R. K. & JOHNSTON, N. C. 1960. 'The chemical constitution and synthesis of queen substance of honeybees (*Apis mellifera*).' *Bee World* **41**, 152-3.

DUPONT-RAABE, M. 1957. 'Les mécanismes de l'adaptation chromatique chez les insectes.' *Arch. Zool. exp. gén.* **94**, 61–262.

GILBERT, L. I. & SCHEIDERMAN, H. A. 1961. 'Some biochemical aspects of insect metamorphosis'. *Amer. Zool.* **1**, 11–52.

KARLSON, P. 1956. 'Biochemical studies in insect hormones.' *Vitamins & Hormones* **14**, 227–66.

—— & BUTENANDT, A. 1959. 'Pheromones (ectohormones) in insects.' *Ann. Rev. Entom.* **4**, 39–58.

KLOOT, W. G. VAN DE. 1960. 'Neurosecretion in insects.' *ibid.* **5**, 35–52.

SCHEIDERMAN, H. A. & GILBERT, L. I. 1959. 'The chemistry and physiology of insect growth hormones.' In *Cell, Organism & Milieu*, ed.
Rudnick, D. New York: Ronald Press.

WIGGLESWORTH, V. B. 1954. *The Physiology of Insect Metamorphosis.*
Cambridge: University Press.

—— 1959. *The Control of Growth and Form.* Ithaca: Cornell Univ. Press.

Chapter XV

ANON. 1960. 'Intelligent talk.' *Times Literary Supplement*, No. 3,070.

BARRINGTON, E. J. W. 1962. 'Hormones and vertebrate evolution.'
Experientia, **18**, 201–10.

BONNER, J. & BONNER, H. 1948. 'The B vitamins as plant hormones.'
Vitamins & Hormones **6**, 225–75.

BOURNE, G. H. & KIDDER, G. W. (eds.) *Biochemistry and Physiology of
Nutrition*. Vols. 1 & 2. New York: Academic Press.

CARLISLE, D. B. 1959. 'On the neurosecretory system of the brain and
associated structures in *Sipunculus nudus*, with a note on the cuticle.'
Gunma J. Med. Sci. **8**, 183–94.

CLARK, R. B. 1961. 'The origin and formation of the heteronereis.'
Biol. Rev. **36**, 199–236.

ENAMI, M. 1959. 'The morphology and functional significance of the
caudal neurosecretory system of fishes.' In *Comparative Endocrinology*, ed. Gorbman, A. New York: Wiley.

FISHER, L. R. & KON, S. K. 1959. 'Vitamin A in the invertebrates.'
Biol. Rev. **34**, 1–36.

HAGADORN, I. R. 1958. 'Neurosecretion and the brain of the rhyncho-
bdellid leech, *Theromyzon rude* (Baird, 1869).' *J. Morph.* **102**, 55–84.

HOLMGREN, U. 1960. 'On the urophysis spinalis and the caudal neurosecretory system of teleost fishes.' *Zool. Anz.* **165**, 77–83.

SANO, Y. 1961. 'Das caudale neurosekretorische System bei Fischen.'
Ergeb. Biol. **24**, 191–212.

SCHARRER, B. 1959. 'The role of neurosecretion in neuro-endocrine
integration.' In *Comparative Endocrinology*, ed. Gorbman, A. New
York: Wiley.

SCHARRER, E. & SCHARRER, B. 1954. 'Hormones produced by neurosecretory cells.' *Rec. Prog. Horm. Res.* **10**, 183–240.

WELLS, M. J. 1960. 'Optic glands and the ovary of *Octopus*.' *Symp. Zool.
Soc. Lond.* **2**, 87–108.

INDEX

A cells, islets of Langerhans, 41.
A-substance, crustaceans and insects, 319, 354.
acetylcholine, 37, 224.
acidophils, pituitary gland, 284.
Addison's disease, 234, 264.
adenohypophysis, 67 (see also pituitary gland); pars distalis, 70, 111, 283, 285, 369; pars intermedia, 70, 262, 281, 282, 369; pars tuberalis, 70.
adrenal cortex, 213.
adrenal gland, 212 ff., 240, 260.
adrenal medulla, 213, 217.
adrenalectomy, effects of, 234 ff.
adrenaline, 37, 57, 63, 66, 191, 218, 224, 253.
adrenocortical steroids, 110.
adrenocortical tissue, 214, 241; histochemistry, 243.
adrenocorticotropic hormone (ACTH), see corticoptropin.
adrenogenital syndrome, 251.
aldehyde-fuchsin technique, 42, 74, 284.
aldosterone, 176, 239, 246.
alimentary canal, vertebrates, 9.
allophores, 257.
alloxan, 50.
alpha cells, islets of Langerhans, see A cells.
analogues, 88.
analogy, 309.
androgenic gland, 330.
androgens, 108 ff., 159, 252.
androsterone, 108.
'anterior lobe', see pituitary gland.
antidiuresis, 77 ff.
anti-thyroid compounds, 206 ff.
appetite secretion, 35.
arginine vasotocin, 88 ff.
artificial oestrogens, 105.
assay of hormones, 34, 235, 244.
atresia, follicular, 96.
autonomic nervous system, 13, 29, 35 ff., 223, 256, 268, 271.
auto-radiography, 180.
auto-transplantation, 18, 20, 120, 301.
Azan technique, 42, 73, 170, 284.

B cells, islets of Langerhans, 41, 49.
B-substance, crustaceans, 319, 354.
B-substance, vertebrates, 262.
basiphils, pituitary gland, 284.
behaviour, and hormones, 139 ff.
beta cells, islets of Langerhans, see B cells.
beta cells, pituitary gland, 284.
bile acids, 103.
bile, secretion of, 29.

bioassay, 34, 235, 244.
biosynthesis, catechol hormones, 223; thyroid hormones, 176 ff.
birds, sexual periodicity, 129 ff.
blood sugar, 39; in lower vertebrates, 64.
brood spots, 114.
Brunn effect, 86.

C-substance in insects, 354.
calorigenic effect, catechol hormones, 229; thyroid hormones, 191.
captivity, and sexual activity, 126.
cardenolides, 103.
carrier substance, 74.
castration, and sexual differentiation, 156 ff.
catechol hormones, 192, 216 ff., 220, 229 ff., 231, 279.
chalone, 29.
'change of sex', 252.
chemical thyroidectomy, 207.
chemical transmission, 75, 120, 225, 232, 296.
cholecystokinin, 32.
cholinesterase, 227, 345.
chorionic gonadotropin, 147.
chromaffin reaction, 221.
chromaffin tissue, 80, 214, 218, 221, 226, 232.
chromatography, paper, 174, 237.
chromatophores, 257, 310.
chromatosomes, 268, 310.
chrome-alum-haematoxylin technique, 42, 73 ff.
chromophils, pituitary gland, 284.
chromophobes, pituitary gland, 284.
circumoesophageal commissures (connectives), 317.
coelomic epithelium, evolution, 249.
colour change, and evolution, 280; amphibia, 259 ff.; catechol hormones, 279; cephalopods, 310; Crustacea, 310 ff.; Cyclostomata, 265 ff.; Elasmobranchii, 267; insects, 310, 351 ff.; morphological, 258, 351; physiological, 258 ff., 351; pineal gland, 279; primary response, 260; pseudobranch, 279; Reptilia, 272; retinal differentiation, 276; secondary response, 260; Teleostei, 268; unihumoral and bihumoral theories, 274.
comparative method, 5 ff.
contraceptives, oral, 126, 355.
corneal reflex, 197.
corpora allata, 337, 346.
corpora cardiaca, 337, 340, 353, 369.
corpus albicans, 97.
corpus luteum, 97, 106, 145.
corpuscles of Stannius, 216.
cortical cords, 151.